UNEASY

SOULS

Stephen Tunnicliffe

Clairmont Press

ii

Published by

Clairmont Press

Clairmont CLUN Shropshire SY7 8JA England

www.clairmontpress.co.uk

1999

Copyright © Stephen Tunnicliffe 1999

The moral right of the author has been asserted.

Printed & bound by Antony Rowe Ltd, Eastbourne

ISBN 0 9519135 5 7

Cover picture by Tim Phillips

Denn ein Gott hat
Jedem seine Bahn
Vorgezeichnet,
Die der Glückliche
Rasch zum freudigen
Ziele rennt:
Wem aber Unglück
Das Herz zusammenzog.
Er sträubt vergebens
Sich gegen die Schranken
Des ehernen Fadens,
Den die doch bittre Schere
Nur einmal löst.

For a god has pre-ordained his way for each person: the lucky man runs headlong to his happy destination; but for him for whom misfortune constricts his heart, he strives in vain to break loose from the pitiless cord, which the ever bitter shears cut only once.

Johann Wolfgang von Goethe: *Harzreise im Winter*

Der Tod ist das Ergebniß, das Résumé *des Lebens, oder die zusammengezogene Summe, welche die gesammte Belehrung, die das Leben vereinzelt und stückweise gab, mit Einem Male ausspricht, nämlich diese, daß das ganze Streben, dessen Erscheinung das Leben ist, ein verbliches, eitles, sich widersprechendes war, von welchem zurückgekommen zu seyn eine Erlösung ist.*
Death is the result, the résumé of life, the total sum, which expresses in one moment all the instruction which life gave piecemeal, namely that all the striving, whose appearance is life, is a futile, vain and contradictory experience, the return from which is deliverance.
Arthur Schopenhauer

CONTENTS

Biographical Note

Many of the persons and events mentioned in these pages, including the two principal characters, Wolfgang Graeser (1906-1928) and Piete Kuhr, later Jo Mihaly (1902-1989) are historical. Most of the letters and documents quoted are extant. The author's principal aim is to re-create the short but brilliant career of Graeser by tracing his life from its beginnings in Naples and Zürich to its tragic end in Berlin. After achieving international fame as the re-discoverer and editor of J S Bach's *Art of Fugue* he is now forgotten outside his specialist field. The sole memoir devoted to him (in German) appeared first in 1929, but has been unavailable for over sixty years. While there is no direct evidence that he ever met Piete Kuhr, their paths certainly crossed in the Berlin of the Weimar Republic. Under the pseudonym of Jo Mihaly, Kuhr became a well-known dancer and published a number of novels and other writings. Her diary of the First World War, written when she was a schoolgirl, was published in German in 1982. That edition is out of print, but an English edition was published in 1998 by its translator, Walter Wright*, and is available from the publisher.

There We'll Meet Again: The First World War diary of a young German girl
by Piete Kuhr (ISBN 0 9532633 04), translated, with an introduction and postscript, by Walter Wright, Oakdene, Fidges Lane, Eastcombe, Stroud, Gloucestershire GL6 7DW (£10.75 UK, £12.25 overseas, post paid)

viii

Prologue

THE MILD spring weather in 1922 seemed a presage of a new calm, the herald of a fresh beginning in the teeming city of Berlin. The dark revolutionary days of the '18-'19 winter seemed far away, and even the street violence of General Lüttwitz's troops, propping up for five days the ineffectual Herr Kapp in March 1920, until the general strike sent them both packing, had receded into history or was reduced to the status of a bad dream. That, at least, was how it looked to Herr Wilke, waiter and general factotum, as he stood on the 4th floor balcony of the luxurious Hotel Adlon in Pariser Platz, enjoying a brief breather and surveying the ant-like crowds hurrying to and fro on Unter den Linden. Helmut Wilke was scant of breath and, thanks to rich pickings in the famous Adlon kitchens, rather overweight, with the pasty, etiolated skin derived from long hours spent in the warm air and artificial hotel lighting.

"Wilke, damn you! Where are you?"

Fat Helmut started at the curt military summons, in English this time. At least this English general, this Herr General Morgan, unlike his Prussian counterparts, was prepared to recognise him as a fellow human being. Wilke's gentle Saxon soul had warmed to the British officer, one of the Control Commission sent to oversee implementation of the peace treaty terms, after he had forgiven Helmut's desertion of his 4th floor post at the time of the putsch. All the staff had been forced out on strike by the socialists and the hotel, for once in its busy life, had been left silent, dark and deserted.

Accommodating the Control Commission in these opulent sur-roundings, all gilt and marble, with the bronze statue of Kaiser Wilhelm still in place, had been a calculated ploy of the Reichswehr officers, an attempt to soften up those responsible for supervising the harsh treaty terms, which they intended to honour more in the breach than the observance. It had not been wholly successful. The Hotel Adlon, in pre-war days home to the aristocracy and frequented by the Kaiser himself, now played host to a more varied but very much less dignified clientèle, the new wealthy of this war-torn country, war profiteers, industrialists and their servile hangers-on, crooks and confidence-men making up the unsavoury majority. Any of the German military top brass who remained were no longer resplendent in their braided, bemedalled uniforms but wore inconspicuous lounge suits. And the less frequent appearances of Hohenzollerns and other titled personages went largely unnoticed, apart from the occasional quiet "Excellency" or "Highness" from a well-drilled hotel flunkey.

Helmut Wilke congratulated himself on having acquired such a soft number in these uncertain times. He was resigned to the insults and indignities that went with it, mostly from Prussian officers or the more ill-bred nouveaux riches. Helmut had been well schooled: as army medical orderly he had endured two years of such treatment, often while easing their discomfort or dressing their wounds. Like so many of his compatriots he tried to blot out those years from his memory, the torn limbs, the stinking gangrenous wounds, the persistent filth, and when the gas attacks began , bestowed indiscriminately on friend and foe as the wind shifted, the blood-clotted phlegm from tortured lungs. His own legacy from this was his perm-anently husky voice. But even that, he thought as he made his way later back to his cramped apartment in a run-down block behind Alexanderplatz, had helped him in the hotel; it was interpreted as discretion, and this was valued where so much business was conducted sotto voce.

Wilke's musings as he walked were interrupted by running footsteps behind him from the direction of Unter den Linden. A uniformed police-man! In pursuit of some petty thief, thought Helmut as the man stopped to catch his breath. But as he did so another man ran up, a great Alsatian dog loping silently beside him, as though they chased the policeman. In spite of his drab clothes Helmut recognised this second man as army, one of the thousands of Officer Corps demobs frequenting Berlin. The dog stood guard, teeth bared, over the shaking policeman.

"So he should be muzzled, eh? I suggest you do this for me, Schweinhund!" The officer spoke with a sneer. "Do you know who it is you have the temerity to order about?"

A small clutch of passers-by had stopped with Herr Wilke to watch the encounter, one of them a blond, fresh-faced lad carrying a violin-case.

"Er . . no, Sir. I was only doing my duty." The policeman, who stood almost a handbreadth taller than his hectoring adversary, quailed visibly and dropped his eyes.

"Your duty! Let me tell you, dummer Kerl, it is not any part of your duty to prevent a Prussian officer from exercising his dog. I demand an apology."

There was a moment's profound silence. The spectators waited.

"Well?"

In spite of himself Medical Orderly Wilkes shrank at the familiar hated tone of command. The policeman seemed similarly intimidated.

"I . . I apologise if you have been inconvenienced, Sir. I was only..." The man's voice tailed off as the other nodded dismissively with a snort of derision and turned on his heel. He was striding off, with a click of his fingers to the still un-muzzled dog, which seemed disappointed to have been denied the chance of sinking his teeth into his quarry. Someone in the small crowd muttered "Shame!" The officer paused, with a steely glance over the faces. All dropped their eyes apart from the lad. As his met the officer's both smiled. A shabbily dressed woman on the edge of the crowd spat on the ground as he passed.

The boy with the violin and Wilke set off in the same direction.

"So the Reichswehr still rules, eh?" Helmut said jocularly, keeping pace with the lad.

"We need the army. We are a military nation." The boy seemed elated by the incident. "Do you not believe this?" He looked at Wilke briefly.

"Me? Oh, I have no idea, young Herr. It is not for the likes of me to have opinions." He shrugged and fell silent. Soon their ways parted and the boy swung himself onto a street-car.

"Why not ask young Graeser? He's keen on Bach, and it is straightforward enough." Professor Klingler threw the remark over his shoulder as he left the room. He seemed irritable at her request. 'These specialists!' thought Margarete, 'no interest outside their main study.' Still, he could have shown some over the aria, the obbligato being on his own instrument. She left the practice room and made her way to the students' common-room of the Music School. All right, Wolfgang Graeser might just do it for her; his teacher obviously thinks he is up to it. Apparently the teaching staff regard him as something exceptional. Well, perhaps he is, she thought, remembering her first conversation with him.

She had noticed his birth-place, Zürich, on the list of admissions. 'Another Switzer!' At least it would help to leaven the mass of Prussians and Russians. She picked him out straight away amongst the new arrivals, a slight, fair-haired boy in a corner holding a violin-case. Painfully shy he had looked, very conscious, it seemed, of his mere 16 years amongst the older students. He was by far the youngest in that year's intake, and had only been accepted by Director Schreker - who was something of a precisian over such matters - on the special recommendation of his deputy Professor Schünemann. Yet there had been, even at that first meeting, something arresting about him to Margarete. Perhaps it was those almost startlingly blue eyes when he looked up at her.

"Another from Zürich, my home town! How nice to have some company."

"I'm German actually. Graeser from Munich." He stood up, clicking his heels in what seemed a deliberate caricature of Prussian militarism.

"Oh, I thought . . ." she faltered. "I'm sure it said Zürich on . . ."

"Sorry," he flushed painfully, reminding Margarete of her 12-year-old brother Ulrich. What a child! But sensitive, too, like Ulie. "Yes, I was born there, but my parents are German. I'm as much Italian as Swiss, for that matter. We used to live in Naples. Who are you, anyway? What are you studying?" He looked directly at her now, and seemed a little reassured by her open smile and casual dress, the sloppy, unrestricted post-war "Wandervogel" style.

"Singing. I'm Grete - Margarete Hanauer. Clavier is my second study, but I'm rotten at it. Not Frau Kayser's favourite student! She suffers me and I suffer her." She laughed.

"Soprano? My mother sings soprano, but she's really a violinist."

After this opening they had become, not exactly friends - it was not easy to break down the lad's prickly reserve with the opposite sex - but at least more or less relaxed together. Margarete, with her rapid chatter, her unruly mop of dark hair and her over-confident, hasty judgments, frequently wrong-headed, was not at all formidable, but she seemed old to Wolfgang with her two years' seniority. And on her side, she felt almost motherly to this gangling boy, alternately childish and arrogantly mature, clutching his violin-case as if it was a shield. Perhaps he would play the obbligato for "Ich ende behende". She knew he was keen on Bach; she recalled with a smile that coffee they had shared at the Romanisches Café, with its noisy cosmopolitan clientèle of students, ex-patriate Russians, actors, transvestites and petty crooks. Wolfgang had started on about the mathematical structure of The Musical Offering. The girl couldn't follow half of it, and the more animated he became the faster he spoke, unconsciously interspersing his speech with Italian words and phrases and moving his arms like a Latin. Soon he was illustrating his ideas by drawing all kinds of geometrical patterns on the table with a finger dipped in coffee. As she smiled at his absorption, Herr Hahn, the autocratic head waiter of the Romanische, spotted him and sent a minion to wipe the table clean. Margarete laughed, both at the event and at Wolfgang's instant rage. He had looked for a moment as if he would hit the waiter, who, startled by this immoderate response, stood there foolishly, cloth in hand.

"Calm down, Wolfgang!" It was the first time she had used his christian name in public, and he changed in an instant, laughing at himself over the trivial episode.

Yes, it was just the sort of music that might appeal to him, with its piquant contrast between the subject-matter, death, and Bach's jaunty setting.

"It's not a college thing. I go outside the Music School for these occasional lessons. Frau Kuhr-Golz used to run her own music school before the war, and she's a fine teacher; she's taught lots of singers in the opera. I have convinced my parents that it is worth the extra money. She has asked me to take part in the cantata - it's for St. Stephen's Day, of course - in her local church, St. Mark's. It's not much of a do, only me and a bass with organ accompaniment and the church choir for the chorale at the end, but Frau Kuhr-Golz thought I really ought to find a violin for this aria because it sets off my voice so well. She's getting someone in specially to hear me."

"You're really serious about it, then? Being a musician?"

"We've had all this before, Wolfgang, of course I'm serious. I'm going to be a singer. You're serious about violin aren't you?"

"No - well, yes, maybe." Wolfgang shrugged his shoulders. "How can one be serious about anything these days? What's the point of being serious?"

Margarete was getting used to these sombre moments, but they still seemed very alien to her own temperament. She fished out the vocal score of the cantata Selig ist der Mann from her music-case - they were chatting on the steps of the Music School in a brief sunny spell on this cold November day. A horse-drawn wagon clomped its way across the Fasanen-platz, Wolfgang could smell the great beasts with their hair-fringed hooves - a homely rural touch in this alien place. The aria request was a good move; the boy was immediately fascinated by the subject of the cantata, a new one for him. It called forth some sardonic comments in his customary mocking style, his voice breaking appealingly as he spoke.

"Ein recht verlaß'nes Lamm - a truly forsaken lamb. Oh, it suits you Grete! So all you want is death?"

"All right, laugh. But it's marvellous music, you just wait till we try it through with Frau Kuhr-Golz. Make sure you're here on time tomorrow; she hates people to be late, and it is quite a long way down to Steglitz."

He was moody again as they made their way next day to the apartment in Steglitzer Straße.

"All this old music, it's all irrelevant now, don't you think. One can't take even Bach seriously any more - well, not when he is writing stuff like this. He's part of a vanished age - an age of belief?"

This time it really grated on her, happy as she was at the prospect of singing with the violin. She stopped and faced the boy, clutching his shoulder so that he almost dropped his instrument.

"Hey, what's up?" He shook himself free.

"Why do you say these things? You don't mean it, do you? What about The Musical Offering?"

"That's different. Bach wasn't concerned then with graves - 'Gruft und Grab' - and going to heaven." They resumed their walk along Bismarckstraße. "Alright, I was joking. But when you think back to the war, and when you just look around you . . ." Graeser pointed to a man on the opposite pavement. He wore a shabby army tunic without buttons, and swung himself along on crutches, the stump of one leg hanging loosely. "I was walking along Kurfürstendamm the other day and a man like that - well, it was his arm, his right arm that was missing - threw himself under the street-car."

"How awful!" Margarete was genuinely shocked. "Was he . . dead?"

"Maybe." He sounded callous, indifferent, and she was about to take him up on it. But the expression on his face, at odds with his words, gave her pause. They lapsed into silence for the remainder of the short walk from the bus-stop.

Graeser was surprised by the singing teacher. From Grete's remarks he had envisaged someone much older, more like Professor Mysz-Gmeiner at the Music School, a heavy, forbidding-looking matron in her fifties with a pronounced moustache. Frau Kuhr-Golz seemed beautiful to the boy, with her upright carriage, dark auburn hair - with just a few grey-silver ones - pulled back severely from her face in a chignon, and pale clear complexion. Her speech was abrupt, academically correct, with just a hint of Silesian intonations.

"We are not warm here." The teacher was not so much apologising for the cold - it was very chilly in the small flat - as explaining her wearing of a fur. The fur coat, once opulent, now showed its age, though scrupulously cared for. "But it is good for your voice, Margarete, not to be too warm. They roast you in that Music School, I think. And -" turning to Wolfgang, "your strings will stay in tune, Herr Graeser." Wolfgang blushed at this unexpected courtesy, covering his embarrassment by busying himself with the fiddle. The carved music-stand she provided was elegant and graceful, "a relic of my Meisterschule before the war. I am the only other relic." She spoke with a bitter smile. "Now let us try your aria, my dear. I must play for you today; Elfriede could not be home in time."

The aria had gone well at this first run-through. Wolfgang was agreeably surprised by Margarete's clear, true soprano, ideal for the music, and responded to it in his playing of the florid obbligato. She found his tempo inflexible, but Frau Kuhr-Golz had kept him in touch with the vocal line. He was far from note-perfect - he never liked sight-reading, he said - but his innate musicianship kept the shape and pace of the piece.

"So you happily bring your life to an end, Grete!" They were on their way back after the lesson. "'Ich ende behende mein irdisches Leben.' It is a dance, not a dirge - a dance of death, a dance of death." He seemed fascinated by the phrase.

"Don't make jokes like that to Frau Kuhr-Golz. She won't see the funny side."

"I wouldn't dare. She is a little . . fierce. Aristocratic. It suits her. She kept me in order." He snorted. "But my tempo was accurate. You were pulling it about." He paused, then, resuming his mocking tone, "but come to think of it, Stephen really asked for it, didn't he! Faced by a hostile crowd with rocks in their hands, all he can do is first to insult them, then claim divine inspiration. It was suicide, not murder. He danced to his death."

"Wolfgang, you're incorrigible." Nothing could puncture her elation after the singing. She laughed, punched him playfully. "How about Piete then, Frau Kuhr-Golz's daughter? What did you think of her?"

The teacher's 20-year-old daughter had come in from work just as the lesson ended. She was tired, a heavy sigh as she let her coat drop on the floor. Then, at a glance from her mother, she picked it up and hung it in the narrow, cluttered foyer. Elfriede - her mother called her Piete - was a striking figure, with her high cheek-bones, dark eyes and quick, strong gestures. There was a suppressed energy about her, a vitality, in spite of her obvious fatigue. She had nodded when Margarete introduced Wolfgang, putting out her hand, which was firm, like a man's hand, but otherwise hardly seeming to notice him.

"That man is horrible, Mutti. I don't think I can stand another week in that place. He looks over my shoulder when I'm typing and breathes down my neck, and he stinks of garlic - ugh!"

"Piete darling, you must hold on longer this time. I can't support you, my dear, I need your help. Food is getting so dear." Piete took her mother's face in both hands and kissed her on the forehead. "But our friends here do not want to hear of our troubles. This young man -" Frau Kuhr-Golz rested a hand on Wolfgang's head as he bent over his violin-case, "has the makings of a fine violinist." Graeser made an embarrassed noise in his throat, and the girl looked at him as if seeing him for the first time.

"Are you at the music school with Grete?"

He nodded. "I'm with Professor Klingler."

"Oh, he's supposed to be one of the best there, isn't he? I heard . . we heard him, Mutti, remember? In the summer."

Wolfgang was intrigued by the contrast between Margarete and this other girl - well, woman, she must be older. Piete, her mother called her, though Grete had said Elfriede when they were introduced. Piete suits her better, he decided. Where Margarete was sloppy and relaxed Piete was slim, braced and tense. He could see Grete putting on more weight - she loved her food - and filling out to a true Wagnerian "diva". Yet the two seemed to be good friends - 'the attraction of opposites' he thought. Wolfgang was tall for his age, but Piete just topped him, whereas Grete's brown eyes were level with his chin when they stood together.

"Wolfgang, couldn't Piete come on Saturday morning, to Professor Klingler's class recital?" She turned to the older girl. "Wolfgang is playing in it, it's for Klingler's students. You wouldn't need to pay anything."

"This Saturday? Oh no, I am with Hans Gérard then. He is giving me an extra lesson. Yes, Mutti" she had registered her mother's withdrawal at the words, "really - giving, because he knows we're poor, and he says I . ."

"I don't understand you, Elfriede." Frau Kuhr-Golz spoke with unexpected severity. (She only calls me that when she's cross with me, Piete thought). "What use is all this . . this dancing" she pronounced the word as if it had a bad smell, "to you? It is nothing but a childish obsession, and you wear yourself out with it."

Piete said nothing. Wolfgang watched to see her reaction, and she met his eyes and smiled faintly, in a way he couldn't interpret.

"She seems nice." Wolfgang's reply was guarded, neutral. "Do you like her?"

" 'Nice'! What a feeble way to describe Piete. She liked you anyway, I could tell. I wish she had come sooner, to play for the aria. Yes, I do like her, we get on well together. And her mother is right, dancing is quite an obsession with her, has been ever since she was little, she told me. She wants to tell stories by dancing."

Wolfgang's reserve vanished at this, as he said with a laugh: "She can do the dance of death for you then. That should liven up the cantata. All the way down the aisle."

"Strangely enough, you are not too far from the truth." Grete hadn't risen this time to his mocking. "One of her first ideas for a dance came to her when she was a kid during the war. She had an uncle in the army, and he brought a trophy back from the Verdun battle, a bloodstained Belgian army helmet. Piete told me she really treasured that gruesome thing, and decided then it would be her first "prop" for The Dance of the Dead Soldier."

"Has she still got it - the helmet?" Wolfgang seemed strangely animated.

"I suppose so. You'd better ask her. She works in Meineke Straße, just round from the Music School, so we sometimes have coffee together when she can get out. Why not come along next time? There is a small café right next to her office - if you can call it that."

"Which, the office or the café?"

"Oh, well, both, from what Piete tells me. But I meant the café. Still, it's a lot cheaper than the Romanische, and more peaceful, even if the clientèle is less colourful."

It was two weeks before this happened. Margarete wanted to arrange another rehearsal of the aria with Frau Kuhr-Golz, and used Piete as a go-between. When they called at the office to see if she could join them Piete was elated.

"He's gone out for the rest of the day, Schmidt der Schmutzfink," this was her boss, "so why not?"

The café had three or four shabbily dressed men at one of the - far from clean - tables. There was a pervasive smell of cabbage overlaying a fainter, but recognisable, one of unwashed humanity. The chairback felt greasy as Wolfgang took it to sit down, wrinkling his nose. Piete noticed his distaste.

"Sorry! I know it's not the Adlon. But it is handy, and cheap, and not too noisy."

Wolfgang felt ill-at-ease, as the two girls chatted and sipped their ersatz coffee. Why had he come, to listen to this girls' talk? His thick cup, like everything else in this down-at-heel place, did not seem too clean. He could hear Mama's 'Don't drink from that filthy cup, Wullie!' Such a commotion she had created in the smart ristorante as she had called the waiter to ask for fresh crockery that time! How old was he then - nine, ten? Hans, his older brother, had laughed immoderately, as usual. And the sun, the hot Neapolitan sun . . .

"Wolfgang, where were you? Piete just asked you something." Margarete's voice recalled him.

"It's always raining here. Oh, Fräulein . . . sorry. What did you say?"

"I'm not your teacher, you know. 'Fräulein' indeed! Do you want me to call you 'junger Herr'? My name's Piete, or Elfriede if you want to be formal. We were talking about the aria you are doing with Grete. You are right, it is like a dance. I was playing it on the piano for Mutti to sing, and . "

Margarete broke in: "Look at the time! Piete, I must go for my piano lesson, Frau Kayser will kill me if I'm late again. You stay," to Wolfgang, who had also risen. "Didn't you want to ask Piete about the helmet?" She dropped some pfennigs on the table and left hastily.

"What helmet? Has Grete been giving away my secrets?" Her tone was jocular rather than severe. Graeser overcame his shyness with an effort, as he explained about the war trophy. Soon they were deep into dancing. Wolfgang had assumed that Piete was having ballet lessons, and could not see any possible link with a 'dance of the dead soldier'.

"I am having lessons in ballet, but I could never be a proper ballet dancer. You have to start training for that in the cradle, and I'm too big anyway. No, what I hope to do is modern dance, free expression." Wolfgang looked blank. "Von Laban, Mary Wigman? Haven't you heard of them?" This was a new world to the boy, gymnastic dance as a direct, sensuous mode of story-telling. He listened with fascination as Piete spoke of the new philosophy of dance and body culture, of her lessons, and her ideas for the dance story using the Belgian helmet. Yes, of course she still had it, he could see it next time Grete came for the aria. Her military Uncle Bruno had also given her his army boots.

"You can't dance in army boots, surely?"

"Why not? You are still thinking of ballet, my lad." And she went on to describe another part of her proposed get-up, her brother's discarded army uniform.

"At the end of the war, Gil - that's what I used to call my brother - came back to our grandma's, where we were living then, while I was talking to a friend of his, a Pole called Androwski, Hans Androwski. You know we lived almost in Poland, east of Berlin. Gil was a sight! His uniform was open over his shirt, the buttons had been torn off taking bits of cloth with them, the shoulder-strips with the official marks were also torn off, his collar was dangling half-way down and he had no forage cap on and no belt. I knew straight away that I needed this torn uniform for my 'dead soldier' dance, this very uniform.It would complete the costume - steel helmet, army boots, battle-dress. I would paint my face, forehead and nose, with rouge for blood, and put some on my hands as well. Oh, I remember it so clearly, that day. That must have been in November too, that dreadful November at the end of the war. You remember, when the sailors mutinied at Kiel and the Kaiser deserted to Holland. And the revolution . . " She lapsed into musing and fell silent. Then, remembering, "But of course, you were only a child then, in Italy still?"

"No, we had to leave when I was eleven, because they hated Germans - especially after Caporetto. We were living in Munich for a bit - well, my father was in Trier with the army. I went to school in Munich. But go on about the uniform."

"Gil - Willi - didn't want to give it me, said he had to hand it in. But why should he? They would only put it on the fire. And my dance was so clear in my head, so vivid. I even bit Gil in the arm, the poor boy. He's never forgiven me for that." She laughed ruefully, her eyes shining as the scene came back to her. "But I got the uniform. I held it pressed tight against me with both arms to stop him snatching it back, and I was crying, I remember - the poor, poor German field uniform. I ran out of the room into the kitchen and threw myself down with it onto the basket of potatoes that Herr Kenzler had just sent in."

Wolfgang was fascinated, oblivious for the time to his surroundings, fascinated as much by the narrator as her tale - with her mobile features and eloquent gestures, especially the hands, large and capable but so expressive, like an actor's. As she finished speaking Piete had hugged herself, and he could almost see the tattered uniform in her arms. There were tears in her eyes.

"And have you tried the dance, the 'dance of the dead soldier'?"

"Not yet, but I will, I will." And with sudden urgency, "Don't talk of this at home, my mother doesn't like my dancing. She thinks I demean myself and the family. They are very proud, the Golzes."

With one of his sudden changes of mood Wolfgang laughed shortly and made as if to leave.

"It's fashionable, anyway, in Berlin these days, death. The dance of death."

"Fashionable? Do you think that's all I am after, being in the fashion?" Piete's eyes flashed, and she grabbed his arm. "What do you know about death? Just listen to me." She almost forced him back into his chair. "I have seen wounded men, wounded soldiers begging for death. When the troop trains came into Schneidemühl station from the Russian front they were full of casualties, stretcher-cases, men with their stomachs torn out . . . And the Masurian marshes, men sucked down, crying for help. Death isn't a fashion, it is horrible, beastly." She paused for breath, looking through the boy, not at him as the images returned. "Children, little babies. I did some nursing in the children's hospital - there were lots of unwanted babies in the war years. Little Gerhard, he died in my arms, the poor little worm - just skin and bone, hardly seven months old, with those big eyes looking up at me." Her own eyes filled with tears again and she brushed them away angrily as she fell silent. The men at the other table had looked up from their card-game at her tirade. Now the slatternly woman came over to clear their cups, sniffing as she did so and wiping her face with a sleeve before opening her cash-wallet, dark with grime.

Wolfgang was glad to breathe even city air, made fresher by the cold November rain, after the fusty café. "Do you have to go back?" He felt the need to make amends somehow to this strange, passionate person.

"I suppose I can stay out a bit longer. I'll see you back to the college." Piete had calmed down, as though the outburst had relieved her in some way. They walked slowly towards Fasanenstraße without speaking. Wolfgang respected the other's thoughtfulness. She felt immeasurably older than this fresh-faced boy with his breaking voice. How could he be expected to understand all that the war, that 'war' meant to her - the blind euphoria of those early months, soon eroded by the harsh realities, the poignant farewells, the broken homes, the shortages, and then the prisoners, the summary executions, the war cemetery outside the town, the wounded and the casualty lists, Werner Waldecker . . . She shook herself to expunge painful memories.

"So your family spent the war, most of it, in Italy? How was it?"

"My father is a doctor. He was in charge of the German hospital in Naples till we were driven out. They lost half a million men at Caporetto. The Italian army was no match for ours. The Austrians had asked for German reinforcements on their Italian front. And we had gas as well." The boy spoke with animation.

"How can you talk so lightly of such things?"

"War is war."

Piete felt like taking him up, but decided to ignore his glib callousness, putting it down to immaturity. Instead, by dint of more gentle probing, she encouraged the boy to open up about his family, his upbringing in Naples, holidays in Zürich, his music, this last stemming from his mother and influencing both boys, him and his older brother.

"Hans is . . nearer your age, I think," looking shyly at her. "He'll be twenty-four in January. But he's at Munich University. He began studying science - chemistry. My father is a research scientist as well as a doctor. But Hans switched to music - Georg Philip Telemann."

Piete laughed at the formal way Wolfgang brought out the name.

"So you'll be a violinist, like your mother?"

He shook his head, but did not reply at once. Then he almost blurted out, "Maybe I'll be a mathematician, or . . or languages, I like English, and Chinese. And philosophy . . oh, I don't know. There is so much to learn, isn't there! And to do. I love mountains, and swimming, and the open air - away from these stinking streets. But it's better in Nikolassee, where we live, the air is fresher, and there's the Schlachtensee to bathe in." They were on the steps of the Music School. A short, swarthy young man carrying a violin-case hailed Wolfgang, speaking with a thick East European accent.

"Hey, Graeser. You are not forgetting Klingler's rehearsal? It is almost time."

"Thanks, I had done, and I'll have to fetch my fiddle and music. I'll follow you, Leo." He held out his hand to Piete. "Sorry, I must go. Why not come out to Nikolassee? My mother . . my parents would like to meet you. And Professor Müller - he is my tutor, he lives near us. We are very quiet at home with Hans away, apart from the practising."

The girl ignored the proffered hand and gave him instead a quick, friendly embrace. "I'd like to, sometime. But I don't have much spare time just now. Thank you, anyway."

She watched him as he ran into the college. It took her mind back to her brother Willi, dear Gil. The same impulsiveness, the same openness to ideas, enthusiasms - those Mexican freedom heroes plastering the wall over Gil's bed! But the army had extinguished all that. She thought of that awful first meeting after he had been called up, not long before the whole stupid farce - tragic farce - ended. 'When Willi came in he never even looked at me, just clicked his heels together in front of the desk, his hands pressed against those ghastly ill-fitting concertina trousers, looking into space. When he was granted leave to have a walk with me - 'leave' for just that! - even then the only thing he was interested in was the horse-meat sandwich I had brought from Grandma. Not once did he mention his piano-playing or composing, and when I asked if he had thought of any more songs - those lovely songs he used to write! - he just kept looking at his watch in case time was up.'

The mournful strains of a cello, slow scales, not all that well in tune, drifted out to her from a ground-floor practice-room of the college. She felt a few spots of cold November rain on her face as she turned away.

The second rehearsal at Frau Kuhr-Golz's had not gone so smoothly. Piete was home and provided the piano continuo so that her mother could listen, sometimes singing a phrase. Differences between Margarete's and Wolfgang's ideas of the aria had become more evident, she approaching it mainly as a vehicle for displaying her voice, he intent on the rhythmic patterning, the counterpoint of voice and violin, and on the relentless - as he conceived it - forward movement of the music. Piete felt torn between the two, appreciating the standpoint of each while trying also to adapt her playing to her mother's demands. The session had started well enough. When Grete and Wolfgang arrived the door of the flat was opened by a cheerful Piete.

"Grete! Wolfgang!" A warm hand-shake for him. "Now we have time for once, and it is pay-day. I have bought some fresh-baked brötchen and beautiful wurst - 'Marrutke's tasty Bologna!' the advertisement says - in your honour. You see," turning to Wolfgang, "I know your Italian taste. So you must join us for supper after the rehearsal."

Wolfgang liked the neatness and order of the small apartment, contrasting so sharply with the shabby entrance to the block and its common staircase and dank stair-well, indistinguishable from a hundred others in Berlin. Piete's mother had unbent to this talented, intense boy with his clean Teutonic looks, fair hair and blue eyes, recognising an unusual musical intelligence. She pressed her daughter's invitation so warmly that Wolfgang overcame his reluctance and abandoned his first intention to refuse.

"But first to work!" Frau Kuhr-Golz was placing the music-stand as she spoke. "You like to stand, Wolfgang? Piete, you bring out that bass-line. You must be cello as well as clavier for us. And it will keep the violin in order."

Wolfgang was intrigued by the paradoxes, as he saw them, in the aria and in the cantata as a whole, the contradiction between the idea of Stephen's martyrdom by means of a particularly bloody and uncivilised death by stoning and the persistent cheerfulness of the music. Even Jesus's bouncy bass aria "Ja, ja, ich kann die Feinde schlagen" (Yes, yes, I can strike the adversaries), presumably those throwing boulders at Stephen - hardly the sentiment for a peacemaker! On another tack, he wondered whether their bass, one of the St.Mark's church choir, would be vigorous enough. Margarete said he was studying choral singing at the Music School but was glad to have a solo spot for once.

"Erich Braun, have you met him? Erich lives here, and as he's already at St. Mark's we can't refuse him. I think he will enter into the spirit."

The violin obbligato had its paradoxes too, opening the aria in those skipping quavers in triple time, but in the relative minor, G minor, instead of B flat major. The soul's longing for death as a dance! What did the great Albert Schweitzer have to say about it?

'... the joyous soul, happy to meet its death, in an aria with an animated 3/4 rhythm, as if it were hastening from this world to its Redeemer, leaping and dancing on its way.'

Wolfgang rejected, or passed over, the Redeemer concept, but the dance, now, that was something. The dance of death . . .

When Grete started pulling the rhythm about again, lingering on 'Mein Heiland, ich sterbe', where the voice and the violin had the same phrase a 3rd apart, Wolfgang put down his instrument in exasperation, quoting the Schweitzer passage to them. Frau Kuhr-Golz, who had been singing with Grete at that point, was annoyed.

"We cannot work if we are to have such interruptions."

Piete eased the tension by getting up from the piano, stretching her arms and proposing a break.

"Herr Schmidt was feeling generous today. He gave me a whole one hundred grams of real coffee. Now is the occasion for it."

After the coffee the rehearsal had been completed without further interruption from Wolfgang. He suffered Margarete's characteristic singer's arbitrary treatment of the rhythm, not daring to incur Frau Kuhr-Golz's wrath again by stopping. But his playing became more casual, the arpeggios in his solo passages less precise. When his phrases were in canon with the voice, Grete stopped.

"Wolfgang, you're too loud when I'm singing." The teacher backed her up and Wolfgang played the passage again, but with an ill grace.

Even when they were all sitting at supper round the small folding table, the simple fare set out invitingly on a white linen cloth by the two girls while Piete's mother went to her room "to change from my working clothes", it had proved impossible to recover the ease before the rehearsal began. Wolfgang, dissatisfied with his own playing and irritated by Grete's rhythmic sloppiness, had retired into his shell. He ate little, and spoke monosyllabically and then only when addressed directly. The two girls chatted about the coming performance, now only three weeks away, and about Christmas.

"Do you remember our war Christmases, Mutti? Those horse-meat balls that Oma used to make for us, and turnips, everlasting turnips." Piete laughed. "At least we can manage a better Christmas Eve this year."

Her mother sighed. "They were hard times indeed. And how guilty I felt when Mother - your Oma - sent me food. But here in Berlin everything was scarce, and I had no money from my pupils, only promises."

"What a stupid waste it all was!" Piete exclaimed, "Men killed . . for nothing!"

"You must not say that, Elfriede. We had to fight for our nation and for the Kaiser. All the gallantry, the sacrifices! For us all, you too! Ludendorff was right. We were stabbed in the back." Frau Kuhr-Golz spoke vehemently, the blood coming into her pale cheeks in two hectic spots. "And Von Treitschke was right too all those years ago: 'The Jews are our misfortune,' he said. He knew, he knew."

"Mutti, how can you say such things? You know that's not true. All our Jewish friends! And what about those two Russian Jews you taught just after the war? Cantors, weren't they, in their synagogue? Didn't they save you from starvation?" Her mother said nothing. There were a few moments of embarrassed silence. Wolfgang cleared his throat.

"My father worked with the Eighth Army Corps in Trier. He says too that we were betrayed from within." Then, as he recollected the incident he had witnessed last Spring, with more animation, "But the army is still in command, whatever the socialists say." He told how the policeman had been made to apologise, with the dog at his throat.

"It was funny to see what a coward he was. They think if they put on a uniform they can rule the roost." Frau Kuhr-Golz nodded vigorously and was about to speak when Piete cried out,

"Shame! And shame on you, Wolfgang. What sort of a country shall we have if we let bullies like that man run it? The policeman was right. It wasn't the poor dog's fault, either. They train them to be savage, the brutes!" She was almost in tears. Grete tried to calm her as she rose from the table, but she shrugged her off, glared at Wolfgang and abruptly left the room. It was left to Margarete to try to calm the situation. She made as if to follow Piete, but Frau Kuhr-Golz restrained her.

"Piete is hot-headed. Leave her to cool down." And to Wolfgang, "Don't be upset. You were not to know how Elfriede might feel about your story. Thank you for your playing. We need to tighten up the rhythm, you are right. The aria will be good. 'Leaping and dancing . .' Dr Schweitzer has such authority with Bach. Margarete, you must leap and dance with your voice. It is to be a pas de deux with Wolfgang's violin, so you must keep in step."

As the S-Bahn rumbled its way through the suburbs and out to Nikolassee Wolfgang's thoughts were in confusion. The Kuhr daughter was wrong, of course. But would Paul, his tutor, think so? He was not sure. His father had laughed when he told him that same story, matching it with others from his army days. He could not shake off the impression of Piete's outburst, her real distress. She was beautiful, too, in her rage . . . The drumming of the train's wheels dulled his senses and he lapsed into reverie. Grunewald! His was the next stop, terminus of the new service. Wolfgang picked up his violin-case, crammed books and papers into his satchel and waited by the door as the clean-smelling train pulled in to Nikolassee.

I   Wolfgang

1

THE LITTLE boy rubbed his sleepy eyes and stretched creased limbs, listening to the faint city sounds from the open window as the dawn sun streamed in, the hot Neapolitan sun, warm even at this early hour and promising another day of heat, dust and smells. Only Maria was awake in the household - he could hear the occasional clatter from her basement kitchen where she made and cooked his favourite pasta - so six-year-old Wolfgang revelled in the unaccustomed luxury of lying in bed. As his eyelids drooped again the distant sounds from the city below and to the east mingled with those of his waking dream, the drumming train wheels, the dark hole of the tunnel and its feeling of empty dread. If he was entering the tunnel, would he ever come out? Was it a dream or a memory? Suddenly he sat up and started fumbling in the shelves by his small bed. Yes, here it was, his own season ticket with Mama's lovely face on it. He called it his own, because his name was there underneath Mama's - Frau Elizabeth Graeser, geb. Obenaus - 70fr. After the long, long journey from Zürich to Naples, days and nights in the stuffy 1st class compartment, mountains, lakes, rattle and roar into the tunnels and out again wreathed in steam, punctuated by meals in the train or station restaurant, Wolfgang had begged the ticket from his mother as a keepsake. He could just make out the date stamped on the creased and tattered card 'Sep 1908'. Almost four years ago! And tomorrow he would re-trace that whole long journey with Papa and Hans, leaving Mama in dusty Naples for . . how long? He jumped off his bed and raced into his brother's room next door.

"Hans! Hansi! Wake up, it's morning. I want to ask you something."

"Get off me, you great oaf!" Hans rolled over, pushing his young brother so that he tumbled to the floor. "What do you want, anyway?"

"How long shall we be away? Remember, we're off tomorrow."

"Course I remember. I'm not likely to forget, am I, seeing the whole trip is for me, so that I can go to a proper Swiss school. I'll be away for ages, years! Don't know how long."

"Not you, silly!" Wolfgang sat on the side of the bed, his cotton nightshirt rucked up, both arms round his knees. "Papa and me. How long will Mama be lonely without us?"

Hans, superior in his 13-year-old wisdom, laughed. "She'll probably be delighted to be free of us all, you specially, Wolfi, with your eternal questions, and . ."

"No, but . . you must know, Hansi. You and Papa were talking about it all yesterday. I heard you."

"Don't call me that! My name is Hans, I'm not a bambino. Ask Papa yourself."

"Ask Papa what?" Miss Jones, their English nanny, had come in as they were talking. "Come on, children, time to be washed and dressed. You were late for breakfast yesterday, Wolfgang. We must not let that happen again."

Thanks to Miss Jones with her precise ways, breakfast had become quite a formal meal, North European style, even in this alien country. Dr Graeser was always first, either sitting at table or fiddling with his treasured German coffee machine and its little blue-flamed lamp.

"Can I put my finger through it, Papa?" This was a favourite trick of Wolfgang's, to pass a finger through the transparent flame without getting burnt. But today Dr Graeser was pre-occupied and distant. He ignored the boy, picking up the bulky Orario Ufficiale to re-check the train times and route.

"Quiet, Wolfgang, your father is busy." Miss Jones made both boys sit to the table, with its customary provision of fruit in the straw-woven peasant dish, pane francese and fresh milk for the children. As they did so their mother hurried in from the garden, taking off her wide-brimmed summer hat. She laid a bunch of black grapes, the bloom still on their plump skins, on the fruit dish.

"There! Warm from the sun, my darlings. You can eat some sunshine today, to help you on your journey to the cold north."

"How long is it before I come . . . before Papa and I come back? Will you be lonely, Mama mia?"

"I shall miss you, Wullie darling, of course I will. But it is only two weeks, and I have Freda here, your Miss Jones, and Maria, and all our friends at the hospitals. Don't fret for me."

"Look, Mama. Here's our ticket from last time, when I was . . how old was I?"

"Oh my goodness!" Wolfgang's mother had taken the battered season ticket and was looking at her photo on it. "What a fright! Did I really wear my hair like that?"

Her husband had looked up as she spoke. "May I see that, my dear. I should like to check it against our current one." Both boys craned to see the new ticket, which was adorned this time with a group photo, their father and both boys. "Yes, all is correct here, and valid for 60 days, to be on the safe side. Your Thomas Cook and Son are very efficient, I must say, Miss

Jones. It is extremely useful having Herr Faerber, the agent, so nearby. He brought the papers up here himself this-morning."

Freda Jones preened herself in this reflected glory. She was a rather wispy lady of indeterminate age, anything between 35 and 50, but it was a carefully guarded secret. The third and youngest daughter of an anglican bishop, Freda had assiduously cultivated her father's Italian hosts when he had visited Naples with her two years ago, and had been offered a post teaching English and 'manners' to the daughter of the house. When soon afterwards Louise, her charge, had left to join a cousin in Rome, Dr Graeser asked Miss Jones's employer, Dr Bertolini, a colleague in another hospital, if she might be spared for his two boys. The Graeser family spoke German most of the time, interspersed with Italian, but Miss Jones used only her own tongue, in precise, well enunciated diction, both from personal inclination and to justify her position in the household. She had found both boys quick and responsive, so tried not to make too obvious her preference for Hans, the older and more equable. Wolfgang was so unpredictable, subject to sudden rages of impatience, especially when he sensed that she had reached the limit of her knowledge on a particular topic. She was prepared to defer to him over music - Freda Jones had dropped out early from the statutory piano lessons at her middle-class home, to the relief of her teacher - but believed it was her due as their governess that both boys should accept her superior wisdom in other matters. Hans had his father's natural courtesy, so was able to gratify her, but the younger boy had been 'difficult', as she put it to his parents, from the moment she had joined the household.

Most professional families in Naples lived on the western hills. The Graesers' substantial villa was in the Via Amedeo, near the German and international hospitals and well clear of the teeming, overcrowded and verminous lower city - this in spite of the drastic clearance and demolition that had followed the cholera epidemic of 1884. Up here, instead of the stench of unwashed humanity and arsenical fumes from the brass foundries, the warm west winds brought with them scents of the countryside, and they were close enough to the sea, only half a kilometre, to relish its salty tang.

2

Carl Graeser had been familiar with Naples for some years before settling there in 1893. As a young ship's surgeon on the oddly named steamship "Popoff", Russian built but owned by wealthy Hamburg shipowners and trading between France and Italy, he had frequently watched the rocky slopes of Ischia slide by as the boat steamed into the Golfo di Napoli, drawing closer to the great amphitheatre of the city before dropping anchor with a clatter of chain in the wide harbour, under the watchful eye of St. Elmo castle, with Vesuvius fuming away over to the south-east.

One such visit had been in the early summer of 1886, made memorable for Carl Graeser by a chance invitation to a birthday party. Thanks to the need in rapidly changing Italy since the Risorgimento of 1861 for foreign capital and professional skills, the small German and Swiss community in Naples had been growing steadily. The railway boom had brought Herr Obenaus and his young wife from their native Munich in 1867, when he took up management of the Naples office of the Romana Railway Company. The following year saw the birth of their daughter Elizabeth, always known as Lily, one of whose earliest memories was of the spectacular and terrifying volcanic eruption when she was only four. As she grew up her closest friend was Heike Dohrn, daughter of Dr Anton Dohrn, the German naturalist who founded the Naples Zoological Station. Its aquarium in the Villa Nazionale, just below where they lived, was a favourite visiting-place of the little girls. In their teens Lily and Heike, one petite and fair, the other tall and red-haired, made a striking couple. They would wander together, arm in arm, through the bustling shopping streets of the upper city, followed closely by the Dohrns' manservant Paolo, who had strict instructions not to let them out of his sight and to make sure they steered well clear of the lower city. This was not easy, because Lily had a lively temperament, and loved to watch and listen to the street musicians, who were more numerous there - and less vulnerable to arrest by carabinieri or the municipal guardie - than in the politer quarter.

It was Lily's 18th birthday, a fine summer morning and the two girls had the pleasant task of going into town to buy her a birthday present from the Dohrn family. Lily, who was shortly to leave to continue her music studies in Leipzig, had expressed a wish for something 'typically Neapolitan' to take away with her. They eventually purchased for 150 lira, close to the maximum suggested by the Dohrns, an elegant hand-made bronze, one of Sabatino de Angelis' famous dancing fauns, copied from an ancient bas-relief in Herculaneum. They ordered that it be delivered in time for Lily's party that evening. As they left the studio Lily, with a mischievous air, spoke rapidly in German to Heike, so that Paolo could not follow it:

"Yesterday Papa took me with him on a visit to an engineer in the lower city. We saw an amazing peasant fiddler there on a street corner. He was playing in all kinds of ways, tunes with the violin behind his back, that sort of thing, but real music, not just tricks. It is not far from here, just off the Corso Umberto. Let's give Paolo the slip and see if he is there again today." Heike needed little persuading, and the escapade was simply achieved by asking the manservant to wait while they used the "ladies' room" in a trattoria then slipping out by another entrance. They knew Paolo would wait in a favourite circulo before reporting their absence. He always welcomed the chance of meeting cronies there and spelling out the headlines in the local papers.

The peasant musician was still at his post, with a voluble crowd round him, many clapping to the tunes, laughing and stamping their feet. There was a sprinkling of foreign tourists, but the two girls soon attracted attention, both by their fresh good looks and their clothes, which were in sharp contrast to the colourful rags of most of the people around them. The fiddler, aware of a rival attraction, came closer. He seemed to be offering to play something especially for them, but the girls could not understand his thick local dialect and were intimidated by his frankly physical admiration and bold eyes.

"Let's get away, Lily. I don't like the way he looks at us." But this was not so easy. The musician had positioned himself across the narrow lane and was twisting his lithe body into an extraordinary shape, hopping on one leg, the other behind his neck, and still scraping a lively jigging tune from his instrument, which almost seemed to grow out of his shoulder. The crowd cheered and stamped, and a bold peasant woman, apparently the player's associate, started to pull at the girls' clothes, stretching out a cupped hand and urging them to pay for their entertainment. They tried to protest, reluctant to risk opening their reticules for the money.

"Can I assist you, ladies?" The girls looked round with relief. Their own language! It came from a slimly built man with dark good looks. He was, perhaps, ten years older than they were and had an air of authority that caused the peasants to drop back respectfully.

"Oh, would you mind? It is a bit embarrassing. They are so importunate once you show interest." Lily smiled up at the stranger. "But I do want to give him something, he is such a marvellous player." The young man took out a silver coin.

"Two lira. Will that do?" The fiddler's eyes lit up as he caught the glint of the coin in the sun.

"Oh, that's too much. We couldn't . ." Lily said in confusion. The man shrugged and threw the coin to the performer, who caught it skilfully, tested it with his teeth and gave the trio of foreigners a sweeping bow.

" I shall be happy to escort you to a more salubrious quarter if you will permit me. Graeser, Carl Graeser at your service."

Both girls liked their courteous compatriot, but it was soon clear that he was more interested in fair-haired Lily with her blue eyes and clear complexion. He accompanied them to the circulo. Paolo was by the window, looking anxiously out. They could not resist laughing at the comic change in his features as he caught sight of the girls. He ran out, scolding Heike with the familiarity of an old servant, and effusive in his "Gracié tante, Signor!" to the respectable gentleman with them.

"But you must come to my birthday party this-evening, Herr Graeser. Please! It is the least we can do. Tomorrow I leave Naples, so it is a farewell party as well." The disappointment in Carl Graeser's face as he heard this was very evident.

"Thank you, I will come. What a pity you are leaving beautiful Napoli. I should like so much . ."

"I shall study violin in Leipzig."

"Ah, so you could appreciate our friend the fiddler."

"He was a natural. Playing the violin for him was like breathing. I shall never play like that."

The young Swiss-German doctor made a very good impression in the Obenaus household. Before leaving that evening he exchanged addresses with Lily and promised to keep in touch.

"I should like to find work on shore now. Sea life is all very well, but one cannot settle anywhere. I am old enough to want to put down roots, and where better to do it than in this lovely place. The medical school here is famous too. I could continue my researches. There is talk of a special German hospital in Naples, to be sponsored by the German Protestant church for Swiss and German people living here, so perhaps there may be a position for me."

It was seven years before Carl Graeser was able to fulfil this ambition. In 1893 the German Protestant church in Naples succeeded in negotiating an agreement with the comune to adapt a disused former nunnery in the Via Croce Rossa near the International Hospital. It would need an experienced director. Dr Graeser, whose career on shipboard had of necessity included both surgery and epidemiology, and who had been involved in research in Bonn before that, was eminently suited to the post. In Toulon he had even met and for a short time studied under the famous German epidemiologist Dr Robert Koch, whose pioneer work on the cholera bacillus had achieved world fame. Carl Graeser was one of that rare breed, a combination of working medical doctor and research scientist.

His appointment coincided with a further outbreak of Asiatic cholera in Naples, so he was thrown in at the deep end and had little time to pursue his acquaintance with the Obenaus family and their charming daughter. The friendship between Carl and Elizabeth had matured but slowly since that first meeting. Before his appointment Graeser had spent much of his time afloat and his occasional landfalls at Naples coincided only once during Lily's time at Leipzig Conservatory with her annual home visit. (Her family had decided that once a year was sufficient for the long and costly train journey, other vacations being spent in Munich with her uncle Willi Obenaus and his large, jolly family.) After completing her music studies Lily found the appeal of returning home to sunny Napoli too hard to resist. She soon found work, in the orchestra of Teatro San Carlo, the great opera house, during the season, and teaching violin, piano and singing. She and Carl remained good friends, but led their separate busy lives.

As director of the new hospital, and soon also occasional lecturer at the university medical school, Carl Graeser led an almost monk-like existence. He sometimes thought in these terms, the more so as his bachelor apartment in the grounds still bore traces of its former catholic occupants and the main nursing staff were deaconesses from his native Switzerland. In addition - inevitably in Naples, where since Prime Minister Crispi's reforms so many of the religious charities and establishments had been secularised - many of the remaining staff were nuns, a situation endured rather than liked by the protestant sponsors. Lily Obenaus met him occasionally and sometimes offered him a free ticket to the opera, but the quiet, intense doctor and researcher, twelve years her senior, was in sharp contrast to her happy-go-lucky musician friends with their unconventional hours and frequent rowdy parties.

It was once again a chance encounter that changed all this. Chance? Fate? Carl would often turn this over in his mind in later life, whose whole fabric was to be so radically shaped by the meeting. 1897 saw the worst wheat harvest in Italy for many years, and by Spring of the following year peasants all over the country, but especially in the impoverished south, were suffering the consequences. There were food riots in many of the large towns. In Milan carabinieri opened fire on one such, killing hundreds and exacerbating the latent hostility between peasants and the military. The reports of King Umberto's injudicious support for the action did much to harm his popularity even in loyalist Naples, where his courage at the time of the 1884 cholera outbreak had become legendary. Naples, with its teeming slums and thousands of unemployed seldom much above famine level, was hard hit by the food shortage. The volatile Neapolitan temperament, so lively and fun-loving, was always subject to sudden change, like its underworld companion Vesuvius. So much of a Neapolitan's life was lived on the streets, where a mood could change as suddenly as a volcanic eruption.

Lily had been rehearsing at the Teatro San Carlo and had just bought a long fresh-baked crusty pané. As she left the bakery she was aware of some commotion. There was the crack of a rifle and running footsteps. A dishevelled man ran towards her from the direction of the Via Roma. As he charged by, without stopping and with astonishing dexterity, he snatched the bread from her arms and ran on. Lily was too affronted to be frightened.

"Stop him! That's my pané, stop him! Thief, thief!" She could see how fruitless it would be to pursue him and was about to resign herself to the loss of her bread, when she saw a carabiniere near her raise his gun.

"No, not that! Don't shoot!" She was too late. The fellow stumbled, fell to his knees, the bread flying from his hands. Lily ran towards him. The bullet had lodged in his leg and he moaned as he tried to drag the leg behind him. She knelt down. Such a young man, hardly more than a boy and pitifully thin under his rags. She did not know what to do. The policeman had picked up her bread and brought it to her.

"Leave him, Signorina. He is rifiuti! Of no account."

"He's hurt. You should not have fired. Just for bread!" She was almost crying. At the same time she was aware that the man stank. Seeing his advantage, his moans increased. Then beside her, like a guardian angel (as she said later), there stood Carl Graeser. He had been told by her parents of the rehearsal and had planned to meet her afterwards, an uncharacteristic impulse for this normally reserved and punctilious man. He quickly took her place beside the wounded youth.

"One moment, please. I shall see if it is serious. Stop your howling, fellow!" His tone silenced the sufferer. Dr Graeser ripped away the boy's ragged trouser to see the wound. "A flesh wound - of no consequence. But it is the dirt that matters, pah!"

"Take this. Please!" Lily gave him her clean linen kerchief. He had already used one of his own to wipe the wound clean, the other served as a temporary bandage to stem the bleeding. By this time a small crowd had gathered, together with two of the comune policemen (guardi), who were arguing with the carabiniere. Dr Graeser left them to it, giving instructions about the bullet wound before offering his arm to Lily. She took it with gratitude, the reaction having left her pale and shaking.

"You have the knack of being there just when you are needed." Lily smiled to Carl Graeser across the table of the Café Gambrinus, where they had taken refuge.

"I wanted to see you. But what's this? Leaving Naples again, your father said?"

"Again? What do you mean?"

"Do you remember our first meeting? With the acrobat musician? You were just about to leave Naples then."

"Ah yes, for Leipzig. But that was just for studying. This is for ever."

"No!" Carl Graeser's reaction was almost violent. He grasped Lily's hand resting on the table as if he meant to hold her back. She laughed nervously but did not withdraw her hand.

Speaking gently she said, "Father's job has really come to an end. When he came to Naples the Romano was a German . . well, a Bavarian railway company in all but name. Now it is no more than a part of the state system, even with the lease to Romano. He has been dissatisfied for years, waiting for a chance to retire. Of course we'll be sorry to leave Naples . . ."

"You (Carl used 'Du' for the first time) must not leave Naples." He released her hand and leaned forward. "Don't you know how much you mean to me?"

Lily blushed, but did not drop her eyes. There was something about the urgency with which he spoke and the way he looked at her, this intense, lean-featured, mature man, normally so self-controlled. Before she could respond he went on, his words tumbling over one another, surprising even himself. He spoke of that first meeting, of how he had been captivated by her blue eyes and bubbling vitality. Of visits to the opera, where his chief pleasure was always to watch her playing. Of hot summer days spent together by the sea. Of their venture together almost to the lip of the crater, stumbling across the scoria and choking in the fume-laden air. Of her part in his elation at being offered the post at the hospital.

"Me? How did I . . ? I don't understand."

"You ('Du') had become for me an essential ingredient (she smiled at the stilted expression, so at odds with the intensity of his manner) of my love for Naples and its people. I loved Naples because . . because I love you." He wanted to marry her. His prospects were good, he was independent and had a position in this great city. He would speak to her father that very evening. He could not allow her to throw away their future.

3

After this declaration things had moved fast and with remarkable smoothness. The Obenaus parents had always liked the quiet-spoken Swiss doctor and had even considered him, privately, as a desirable son-in-law.

They were a bit taken aback by his inability to accept their wish for 'a proper Bavarian wedding' in Munich for their first child. His duties at the hospital and the university, he told them, made it impossible to leave at this time and he could not contemplate a long engagement. ("I am 42. I shall be an old man when I become a father.") So instead the hospitable Obenauses had to be content with a lavish ricevimento in their spacious house and garden - their last before leaving Naples - after the necessary civil ceremony. The important question of somewhere for the newly-weds to live was settled by their taking over the Obenaus establishment until they were able to find and purchase a house of their own choice. Lily had, in preparation for the move, resigned her post at the San Carlo opera house. In the following year she gave birth to their first child, a son. Hans, with his fuzz of black hair and wrinkled face, came crying into the world in March 1899. The little boy, almost comically like his father, flourished in the Neapolitan sunshine, doubling his weight satisfactorily in the first few weeks and evoking all the usual responses from Maria and the other women servants. Frau Obenaus senior had braved the journey from Munich and spent several months with her daughter. She had wanted Lily to have the baby at Munich, "where you will have proper nursing," but had had to defer to her son-in-law, who thought the journey would be too much for her.

1900, the turn of the century, had an inauspicious ring to it. In May their link to the underworld - as Lily always thought of Vesuvius with its smoky summit and sulphurous fumes - made itself manifest with another spectacular eruption. Heralded by vibrating rumbles for some hours beforehand, stones and dust were hurled hundreds of metres into the air, falling back into and around the cone while the lava stream glowed red as it flowed. The whole city was layered with ash, and Dr Graeser was inundated at the hospital with pulmonary ailments. The first night after the eruption the Graesers slept little, hypnotised like most Neapolitans by the lurid glow in the eastern night sky and listening to the periodical distant thunder of later small eruptions. Two months later, as if Vesuvius had given the signal, came the assassination near Milan of 'Umberto the Good', as many older countrymen still thought of their king. The state mourning did little to curb the natural gaiety of the Neapolitans, but there was much superstitious gossip about evil omens for the new century, and San Gennaro had more than his usual lavish tribute of candles in the cathedral. Maria, the old servant inherited by the Graesers from the Obenaus household, made a point of lighting one for her 'Signorina Lily' (she could not be persuaded to change to 'Signora', even after the baby was born), who was trying to cope with the early stages of her second pregnancy in the oppressive August weather. Her husband had been anxious about her for some weeks, with the double burden of the pregnancy and the disruption of moving to their new house near the hospital. It took its toll, and she suffered a miscarriage after three months. For weeks she mooned about the unfamiliar place like a lost soul, rocking little Hans in her arms, unable to settle to anything. She would pick up her violin, only to abandon it after a few notes, or play some desultory chords on the shining new Bechstein pianoforte, a house-warming present from Carl imported specially from Germany.

It was five years before the Graesers looked forward once again to an increase in the family. Hans was excited at the prospect of a little baby brother.

"But Hansi my sweet, perhaps it will be a baby sister for you." His mother looked down to where he was crouching by her feet under the piano. She had just been playing and singing some nursery songs.

"Well, that will be even better, 'cos she will look just like you, Mama." Lily blushed, and took him on her knee.

Carl Graeser's sister Juliana was matron of a highly respected maternity hospital in Zürich and succeeded in persuading her brother that Lily should have the benefit of more up-to-date equipment as well as a more tolerable climate for this second confinement, in view of the miscarriage and her age. As the baby was due in early September her husband decided to arrange his annual holiday to cover the same period. Fortunately Dr Scotti, Principal Medical Officer at the neighbouring International Hospital, was happy to cover for him, thanks to a good working relationship built up over the years. The International Hospital was a far bigger concern than the friendly 'Hospital der Deutsch-Evangelischen Gemeinde', and Dr Scotti, who had attended the opening of the latter twelve years before and made regular donations to its funds, liked the more relaxed atmosphere of the smaller Krankenhaus with its quiet-spoken Swiss deaconess nursing sisters.

Once again the family took to the railway, the spare middle-aged doctor, his wife Lily, her relief only a fortnight or so away, looking with her burden far younger than her 37 years, seven-year-old Hans and the young Italian nursemaid Violetta - Hans reduced it to 'Letta - who was alternately excited and scared at the unaccustomed sights and sensations of the journey, so different from her tiny one-roomed 'house' in Neapolitan Santa Lucia with its sparse, gaily painted furniture and ever-open door. The little boy tried to count the bridges and tunnels, but soon lost count and went fast asleep, sleeping his way through Milan and across to the Alps. After a welcome breakfast at the Bellinzona station ristorante - everything still seemed comfortably Italian here - the train began the long climb to Airolo and the great St. Gotthard tunnel, now a quarter of a century old.

"Feel here, Carl!" Lily took her husband's hand and rested it on her bulging tummy. "I think he responds to the tunnels."

"He? Why do you say that? A little sister for Hans is what you said before."

Lily smiled, but said nothing.

"Can I feel him, Mama?" Hans snuggled close to his mother, reaching out his hand.

"Wait for the next tunnel, Hansi darling."

The train was rumbling over the Ticino bridges, back and forth across the swirling current. Then came a veritable corkscrew of looped tunnels as they laboured upwards to the lovely Faido valley, festooned with waterfalls. There seemed no doubt that the curled up little creature in Lily's womb reacted to the tunnels.

"I wonder if he knows something," Lily mused. Carl Graeser told her that there was already considerable evidence of pre-natal memory.

As the train, refreshed from the long pause at partly ruined Airolo, set off for the 15 kilometre tunnel a thousand metres under the St Gotthard Pass, Lily tried to relax. The baby would not allow it. At the moment the mountain swallowed them it gave a kick so violent that she cried out involuntarily. 'He will remember this all his life,' she thought, with something like a pang of dread. The enveloping roar of the tunnel induced a sort of drugged stupor, affecting them all. Soon they felt a difference in the train's movement.

"That's it," said Graeser in relief. "Downhill from now on, we have reached the highest point."

The train emerged into dazzling sunlight and steamed towards Göschenen.

"Look there, Mama! What is that great thing? Is it a river?" Hans was staring out of the left-hand window. His father lifted the little boy up to see better.

"That's a glacier, Hans, the Damma Glacier. A frozen river. And over there, look, right in the distance, that great mountain with clouds round it, can you see? That is called Jungfrau."

Violetta, who had been terrified by the long tunnel, had revived with the sunshine. She came to the window and Hans pointed.

"Look, Letta. It's called Signorina." This caused a general laugh, and the high spirits persisted until the train pulled in to Göschenen station.

The rest of the journey seemed tedious after the excitement of the Alpine crossing and they were all glad when the huge steaming locomotive hauled them into the echoing Hauptbahnhof in Zürich. Carl's sister and her husband Dr Escher were there to greet them and to shepherd the little group of weary travellers to their spacious house near the Hohen Promenade, looking over cool green Lake Zürich. The journey left the expectant mother exhausted and wan, so Carl decided she should be settled straight away in his sister's maternity home nearby. The birth, a hard and pain-filled one for Lily, came prematurely a few days later. As she had known, it was a boy. They named him Wolfgang after Lily's father.

"But also after Mozart! I know he will be musical." Lily smiled up at her husband, looking pale and washed out but singularly beautiful against the white bed-clothes.

4

When the time came for Dr Graeser to resume work, his wife was still too frail to face the journey. She followed with her baby two months later. Her apprehension about the effect of the Alpine crossing on her new charge had been another reason for the delay. It was amply confirmed during the train journey. Eventually she took to holding little Wolfgang's soft head close to her breast and covering his ears whenever they approached a tunnel entrance. Even so, she felt his tiny heart beating faster each time. When they reached the St.Gotthard he set up a wail which lasted for the whole twenty minutes or so of their 'immersion'. Lily was relieved when they at last reached Naples, cool and pleasant in the autumn weather.

Hans loved his baby brother and always wanted to watch when his mother did anything for him. He would take the baby in his arms;

"Hold him carefully, Hansi darling. And remember, his bones are still soft, especially on his head."

It was a touching sight, the seven-year-old lad with his dark hair and brown eyes close to his fair-skinned, almost bald, blue-eyed baby brother. Soon it became clear that this attention was suffered by Wolfgang as a make-shift for his father. He was the favourite. Whenever Carl Graeser was able to spare a moment in the nursery the baby crowed with delight, holding up his arms until his father took him up. At that time the fifty-year-old doctor had a vigorous moustache in the Italian style, and the baby delighted in pulling at it, to the great amusement of the older brother.

The family made their next visit to Zürich two years later. Once again Wolfgang, now old enough to make his feelings more explicit, reacted adversely to the train journey; his mother resolved not to subject the little boy to another such ordeal until he could cope with it better. The Christmas of that year, 1908, was a memorable one. The German community in Naples always used Weinachtszeit as an excuse for home nostalgia: the Advent Calendar, gingerbread, the statutory Stolle cake, even the Christmas tree. Fir trees were not available; the Graesers' Weinachtsbaum was a poplar sapling, suitably decorated with the carefully saved trinkets and crowned with a tinsel star by Lily, enthusiastically helped by Hans. On Heiliger Abend, after the service in the German church came the present-giving. Little Wolfgang's special present was a large box of smooth wooden bricks. He unwrapped the big parcel with great excitement, shouting in delight,

"Papa, Papa, look!"

Carl Graeser crouched down beside him and together they started to build. Meanwhile Hans had been given his present, which had to be brought into the room from its hiding-place. It was a shining new bicycle imported from Germany. He was inordinately proud of it. His father left Wolfgang in order to explain its finer points.

"You will have to practise using the rear brake tomorrow morning. It works with the pedals."

"Wollie have a ride!" Wolfgang had followed his father and was pulling at the front wheel. Hans snatched it away.

"You are not big enough - is he, Papa?" Hans tried to pull the machine away from the little boy. His mother called,

"Here, darling. Let's make a house."

"Wollie want a ride, Wollie want a ride! Papa, lift me up!" He held out his arms in his customary imperious way, but this time Papa did not respond. The boy's face darkened in a scowl. He returned to his bricks, picked out a big one and hurled it at the bicycle.

"Nasty bikle! Nasty bikle! I hate you!" Lily tried to calm him, but the child almost went berserk. He stamped his feet, screamed and lay on the floor, and when his mother tried to pick him up, bit her finger and rolled away. Carl Graeser took him up, but as he held it the little body went rigid and the boy held his breath until he was blue in the face. Both parents were alarmed. Carl took the boy out of the room and finally succeeded in calming him down enough to hand over to the nursemaid to put to bed. Later they discussed the matter:

"No, there is nothing physically wrong, my dear. I am certain of that. Wolfgang is quite strong in fact, as you saw when you tried to pick him up." Carl laughed shortly.

"He is his father's boy, that's for sure," said his wife with a sigh, "but I do worry about him. He is so . . so quick, so sudden. I don't know how to put it." She went on to describe several incidents, some reported to her by Felicia, the nursemaid. "It is as if his mind is working all the time, faster than he can find words, or even actions, to express himself. You can see his frustration building up, then it bursts."

"But he loves you too, my dear. He relies on you - as I do. He needs your calmness and love and will need it more as he grows up."

Carl Graeser was right. Although Wolfgang clung to his father whenever he could, it was the mother who provided a kind of emotional sheet-anchor. Three days after the Christmas Eve outburst came the appalling Messina earthquake only 300 kilometres to the south. Neapolitans were no strangers to earthquakes; and many working in the hospitals, as elsewhere, had relatives in Sicily. Wolfgang kept hearing the word and kept asking questions.

"Hansi, what does the earthquake do?"

"Kills people. Makes buildings into ruins."

"How can it do that? Does it pick them up and throw them?"

"It's not a person, silly. It is a natural phenomenon," Hans was rather proud of this phrase, "like Vesuvius. You know how it rumbles. Well, when the earthquake rumbles, great cracks come in the earth." The older boy was warming to the theme now. "You stand there, Wolfi. You are on one side of Via Amedeo and I'm on the other. Do you understand?" The little boy nodded. "Now look! All of a sudden there's a great big hole, just there." Hans pointed between them, "Don't go too close, you'll fall in and die." Wolfgang looked scared and cowered back. "That is what happened in Messina. Not just people, whole houses, churches . ." The little boy's eyes had grown rounder and rounder. He burst in,

"And hospitals?"

"Yes, hospitals too. Everything!"

That evening Lily heard sounds in the nursery after Wolfgang had been put to bed and went to investigate. The door of the room was ajar. Wolfgang had left his cot and was piling his bricks up in a wall. He was totally absorbed, and for a while she watched, fascinated. After building as high as he could the little boy swung his arm, knocking the bricks to the floor. At the same time he made his imitation of the Vesuvius rumbles and fell to the floor on top of the bricks. He lay so still that the watcher thought he had hurt himself and ran in to him. He looked up at her, as if out of a dream.

"Quake, Mama, quake!"

By this time Hans had begun to attend the small German Grundschule in Naples, cycling proudly down from the Via Amedeo at 7 each morning. The school had been founded some years before to cater for the increasing number of Swiss and German ex-patriates, their number swollen by third and fourth generation descendants of the Swiss mercenaries who had joined the struggles against Bourbon domination. Many had inter-married here, captivated by the free and easy Neapolitan life-style, so different from the strait-laced, sometimes Calvinist environment of the cantons. Yet some of them still held on to the German language and culture. Dr Graeser was always ready to welcome these Swiss Neapolitans in the hospital, making use of the circumstance when soliciting funds from Swiss-based organisations.

Wolfgang was interested in everything. He had soon identified his father as the prime source of knowledge, badgering him incessantly with questions as well as exasperating the Italian nursemaids, who found it hard to deal with this lively, beautiful but unpredictable child, so different from their own sleepy olive-skinned bambini. Soon Dr Graeser made a habit of taking Wolfgang with him to the hospital or to his small research laboratory in the grounds, where there was more to occupy his mind and where his insatiable curiosity was more controllable. Since the Messina earthquake one of his recurrent obsessions had been Vesuvius, their link to the bubbling turbulent underworld, as Wolfgang imagined it. When he was five years old his father over-ruled his wife's nervous scruples and took the boy up to see the crater.

"Are you sure it won't give him more nightmares, Carl?" She had had to cope with many disturbed nights immediately after the traumatic Christmas of 1908 and from time to time since then.

"Quite the reverse, my dear. I spoke to Eugen about it last year in Zürich. Do you remember? He thinks we should do all we can to bring the boy's fears into the open. Seeing for himself is what Wolfgang needs." Carl Graeser had known Eugen Bleuler, just a year his junior, ever since their schooldays together in Zürich. Professor Bleuler was now in charge of Zürich's Burghölzli mental hospital and an internationally respected psychologist.

"But Eugen . . Professor Bleuler has to deal with abnormal cases all the time. Our darling Wullie isn't ill!"

"No, of course not. But he is abnormal in a sense, abnormally quick, intelligent. Bleuler was telling me about the new work they are doing there and in Vienna on the way the mind works. There is a colleague of his, a namesake of mine actually, Carl, Carl Jung. He has done some research on the unconscious, the hidden layer of consciousness in our brains."

Lily had stopped attending by this time, realising that the expedition would go ahead whatever her objections to it. In the event, it did seem to calm her son. In deference to her opposition, Carl Graeser had prepared the ground by reading to Wolfgang from Goethe's Italian Journal his vivid accounts of trips to the Vesuvius crater. Wolfgang was fascinated, especially by the description of the lava flow.

'I felt a great desire to get near the place where the lava was issuing from the mountain. My guide assured me that this was safe, because the moment it comes forth, a flow forms a vaulted roof of cooled lava over itself, which he had often stood on. To have this experience, we again climbed up the mountain in order to approach the spot from the rear. Luckily, a gust of wind had cleared the air, though not entirely, for all around us puffs of hot vapour were emerging from thousands of fissures. By now we were actually standing on the lava crust, which lay twisted in coils like a soft mush, but it projected so far out that we could not see the lava gushing forth. We tried to go half a dozen steps further, but the ground under our feet became hotter and hotter and a whirl of dense fumes darkened the sun and almost suffocated us. The guide who was walking in front turned back, grabbed me, and we stole away from the hellish cauldron.'

"What a pity the lava isn't flowing out now, Papa. We could do that too, and perhaps we would see it under us, like Goethe wanted to."

"You want a taste of the hellish cauldron do you?" His father laughed. "No, they don't permit that sort of thing nowadays. Goethe was there more than a hundred years ago, before it became popular with sightseers. We shall see plenty of smoke and smell the fumes, and you can bring back some pieces of lava as souvenirs."

The following year Hans was 13. Dr Graeser decided that he needed more sophisticated education, particularly in the sciences, for which he was showing a marked preference, than could be offered at the little school in Naples with its small staff and primitive equipment. It was arranged for him to attend a well respected boarding school in Canton Thurgau, near the Bodensee (Lake Constance). With the prospect of Wolfgang now attending school in Hans's place - Hans even magnanimously offered him the loan of his bicycle! - Lily felt able to take on more music pupils and engagements. Miss Jones agreed, somewhat apprehensively, to stay on for a while and provide extra coaching, especially in English, for her younger pupil.

The trip by Dr Graeser and his two sons to Switzerland in the summer of 1912 passed off without serious incident. Hans, a quiet serious-minded 13-year-old, resembled his father even more with his spectacles - he was short-sighted - and had something of Carl Graeser's studious temperament. He had been looking forward to his new life at the school in Glarisegg, and was sufficiently excited by the place and the other students not to mind the parting from his father and young brother. Wolfgang plagued his father with questions throughout the long journeys, but seemed to have mastered his early problems with the tunnels. His sixth birthday came while they were in Zürich and his uncle Escher, knowing the boy's inquisitive mind, gave him a stop-watch.

"You can time parts of your journey back with it, Wolfgang, and work out the speed of the train." It was well chosen. Wolfgang resolved to measure all the tunnels - there were more than thirty altogether - with the help of his new present, then he worked out various statistics to tell his teacher and Miss Jones.

It soon became evident that the curriculum of the little German school in Naples could not keep pace with Wolfgang's incessant mental activity. His father tried to supplement it, introducing him to parts of his practical research work, and Miss Jones plied him with English books, many of which, like her own favourite "Little Lord Fauntleroy", he abandoned after a page or two, to her chagrin. Almost the only children's book she managed to interest him in was Alice in Wonderland and Through the Looking-Glass. He devoured it in a few days then kept talking about it. A little later Freda Jones was startled to find an unfinished story by her pupil, boldly headed "Alice Through the Volcano", containing a mixture of scientific facts and blood-curdling accounts of people falling into bubbling lava and crevices opening up to swallow people, animals, buildings . . . She decided to show it to the boy's parents. When he found out she had done so Wolfgang went into one of his rages, throwing books across the room, stamping and shouting. For weeks afterwards he refused to speak to Miss Jones and only relented on his father's insistence.

5

The incident was one factor in Dr Graeser's resolve, early in 1914, to acquiesce in his sister's suggestion that Wolfgang should spend a longer time in Zürich, where on their previous visit he had struck up a close friendship with his cousin Georg Escher. He arranged to send his son for a six month stay. Miss Jones would travel with him as her last official duty; she had been getting increasingly nervous of the political situation and wanted to return to the bosom of her family while she could. The political unrest had been another reason for Carl Graeser's decision. Like many other Swiss and German residents in Naples, he placed little confidence in the 1882 Triple Alliance standing up to much strain, knowing at first-hand from Austrians in Naples the inveterate hostility between Italy and the Habsburg Empire, and aware also of the hold the Vatican had on French allegiance. They discussed such things endlessly at the German Club in the Via Roma.

"North Africa will be what decides it, peace or war." Dr Dohrn, son of the founder of the Zoological Station in "La Villa" and brother of Frau Graeser's friend Heike, spoke dogmatically. "Our gun-boat diplomacy in Agadir three years ago did not endear us to the French, nor did the Kaiser's courtesy visit - if you can call it that."

Carl Graeser, who had been listening up to then, took his pipe from his mouth.

"I don't agree. Giolitti is always looking south when he should look nearer home. Italy has been trying to ape the English by establishing African colonies, but they can't hold them. What happened at Adowa showed that clearly enough."

"That is old history," answered Dohrn. "Twenty years ago, wasn't it? They still hold Tripoli, in spite of the Turks."

Pastor Ellger from the German church joined in, in his rather high-pitched, querulous voice.

"In my view Giolitti is a man of peace. In the Turkish war he was over-ruled by the military and the catholics, but he has pledged himself to honour the treaty with our country and Austria. And he is a man of his word."

Dr Dohrn gave a scornful, barking laugh. "He is a trimmer, Pastor, a manipulator. In any case, what happened in Sarajevo is more important than anything Giolitti can say - or do for that matter."

This caused a lull in the conversation. There were Austrians as well as Italians in the room, and the assassination of Archduke Ferdinand the previous week was still, by common consent, a topic to be treated with circumspection. Carl Graeser knocked out his pipe and made to leave. He paused to speak to Dr Dohrn.

"I fear you may be right. My wife heard from her family in Munich only yesterday. They are all expecting war there, troop movements every day and a feeling that the waiting is over."

A Prussian doctor on a visit to the International Hospital, Dr Walter, overheard the remark:

"A good job too, if you don't mind my saying so. We have waited long enough. Say what you like about the Kaiser, he is no coward. And we are strong enough to deal with Russia as well as the others in the Entente. The Serbs deserve everything that is coming to them. And if the war spreads eastward Japan is bound to come in with us." He looked round and dropped his voice. "When Italy sees which way it is going . . ." nodding significantly, with a glance towards an Italian guest, Count Bersiglieri, on the far side of the room, then raising his voice again. "The Triple Alliance has stood the test of time. Mark my words, by Christmas Hindenburg will be crowned with laurel and we shall all be celebrating victory."

Carl Graeser was not as supportive of the Prussian doctor's assessment as others in the Club. He was thoughtful as he made his way back to the Via Amedeo. It was a good thing the two boys were out of Italy just now. Switzerland would remain neutral whatever happened, and the border would stay open. But was he himself a Swiss or a German? Not an Italian. In spite of his twenty years in Naples the doctor never identified that closely with the country. But he also felt detached from his so-called home country of Switzerland. 'I could never live there again, that's certain, nor could Lily. If things get difficult here,' Graeser, knowing by now something of Italy's opportunist foreign policies, dismissed the Triplice in his mind as worthless, 'we shall have to get to Munich somehow, to Lily's people. The army will be needing doctors.'

When he reached home another thick letter from Wolfgang awaited him, to add to the pile accumulating on his desk. He was proud of his seven-year-old son's long letters. They had talked about keeping in touch before Wolfgang and Miss Jones left Naples. Wolfgang said,

"I shall write to you, Papa, but Mama can read them. Hans always writes to Mama."

Carl laughed. "The main thing is to write regularly. Hans has been very good about that. We shall look forward to hearing from you too now, and of course you will hear from us every week."

The parents were amused at the contrast between the boys' styles of writing. Hans' letters were brief, practical, curiously impersonal and very neat, Wolfgang's long, expansive and written in a fluent, rather messy hand, with sundry crossings-out and blots. Carl took the letter in with him to his study and settled down to read it before his wife returned from the San Carlo.

" . . . Georg has been showing me how to draw. He is one of the best artists in the school and the teacher is always putting his pictures up. Yesterday we took our bikes and sketch-pads up towards the Zürichberg and made lots of sketches, looking over the lake and across to the mountains. The lake looks green from there . . . Dr Escher and Auntie talk a great deal about the coming war in Germany. Is there going to be a war, Papa? I have been looking at the map to see where Sarajevo is, where that student killed the Crown Prince of Austria. The student is called Princip, did you know? We saw his picture in the newspaper, he looks like Andreas Wundt, one of the older boys in our school. How can he be a murderer, I do not understand. Papa, please explain why a Serb should want to kill the heir to the Austrian empire. Will Italy be in the war? Dr Escher says that all the Roman Catholics in Italy will not want to fight French Catholics, so Italy will not want to honour the alliance with Austria and Germany . . . Please tell Mama that I practise my violin every day!! Dr Strauss is very strict. He has given me a sonata to learn by my namesake Wolfgang Mozart. It is called Sonata in E minor, K.304. I think K. stands for Opus but that does not make much sense. All the beginning is in unison with the clavier piano, then I play the tune. Aunt Juliana sometimes plays the piano for me, but tell Mama she is not nearly as good as her. There are only two movements, the second is a minuet and trio. The trio is the second part, then you go back to the minuet. The trio is lovely, in E major for a change. Georg says I play out of tune, but he does not really know . . ."

So it went on. This letter, like the others, covered several sheets of writing paper. Carl smiled as he read, seeing the writer so clearly scribbling away in his impetuous style and with his forest of ideas, that unruly lock of fair hair flopping over his forehead. The doctor had already proposed to his wife that they try to make a collection of Wolfgang's letters and have them printed. Lily was at first startled by the idea.

"They are so personal, Carl, intimate almost. I don't think Wullie would take kindly to it."

"They would not be for the general public, my dear, just for our own circle. He gives such a vivid picture of what it is like to be that age in these troubled times. They would make a sort of chronicle."

Wolfgang spent his eighth birthday in Zürich and returned to Naples in late autumn, accompanied this time by his cousin Georg and one of Dr Escher's staff, a Milanese who had agreed to take the two boys on to Naples before going home. When he heard of his father's idea to print the letters Wolfgang was happy to agree, rather proud at the thought of his work actually appearing in print.

The German community in Naples, among whom the Graesers always numbered themselves, had had a temporary reprieve when the official statement of neutrality went out on August 2nd, but the old carefree life seemed to have vanished under the shadow of war. Frau Graeser was made aware of the change through a trivial enough but disturbing domestic circumstance. She had taken over two or three of the staff from the Obenaus household, who had been happy to move in with them to the new house in Via Amedeo. In October, soon after Wolfgang's return from Zürich, old Maria the cook asked to see her. She always walked from her home in the lower city, arriving at 6 a.m. as regular as clockwork. After the family breakfast Lily asked her to come up. She appeared, embarrassed and red-eyed. After dropping a curtsey she muttered with her head down:

"I must leave you, Signorina . . beg pardon, Signora."

"Why, whatever is the matter, Maria? Has something upset you? Has Wolfgang been annoying . ."

"No, Signo - . ., not the sweet bambino . . . ragazzo. Never! It hurts me to leave him, dear young boy. And you, Signorina."

"Well then," Lily was at a loss. "Do you need more money? Higher wages?"

"The doctor is very generous, Signor . . . Signora. My man Francesco, he says to me 'You work for those foreign people. They are our enemies.' He says . . . I must not tell you what he says about Germans, Signorina. Our holy Father (she crossed herself) says too, and Father Agnello in our church, we must help our brothers and sisters in France. So I must leave you. I am sorry." Her face had closed up and Lily realised there was no more she could say or do.

Life went on in spite of the war, but little by little the Swiss-German community shrank as their members found means of returning home, and little by little they began to feel for the first time like aliens. Lily took some comfort in her musician friends, always an exotic mix of nationalities. They tried to shrug off the rising tide of chauvinism, but it was impossible to ignore. It was summed up by an injudicious remark in a speech by the Prime Minister, Professor Salandra, who had replaced Giolitti when war became imminent, which became a catch-phrase: sacro egoismo. In May 1915 came the declaration of war against Austria-Hungary, and the prospect of actual fighting on the north-east border. The Graesers were not insensitive to the contrast between the confused, often ignorant attitudes around them in Naples and the harsh realism of the war in Germany, reported to them almost daily in the letters and newspapers sent from their families and other friends. Dr Graeser was glad that Hans, at least, was out of harm's way in Switzerland.

Hans was less of a worry than Wolfgang, with his questing mind, bubbling energy and unpredictable changes of mood. Wolfgang had, on his own initiative and with little guidance, developed his artistic talent considerably, drawing and painting now with fluency and assurance. He still concentrated on landscapes, in particular the peaks and snowbound vistas of his native country. Some of the paintings were beginning to assume semi-abstract patterns, blocks of white, blue-white, and black or blue-black slabs of rock, green lakes and glaciers. Often he gave the pictures no title beyond Study I, Study II and so on, not wishing to say on which actual mountain scene or panorama they were based. In Naples he had also done a series of Vesuvius paintings, some of them lurid attempts to portray a major eruption like the one in the year he was born. A few incorporated curiously mediaeval-looking devil-like figures leaping in and out of the flames. He named this series simply "1906 Nativity".

Lily Graeser found the obsessive quality of these paintings disturbing. Wolfgang had accumulated quite a sheaf of sketches of Vesuvius, done both from their garden and from further east, closer to the volcano. He composed and painted the actual pictures in his own attic room, on the door of which he had fixed a large sign: STUDIO - Keep Out! On one occasion his mother had gone there to fetch him for a music lesson. He had not noticed the door opening.

"Wullie darling. Time for your violin lesson. Can you leave the painting now?"

Wolfgang started, making a splash of colour on the composition. He muttered a reply of some sort, busying himself in removing the blot. But it was the way he had looked at her with those sharp blue eyes, a strange haunted look that went straight to her heart. She hurried to him, put her arm round his neck and kissed his tousled fair hair.

"Come, dearest. Let us do some playing now. You look tired, and it is so stuffy up here." It was almost as if she had woken him from some strange dream - or nightmare.

By now Wolfgang had grown taller than his mother and he looked older than his ten years. There were often two vertical lines on his forehead, giving him a pre-occupied, studious air. He was always happier when playing or listening to music and would have sudden onsets of exuberant high spirits. When outside, rushing down to the bathing-place at the Posilipo or pedalling furiously on his bicycle away from the city to the west, these outbursts could become almost manic, especially if he was with school-friends. These days his father had less time to devote to him, beset as he was with financial and staffing problems at the hospital. Nevertheless he was proud of his brilliant, multi-talented son and did what he could to supplement the rather limited capabilities of the German Grundschule. In both mathematics and languages Wolfgang far outstripped his fellow-pupils, as well as - Dr Graeser suspected - his teachers. He arranged for the boy to have extra mathematics lessons with a student at the university, and always ensured that there was French and English reading-matter at home, both books and journals. Wolfgang read voraciously and indiscriminately at this time.

6

"I think we must get Wolfgang away from Naples this year. Juliana is happy to take him again." Carl Graeser and his wife were contemplating the future as 1916, the third year of the war, began. "I don't like the look of things here and it seems uncertain how long we can remain in Naples."

"He loves his cousin." Lily was trying to convince herself of the merits of the scheme. She always had a lurking dread in her for this second child. "But he seems so . . so vulnerable, Carl. It is hard to put into words. Those strange Vesuvius paintings, don't they worry you?"

"Worry me? I think they are remarkable certainly, my dear. Astonishing for a boy of his age, so lively, adventurous. What is there to worry about?" He did not wait for a reply. "I showed them to Werner the other day. He is something of a connoisseur, you know, in touch with French art, Modigliani and so on. He was impressed, said I ought to have an exhibition of Wolfgang's work. But there is no chance of that here. Perhaps when the war is over . . ."

"Will it ever be?" Lily spoke despondently, then, bracing herself, "You are right, Wullie will be better off in Zürich."

Wolfgang left Naples in April, this time accompanied by one of the Swiss deaconess nursing sisters from the hospital. In June the weak coalition government led by Antonio Salandra fell and was succeeded by an even weaker administration under the nominal leadership of 78-year-old Paolo Boselli. Power was effectively in the hands of the army under General Cadorna. The campaign by the Isonzo river in the north-east dragged on indecisively. Meanwhile the Graesers, in common with other Germans in Naples, received more and more sombre bulletins from the western theatre of war. The fighting at Verdun seemed an everlasting, static slaughterhouse; three of Lily's cousins had lost their lives there. Soon after Boselli's takeover came news of the Austro-Hungarian defeat by the Russians at Lutsk near the Carpathian mountains. Emboldened by this and by Italy's repudiation of the Triplice, Romania declared war on Germany and Boselli followed suit for Italy.

"That decides it!" Dr Dohrn was again giving the - already depleted - German Club members the benefit of his views. "Now this country is at war with us it will soon be too hot a spot for any Germans, even down here in Naples. Or German speakers, for that matter." The last shot was for Dr Graeser.

"I can corroborate that." Anton Schmidt, a young lecturer from the university chimed in. "On my way here I called in for some cigars at the government place down the road, what d'ye call it? Spaccio Normale, and they refused to serve me. I asked in German, as I've always done. The assistant just turned his back."

"We are needed at home now. It is the duty of all Germans to rally to the Fatherland." Major Schwartz was the oldest member of the Club. Thirty-five years' residence in Naples and an Italian wife had not succeeded in expunging his guttural accent, and he wore his grey hair close cropped in a passable imitation of von Hindenburg. "If I were younger I should be on the next train."

"Well, I leave in a week's time," said Dr Dohrn. "What about you, Graeser?"

"I am not in quite the same position, Dohrn, as you know. I have no-one to whom I can hand over the hospital at present. As a Swiss national I have at least nominal security here."

"Nominal, I grant you that, nominal. Try saying that to one of those swaggering carabinieri. It is a new pastime now, harrassing foreigners, unless they are French or English. Or Americans, of course. Your wife is German, I think?"

Carl Graeser would have liked to dismiss Dohrn's words as his usual rhodomontade, but they chimed uncomfortably with his own and his wife's observations. At the hospital the remaining Swiss nursing sisters, who formed the backbone of the nursing staff, were recalled for safety by their community and had to be replaced by less competent Italian nuns. In the city the hostility to Germans and German speakers became more and more pronounced.

In the event the decision to leave was taken out of Carl Graeser's hands. Early in 1917 the comune informed him that his hospital was to be placed under the control of their Chief Medical Officer and might be requisitioned for war wounded. They had already had to cope with some of the latter, pathetic half-starved survivors from the Isonzo fighting, often with appalling wounds. Dr Graeser was glad that he had accepted his sister's suggestion the previous autumn to keep Wolfgang in Zürich rather than risk the return journey by himself. At home they had lost all but one of their Italian servants, and Lily had had to end most of her teaching and playing in order to keep the house together. Food was in short supply, much of it severely rationed or only available at inflated cost 'under the counter'. The same was true of coal: when it was delivered it was poor stuff, full of dirt and stones.

In October the Italian 1st Army under General Cadorna, ever the optimist, initiated another major attack to the north of Montefalcone and Trieste, with the aim of scattering the weakened 11th Austro-Hungarian Army. Cadorna, ensconced in his fortress well away from the field of battle, ignored danger signals from his own staff, dealing with them summarily by dismissing 'cowardly' officers wholesale and replacing them with others less experienced. He totally misread the changed strength of the enemy by the addition of German reinforcements under General Otto von Below, tough battle-hardened troops with heavy artillery, including gas.

The Graesers, alone in their big empty house, trying to keep warm at the end of October, had a graphic account of the ensuing catastrophe from the 18-year-old son of their last remaining servant, the gardener and handyman. Although a true Neapolitan, Hanno Sprenger was one of the descendants of Swiss mercenaries who had settled there.

"That sounds like someone outside, Carl."

"At this time of night? It is pitch dark out there. You must have imagined it, my dear."

"No. There it is again." This time Carl Graeser had to acknowledge it. He strode to the door and called through it.

"Who's there?"

"Signor, please, Signora! Help, please!" Carl unbolted the door.

"Who are you?" At the same time his wife cried out, "It's Antonio! He looks frozen. Come, we have a fire here."

Sprenger's son Antonio, conscripted only six months before, had suffered from his fellow recruits because of his German-sounding name. His platoon, in common with others, had waved white cloths and handed their arms over to the advancing Germans. Before doing so they turned on 'the dirty German' in their midst and would have summarily shot him had he not managed to wriggle free and escape in the fog. The boy was a sorry sight, thin and shivering, with bare feet and torn clothes, hardly recognisable as a uniform. Emboldened by the warmth and such food as they could provide - little more than bread and olives, with a mouthful of local wine -

he started his tale. Once away from the Front he had hitched rides on farm vehicles and lorries or walked, using simply the word 'Napoli' and hoping for the best. He had not dared to go straight home in case the authorities had posted him as a deserter. The Graesers questioned him about the battle.

"Our searchlights kept sweeping across. We could see soldiers, German soldiers with helmets (he gestured to show the bucket shape), coming through the river. Then there was gas, clouds of choking gas (the boy gripped his throat, his eyes staring) all mixed with the freezing fog. I lay in the mud to get under the gas and crawled away. We had no shelter, just mud and iron sheets. We made holes in the rock to hold the sheets. There were many dead, many wounded, crying out . . ." As the images came back he scrambled up, looking wildly about him. Lily took the boy's hand gently and pulled him back by the fire. "Then we knew it was the end. I wanted to go to the Germans with the others, but they turned on me."

Frau Graeser made up a bed for him by the fire with some blankets. The next morning he went to his father as soon as he arrived and they heard no more of him. Later that morning Dr Graeser was summoned to the City Hall and informed that the German hospital was to be requisitioned 'with immediate effect.' His house also would be required. Since his wife was an enemy alien she should be interned. However, in view of his service to the country they were prepared to permit them to leave together.

"And our possessions? Our furniture, my car, my research instruments, laboratory?"

"Confiscated, Signor. Your fellow-countrymen have taken more than that from Italy at Caporetto. They have taken our honour, our young men."

Dr Graeser barely had time to telegraph the Eschers in Zürich before they left Naples, carrying whatever they could rescue and had room for in their hand luggage, trunks having been denied them. By some administrative oversight, helped by a sizeable exchange of lira at the station, they did succeed in despatching one large cabin trunk to Zürich, labelling it 'Medical apparatus'. Its contents proved a godsend in the following days of travel, first to Zürich, with an emotional reunion with Wolfgang and Carl's sister and brother-in-law, then all three of them on to Munich. The border crossing at Lindau was stiff with armed militia, and there was a disconsolate queue extending right across and out of the station and along the wall outside. Their hearts sank when they saw it.

"We shall be here for hours." Lily, tired out from the last few days, was almost in tears. She sat on her case and put her head in her hands. Wolfgang stood stupidly, not knowing what to do. Carl had gone into the station to investigate. He returned with a spring in his step, followed by Lily's brother Karl, very smart in his army major's uniform. After the greetings he told them he had managed to 'borrow' an army staff car and could take them all the way to Munich.

II Piete

1

"That's gold, that is!" The little girl was squatting on her hunkers by the heap of grain, running the silky seed-corn through her fingers and delighting in the touch and clean smell of it. By contrast, the grinning farm-labourer who spoke seemed to her uniformly drab in colour, standing huge beside her in his clumsy wooden-soled boots and coarse clothing.

"Liquid gold?" Piete loved words, loved the sound of 'liquid' - flüssig - , which she had heard her Oma use that morning at breakfast. She looked up to the man's brown face.

"Ar, young missy, liquid gold. That it is. You'm got a field of corn in them little hands o' yourn."

"A whole field? . . ." The girl jumped up, her pigtail flapping. As she did so a mouse ran out of the golden heap.

"Ach, the varmint. I'll have 'un!" The man moved with sudden agility, bringing a heavy foot down on the creature.

"Oh don't! Poor little thing!" Piete was too late. He lifted his foot to reveal the tiny corpse, its head mangled and bloody. She bent down and lifted it by the tail.

"Leave un be, missy. Your clean shift'll be smutted. Here, I'll burn it." But the little girl was oblivious, sobbing as she stroked the soft grey fur with a gentle finger. She drew back from the man as he reached out his hand.

"You great brute! You killed him, you killed him. What harm had he done to you?"

The man shrugged his shoulders, taken aback by the vehemence of the attack, and even a bit intimidated by the girl's flashing eyes. She was, after all, Councillor Golz's grand-daughter and the barn was on his property. He tried to soften his tone.

"See here, Miss Elfriede." He bent over the grain heap, pushing some of it aside with a calloused hand. In spite of herself she was intrigued. She laid the little thing, now stiffening, tenderly on some wisps of straw and looked where the man's blunt finger pointed. Traces of mouse droppings, some chewed grains.

"'Im's a thief, and a mucky one. Which do you want, which do your grandma want, corn for her bread or a barn full o' mice?"

Piete had to recognise the logic of it. 'Corn for our bread.' Of course, the seeds must be saved. In a more friendly tone she asked,

"How many grains will one seed make when it is planted in the field?" The man scratched his stubbly head.

"Why now, there's a puzzle. If 'e falls good and takes root . . if 'e grows into one ear o' corn . . . . Let's see, twenty, thirty grains?"

"Thirty! All from one little speck like this?" The child had crouched down again and was rolling a tiny seed between pink finger and thumb. She cupped one small palm and carefully counted thirty of the cool gold grains into it. The man seized his advantage.

"Ar. And how many ears of corn now did that varmint rob us of? Answer me that, young missy."

She looked at the golden heap, then at the stiffening little corpse. There was nothing to say. Suddenly she jumped up, went over and lifted the mouse gently in her hands.

"Well, he shall have a proper funeral. Marie can help me, and Willi must be the pastor and say the funeral words from a little black book . . Oma's prayer-book will do." She nodded to the man and ran out of the high cool barn into the April sunshine.

It was 1908. The affairs of the great world outside - Casablanca? Where was Casablanca, where it seemed from the newspaper Germany had been insulted by the French? - seemed faint and far away in rural Posen, where life went on as it had done for decades in the farms and great estates. This was Prussia, and the Poles knew their place while Prussian efficiency ensured their jobs. Away to the west along the railway, Kaiser Wilhelm II in Berlin ruled in his fitful way, and Germany prospered. In Schneidemühl, the small market town where Elfriede lived with her grandparents, town and country blended peacefully. Even as a six-year-old she was free to run more or less where she wanted in the sleepy little town, with its 20,000 or so inhabitants. No-one would interfere with little Piete, grand-daughter of Master-Builder Golz, who, besides being a Town Councillor and a Freemason, was the architect behind many of the town's more imposing buildings, like the Masonic Lodge "Loge Borussia" and the fine army barracks, home to the 149th Infantry Regiment. It seemed proper to the burghers of Schneidemühl that Councillor Golz should choose the handsomest of the six jolly Haber girls as his bride, thus linking two of the best families. The oldest, Louise, had already married Georg Otter, well respected for his position in the Post Office. The wedding reception was held, of course, in Loge Borussia, just completed in time for the great occasion.

Piete's planned funeral never took place. All her cajoling could not persuade Willi to leave his own obsessions and join her game to act as pastor. He was tinkering at the piano when Piete ran in, the mouse carefully folded into a lace handkerchief 'borrowed' from her grandmother's lavender-smelling drawer. Finally he shouted at her,

"Go away, I'm composing." Willi knew this would always silence his sister. She was so proud of her artistic older brother, with his lovely tunes and slim white musician's hands.

"Piete, have you been in my bedroom with your muddy feet?" As she came in Frau Golz spoke crossly for once. "And what is that you have in your hand - one of my best handkerchiefs! You naughty little girl." She snatched the square of delicate lace, and the mouse fell to the floor.

"Oh! Whatever next?" Piete stood in dismay as her grandmother looked at the offending object. She was always devastated when her Oma was cross with her.

"Marie! Marie!" The servant rushed in, scared by the urgency in her mistress's tone. "See there! Take it up and see that it is burnt. Do you hear? Burnt in the stove!"

Marie curtsied hastily and carried off the corpse. Piete, chastened, was sent out to wash her hands.

Such a fine funeral she had planned! She remembered that day in Karlstraße - it must have been one, two years ago? Oma had let go her hand as they stood by Schachian's shop. The little four-year-old had been captivated by a jointed wooden toy being demonstrated to a customer by Herr Schachian himself. Her grandmother was deep in conversation with her own sister, Aunt Emma Haber, who owned the fancy goods shop next door. As Herr Schachian disappeared into the dark interior of his shop Piete caught sight of a patient black horse standing outside a house just round the corner. Behind it was a hearse, draped in black. She ran up to it and stroked the horse's soft nose, but found herself taken by the hand and led with others through an open front door. When she tried to say something she was hushed severely by a gaunt lady dressed in black. Suddenly there was a big box in front of her with a man lying in it in his Sunday clothes. A lighted candle was placed either side of where his head lay. Some people were crying, and another man stood by with a black book in his hands. Were they going to bury this man in the box? The little girl opened her eyes wide and stared fascinated at the resting body. He looked so peaceful. Didn't she see him open his eyes just then? Perhaps he wasn't dead after all! Perhaps they had all made a mistake and he would be buried before he could tell them.

"He's alive! Look, all of you, he's alive!"

The child's shrill voice startled them all to sudden silence. Then the pastor spoke in solemn tones,

"'Out of the mouths of babes . .' This child has spoken truth, my friends. Weep no more, for he has found everlasting life.." Frightened by these portentous words and by the stir she had made, Piete squeezed herself between the trouser-legs and skirts and escaped.

Piete loved the open air and adored all animals, however small or large. The great brown coach-horses Hans and Liese were two of her favourites. They would nuzzle at her when Schulz, her grandfather's coachman, let her help with the grooming of their sleek coats, for they knew she would have a sugar-lump for each, purloined from the silver sugar-bowl on Oma's tea-table, or at least a sliver of carrot begged from Marie in the kitchen. Coachman Schulz and his diminutive apple-cheeked wife, no taller than six-year-old Piete with her long legs, were always welcoming. Had not their own Gurtel nursed her as a baby! And for her part Piete, or Miss Elfriede, as the couple always called her respectfully, loved to scamper out into the yard and up the stairs to their cosy flat above the coach-house, to be regaled with gingerbread or a coarse home-cooked biscuit smeared with raspberry jam.

When she sat up on the box beside coachman Schulz as the shiny black Golz coach with its two brown horses pulled out from the yard of "Villa Golz" into Zeughausstraße, Piete liked to think that the common folk doffing their caps were paying homage to her rather than to her grandfather, ensconced in the dark blue velvet interior. It was far nicer in the open air, beside old Schulz with his brown woollen waistcoat and gnarled hands. Sometimes he would let her hold the stiff black leather reins, and she fancied herself a princess 'like Princess Sissi in Vienna' visiting friends in her summer barouche. The coach, bound perhaps for one of the grand houses in its estate outside the town or to survey one of the Golz-owned plots of land on the outskirts, would pursue its stately route up Posenerstraße to the town centre, left along Friedrichstraße and out past the town cemetery with the Golz-Haber family vault prominent amongst the sarcophaguses. Ten minutes in any direction and town became country, the town smells - baking bread from Zahl's, horse-dung, spices, and if the wind changed the choking stench from the starch factory - gave way to cut hay and the gentle perfume of the potato flowers, all overlaid by heady whiffs from the two shiny rumps in front of them.

She could never think of her grandfather as Opa and would not dare address him so, with his impregnable waistcoat and shiny watch-chain, the Masonic badge dangling from it. Many important people came to see

Councillor Golz; the big silver bowl in the drawing-room was seldom empty of visiting-cards. The Frau Councillor also had her circle of visitors, wives of the town's notables like Frau Councillor Schön, old friends like Fräulein Ella Gumbrecht, who taught at the elementary school, as well as others from the extensive Haber family, her oldest sister Louise the inventor, or Clara Schwarz in town from Bromberg for some shopping. Frau Louise Otter lived nearby with her husband Georg, retired from the Post Office, who appeared very rarely, trotting along a few steps behind his wife as they took the air on a Sunday afternoon. He was happier in the room allocated to him by Louise, who hated the smell of tobacco and would not allow his favourite indulgence anywhere else in the house. Piete would sometimes wave to him as she passed the window, or call out 'it's a lovely day, Uncle Georg!' The old man would take his pipe from his mouth and wave it about, with a friendly smile.

Most of the Poles, like the Golz's servants Emma and Marie, were Catholics and went to the Catholic church on Sundays, with its incense, candles and gaudy statues. Their Prussian masters attended the three more sober Protestant churches or the Lutheran church, while the Jews, many of them shopkeepers like Johr and Gabriel the butchers or old Herr Edel, whose grocer's shop Piete loved, with its strange, clean, sour smells and sacks of flour, sugar and other dry goods, gathered at the synagogue every Saturday. On great festivals, like this Whitsun of 1908, the Golzes and Habers would occupy the family pew in the great 'town church' in Neue Markt. Piete and Willi, inseparable as ever, held hands as they sat between Grandfather Golz and their dear Oma, while the pastor droned on, for ever it seemed to them, in the high pulpit.

"Hey, Willi!" Piete whispered, stifling a giggle. "Suppose he was suddenly struck dumb. We'd just see his mouth opening and shutting, and nothing coming out."

"I'd like to put a spell on him," said Willi fiercely. Then more quietly, after a sharp nudge from Grandfather, "I'm going to be a magician. I want that conjuring set we saw in Schachian's yesterday, then I'll practise and practise. Have you got any money left, Piete?"

"No. Why not ask Mutti? She's got lots of money in Berlin."

Once back in Villa Golz they raced upstairs to Willi's little attic room, and he set to work on the letter to their lovely rich Mummy in Berlin.

Whitsun is a mighty Feast
My Mummy is the very best!
Give a cheer for Mummy, who
Sings so beautiful and true.

There's no-one better in the world
In wood and meadow, land and field.
She's awfully, awfully good, so that
Even God takes off his hat!
Put out the flags when she is here!
The sky too opens up for her.
Mummy dearest, when you come,
  please bring me a conjuring set costing 1 mark 25.
 Your very loving boy and little poet, WILLI

Piete was impressed. "It is a real poem. Perhaps Mutti will make it into a song."

"It's not a song, silly. It's a poem. If I wanted a song I would compose one. And then Mutti would sing it."

Their mother's visits were always great occasions for the two children. They loved her city elegance, making the native Schneidemühlers look dowdy and plain when they walked out with her. In the morning they would both race into Mutti's bedroom, to be first next to her and snuff up her delicious perfume. After the inevitable sad parting, straining their eyes for the last glimpse of Mutti's fluttering handkerchief out of the train window, until it rattled round the bend and out of sight, Piete would change Mutti's pillow for her own, to keep the precious smell a few days more.

2

Yet even here in the bread-basket of Prussia life moved on. They were clearing ground for a brand-new factory, for building the new aeroplanes it was said, out beyond the Stadtpark; and trains to and from Berlin rumbled by day and night, heard clearly by Piete in her small cot-bed in Villa Golz, where she lived with Willi and her Oma.

Greetings and farewells! The big railway station, with its clouds of steam and clanking trucks, always signified both for Piete. In 1910 the Danzig express brought two surprise visitors to quiet Schneidemühl. She and Willi had heard the steam whistle as they sat in the Golz builders' yard. They were planning a circus act. Willi was to be ring-master and Piete wanted to be a performing leopard like the one in the Russian circus, jumping through a flaming hoop.

"Hey you two!" They looked up. Two tall lads in sailor suits, packs on their backs, leaning across the fence. "Are you Willi and Piete Kuhr?"

"Yes. Why?"

"We're your brothers. We have just come to stay with Grandfather Golz."

Willi jumped up. "We live with Grandfather. Our brothers are in Danzig, they live with Father."

"No we don't." Ernst, the taller of the two, laughed. "He can't pay for us any more, so Hans and I are staying here with you."

The newcomers had little time for eight-year-old Piete with her games and plaits, but Hans, who at 14 looked grown up to Piete, soon made friends with Willi. He was excited by his knowledgeable big brother and his talk of the capital city, its harbour and the great ships from all over the world.

It was as if the brothers' arrival had been a signal, the beginning of big changes in Piete's life, chasing away the safe, warm years of her early childhood. Not long after their arrival, Grandfather, who had always seemed as permanent and solid as his own buildings, became ill, so that he and Oma went off in the train to take the waters at Karlsbad, leaving the children boarded out with friends and relatives. No-one could take them all, so Piete, who had begun to attend the girls' grammar school, the well respected Empress Augusta Victoria School, was taken in by Fräulein Ella Gumbrecht.

The flat was in a noisy building. Piete slept on a creaky truckle-bed in Fräulein Gumbrecht's bedroom, but her nights were restless, disturbed by her companion's heavy snoring and by the unfamiliar nocturnal sounds of the old apartment block - bangs, shouts, sometimes raucous laughter - at all times of the night. At 6 a.m. Frl. Gumbrecht rose, with much grumbling and muttering.

"Elfriede," (she never called her Piete, like everyone else did) "up you get. You know where the bread is. Get yourself off to school in time. I have to leave now."

This was all very well. Piete would look at the ugly carved clock over the stove. 'Five minutes before I need to get up,' . . and for once the building was quiet, at this hour of the day. She woke again with a start. 'Oh no! 8 o'clock! Fräulein Finsch was horrible yesterday. She said she would send me to the head if I was late again. I wish Willi was here, he'd know what to do.' Piete scrambled into her clothes. No time for breakfast, though her tummy was rumbling. She swallowed some water. A note, that was it! She would pretend Frl. Gumbrecht had written it. She sat at the table, chewing the end of the pen, then set to work.

> Dear Frl. Vinsch
> Piete Kuhr could not attend the first lesson because she was very sick.

Signed. Frl. Ella Gumbrecht

Fräulein Finsch looked at the scribbled note, then at Piete.

"Who wrote this?"

Piete tried to stammer out 'Fräulein Gumbrecht' but her mouth dried up and the words just would not come. Her heart sank.

"You wicked, wicked girl. Straight to Herr Enderlein with you now, and tell him what you have done." She thought of trying to explain that Frl. Gumbrecht often forgot to wake her, that the building was noisy, that . . . Then she straightened her shoulders and looked up. 'Why should I try to explain? They won't believe me. I've done nothing wrong really. And I can't tell on Fräulein Gumbrecht.'

Her defiant attitude when she faced the headmaster did her no good.

"Forging is forging, my girl. You seem not to realise the seriousness of your offence. I have asked your teacher, Fräulein Finsch," he spat out the 'f' of Finsch, shaking her 'forgery' under her nose, "to instruct the class not to speak to you for the next three months. Do you understand?"

"Yes, Herr Enderlein."

The event cast a cloud over her schooldays. Indeed, the clouds generally seemed to be thickening. Karlsbad did little for Grandfather Golz, and in February of the following year he died. Villa Golz was sold, coachhouse, horses, stables, and all. Coachman Schulz was given his small pension and had to leave the cosy coachhouse flat. Piete, Willi and their beloved Oma moved round the corner into number 17 Alte Bahnhofstraße, where Aunt and Uncle Otter lived. The funeral was a very grand affair. All the town councillors, their wives and families came, together with friends, acquaintances and business-men from far and wide. The free pews in the town church were filled to overflowing with tradespeople, servants and workmen - for Master-Builder Golz had been a popular master and his family always spent liberally in the little borough. Afterwards, the Freemasons' Hall, "Loge Borussia", provided a suitably dignified setting for this last tribute to its creator.

To Piete it seemed that, of a sudden, death was in the very air of Schneidemühl. Earlier in the year there had been her Polish school-friend Toni Renkowitz. Toni had died from such a trivial accident, a prick with a pen-holder near her eye. Yet there she lay in her white coffin like a wax doll, so different from the laughing, red-cheeked Toni that Piete had known. Then, two months after Grandfather had been laid to rest, joining his two little children in the marble and sandstone Golz-Haber mausoleum, came the dreadful news about the ocean liner "Titanic". Piete could see it all so vividly in her mind, the great iceberg, the people running and scrambling for safety as the ship, like a great whale, sloped ever more steeply and sank, leaving little boats, lifebuoys and bodies scattered like corks in the icy water. For many nights after she had seen the pictures in the paper she woke crying from nightmares of engulfing waves and desperate shouts for help.

In the summer Hans and Ernst both left the Golz household. The restricted space and smaller rooms in Alte Bahnhofstraße had made their continued stay more of a trial, and they both wanted to join the Merchant Navy. Their father - Piete and Willi never thought of him as their father - Herr Richard Kuhr had influential friends in Danzig shipping circles and was able to place both young men in ocean-going ships, Hans in a trader plying to South American ports, Ernst 'half way round the world', as their mother put it, to Australia.

Another farewell! Just before school began again after the long summer break, Piete and Willi were at the station, waving goodbye to their darling Mutti, who had to return to her 'Meisterschule für Bühne und Konzert' (Leading School for Drama and Music) in Berlin's Charlottenburg, to prepare for the new school year.

"Come children! Even the steam has vanished. Grete must be halfway to Berlin by now."

Their grandmother took Piete by the hand. Willi ran ahead and was soon through the subway and away.

"Can we go by the road, Oma? I don't like the subway, it's too echoey."

"You should be proud of it, dear. Such an elegant design! Your grandfather will be sadly missed in Schneidemühl." Nevertheless she humoured Piete's whim and they set off for the walk. Soon they heard a shout and a clatter of galloping hooves. Frau Golz grabbed the child and pressed her back against the wall as a big cart-horse, mouth flecked with foam, charged along the narrow lane, the farmer half on, half slipping off its back and tugging frantically at the halter. As it saw the two figures the beast seemed to try to halt its headlong progress. A hoof slipped on the cobbles and it lurched against the wall. The cart-horse had stopped, eyes staring, chest heaving, and before Frau Golz could stop her Piete was at its head, stroking the sweat-soaked hide and crooning softly to the terrified animal. But where was the rider? Frau Golz was first to get to the fallen body, hunched by the far wall. His head had been crushed between the wall and the horse's shoulder as the animal skidded to a halt. The skull had split open like an egg, and grey stuff was oozing out. The limbs twitched and were still.

Frau Golz looked up from where she knelt, to see Piete, round-eyed, expressionless, staring at the mangled corpse.

"Go away, Piete! Go away this instant! Go and fetch help - a doctor! Quickly!"

It was as if Piete woke from a trance - or a nightmare. She looked about. People had started to gather round. A rough worker led the horse off, now docile enough.

"Make way there! I am a doctor. Make way!" A fussy little man pushed his way through, and her Oma signalled to Piete to go. She trailed slowly back to Alte Bahnhofstraße.

3

Summer 1914. Germany goes to war. At first the war was exciting for the two children. Willi and his Polish friend Hans Androwski talked about it endlessly. Hans was the cleverest person Piete had ever known. He was very thin and wore spectacles, and he looked very grown-up. He was always top of his class at school. But this time his ideas were quite shocking.

"It's the Kaiser's war, not ours. Why should we go and get killed, when he rides around in Berlin showing off? The Russians are our friends, anyway. I'm Slav."

Piete thought he was just saying things like that to shock her, because everybody else said it was Germany's great chance to prove how strong it was. Germans had to help their Austrian neighbours, whose Archduke Ferdinand and his wife Sophie had been shot in cold blood when they were making a friendly visit to Serbia. When Piete tried to say this to Willi and Hans they just said,

"Go away. Girls can't understand things like this. Go and play with your dolls." This last from Willi, 'and he knows I don't play with dolls.' Piete felt aggrieved. Just because she couldn't talk cleverly and answer them. She took refuge in her mother, who was on holiday with them at the time because she had had to cancel a planned trip to Sweden when the news broke in July.

"We must be proud of our country, my darling. It is not just Prussia now. Germany is a great nation and our Kaiser is an emperor like Franz Joseph of Austria-Hungary. Androwski can't be expected to understand this, he is only a Pole."

"But Mutti, Hans and Willi say that girls don't matter when it comes to war. We can fight for our country too, can't we? It is our country as much as theirs."

"Of course, my love." Her mother smiled. "It is for us to work here at home, though. Bruno, your uncle Bruno, will fight for us, so will all the soldiers in your grandfather's barracks, the 149th Regiment of Foot. We must cheer them when they set off for the front."

Piete liked this idea. It was fun seeing all the smart uniforms and running along beside the marching soldiers and throwing flowers to them. She wished she was a boy, so that she could look forward to marching with a gun and bayonet and to wearing a uniform with shining brass buttons and a helmet. But was this all that girls could do, cheer and give posies to the soldiers? She spent some precious pfennigs of her pocket-money on two black, white and red flags on two little sticks - the shops were full of such things now - and pinned them up criss-cross over her bed-head. Then her mother gave her another idea.

"We must all devote our skills to the Fatherland. I shall teach my students about our great German composers, Wagner, Brahms . . . oh, so many of the finest the world has known."

"I am best at German in our class, Mutti. Couldn't I write something? A story about a German hero or about winning a battle."

"There will be victories enough, Piete dear, you can be sure of that. Why not keep a diary and put them all down as they happen? That could be a valuable record, and when you grow up you could show it to your children. Most people say we shall have conquered the enemy by Christmas, so I shall have it typed for you, and you can give copies as Christmas presents. "

On August 1st, when Germany declared war on France and Russia, Piete wrote the first page of her 'war diary'. She tried to copy out all the important bulletins in the newspaper so that it would be a true record, as Mutti had suggested. As it was holiday time at first, she could spend time on her writing. Her little friend Gretel Wegner, who lived at the back of their house in Alte Bahnhofstraße, admired her industry, but she was too young to understand how important it was. Willi thought it was a good idea, and Androwski moderated his tone when Piete was with them, seeing how his cynicism about the war could distress her. So the diary grew page by page. It soon became her own special confidante, her 'dear Diary', in the absence of anyone with whom she could really share her views and thoughts about the war as events unfolded. She loved her grandmother, but Oma was too busy all the time and too old to understand her more intimate feelings. Her mother always had to go away again, back to Berlin. Although she and Willi were still close - the Kuhr twins they were dubbed in Schneidemühl - he never took her ideas about the war seriously. And anyhow he was bound up with his own interests, writing poetry, composing songs and finding out about Mexico, where he planned to go when he grew up.

"They have had a revolution in Mexico. That is what we need here. Soon there will be another one in Russia, like they had in 1905, then they will help us." Willi was passing on Androwski's ideas. "But I suppose if the war goes on I shall have to fight too."

"Course you won't, Willi!" Piete was horrified at the idea. "You are not fit enough for the army. Anyway, Mutti and all Oma's friends think it will be over by Christmas. Soon it will be victory parades instead of trains to the front. What is a revolution? Will that help to end the war?"

Hans Androwski tried to explain about revolutions and the need for a different kind of government.

"Will the Tsar put workers in charge of everything, then?"

"The Tsar is why they want a revolution. Don't you know how he ordered thousands of workers to be shot in 1905?"

"She doesn't know anything. It is a waste of time trying to explain, Go and play soldiers with Fritz and Gretel, Piete."

She ignored Willi's interruption. "What will happen to the Tsar then?"

"Oh, he will be executed. Shot. Probably his family as well."

Like the Archduke Ferdinand. Violence, death. It seemed to Piete there was no end to it, whether or not there was a war.

Although the diary was begun for her mother, she soon began to realise that even darling Mutti could not understand all that she was writing about. At first she kept sending pages to Berlin as they were completed and her mother had them typed. Soon came less enthusiastic responses. "You need to tell more of the heroism of our troops and less of the unpleasant things. Our gallant soldiers are fighting those who want to rob us of our country. When they die in battle they die as heroes. Never forget that!" Piete took the letter up to her room and read it over and over. 'What is a hero's death? Mutti says her singing pupil Siegfried Dahlke died the death of a hero, a true Siegfried. But when he is dead he's dead, just that, like a lump of wood or stone. He can't know he is a hero any more.' She took up another of her mother's letters. "Such great, noble and uplifting times have never before been experienced by any nation." Of course, Mutti was in Berlin a long way from the war and could see the Kaiser taking the salute and other 'uplifting' things. It was different here in Schneidemühl, close to the Russian front.

The days, weeks, months went by and Piete dutifully recorded the victory reports, copying them down from the bulletins posted at the newspaper office. As it was to be a true record for her children, she also committed her thoughts and feelings to the diary's pages. She could not bring herself to write about heroes and 'uplifting times', though she knew her mother would have liked it, to show to her Berlin friends, especially the high-ranking military men and their wives.

The war was not over by Christmas. Instead, it became part of the fabric of life, with its deprivations, its casualty-lists, its - less and less frequent - celebrations, which in the early days meant a day off school for Piete and Willi and their friends. The first such holiday had come just a month after the diary had started, Hindenburg's great Tannenberg battle on the Russian front in East Prussia. Thousands of prisoners taken, and thousands more trapped and drowned in the Masurian lakes and swamps. The news had come shortly before the Sedan Day holiday. Two victories to celebrate together! Piete had walked around in a daze almost, bewildered by the contrast between all the cheerful faces - flags flying, the band playing - and the horribly vivid images in her mind of Russian soldiers, some of them no older than Willi, she had been told, sinking to their deaths in the Masurian swamps.

Piete loved helping her grandmother, who was in charge, and the other ladies with the Red Cross buffet at the railway station. She would put on her apron, tidy her hair and run through her grandfather's subway to the station every day after school. On 31st August, just before Sedan Day, a troop train had stopped in Schneidemühl with soldiers from the Russian front. One of the soldiers was a young lad who looked no older than Willi. He jumped down as the train clanked to a halt, and started running about, shouting and screaming.

"I heard them shrieking! I heard the Russians shrieking in the swamp!" Piete watched, terrified yet fascinated, as the boy started bashing his head against an iron lamp-post, his army identity disk swinging loose on a string round his neck. She couldn't move. In spite of herself she found her mind going back to the dead farmer. Perhaps this soldier's head will split open too. He was wearing no more than a grey shirt and army trousers, torn and filthy. Frau Kuhr brought him a mug of steaming coffee, slopping it on the asphalt in her haste. She put her arm round the lad's narrow shoulders and helped him to swallow it down. He looked wildly at her.

"I saw them, Grandma! Sinking and screaming. Aah! they went, aah! aah!" He tried to bang his head again, though blood was already streaking his face, mingling with the coffee.

"You're dreaming, lad! Drink up now, and be quiet." She led him gently to the two orderlies he had escaped from. Piete came out of her trance.

"But they did scream, Oma. They said in the news about it." Frau Kuhr had not known that Piete had been in time to witness the scene. In the stress of the moment she spoke roughly.

"What are you doing here? Get back home at once. Haven't you got homework to do?"

Piete felt rejected. She had been trying to help, hadn't she? She bit back the angry retort that came to her lips, tore off her apron and ran out of the station forecourt.

Nine months later came the news of the great liner 'Lusitania' sent to the bottom by a German torpedo, because, it was said, it had been carrying arms and ammunition. Her 'Titanic' nightmares began again, the cries of the drowning this time mingling strangely with the screams of Russians being sucked slowly down into the mud. These were vivid, yet confused. She would wake sweating and wide-eyed in the darkness. Once she crept to her grandmother's room and asked if she could sleep with her for a while. She could not bear to recount the visions of her dream, nor could she put them in her diary.

Death by drowning! Even as a little girl this had been fearful to Piete. At Kolberg once, when Willi had whooping-cough and their mother and grandmother thought the sea air would help, the two children had been fascinated by the tales of an old sailor.

"Drowned folk always return," he would say to them solemnly.

"Do they come alive again, then?" Little Piete was fascinated by the idea.

"No lassie, not alive, though sometimes it looks like it." He paused, puffing his pipe and gazing through the smoke to the horizon. "Ah, I mind when the old 'Vittoria' was lost with all hands. They come back to shore they did, in threes and fives and eights. Just down there," he pointed across, "past the headland." He turned to the boy and spoke confidentially. "It's the gases keeps the bodies up, you see, like balloons bobbing in the water. It's as if they want to come."

"And did people pull them out of the water?"

"Why yes, o' course! They want their folk to have a Christian burial, so their souls can rest in peace. Uneasy souls, we call them when they come back. Uneasy souls!"

When their mother and grandmother took to the sea together soon after that conversation, leaving the children in the nursemaid Emma's charge while they slowly advanced into the waves in their flounced costumes and bathing-caps, little Piete set up a howl and would not be comforted. Mummy was drowning, and Oma! The cries got louder, other hotel guests gathered round in concern and her mother was obliged to abandon her bathe.

4

Frau Golz's only son Bruno, scholar and philosopher, who was studying at Halle, added himself to the hundreds of thousands who volunteered for service in the heady first month of the war. Dr Golz, Piete's beloved Uncle Bruno, was by nature a thinker, an observer, and Piete cherished his occasional visits to Schneidemühl as windows of sanity in the sombre war edifice. He nearly always brought some small gift for his favourite neice, usually a book, knowing her taste, Wilhelm Raube's stories, poems by Eichendorff and Arno Holz, even once an old leather-bound copy of The Sorrows of Young Werther, which she read with fascination. When she came to the last sad letter, with its "Charlotte, Charlotte, farewell, farewell!" she was in tears, imagining first the desolate Werther putting down his quill only to pick up the loaded pistol and hold it to his head, then the shock to his unattainable beloved. Piete could not decide whether her sympathies lay more with Charlotte, whom she considered rather feeble, or with her upright husband Albert.

Owing to the erratic mails, short notice of leave and strict security, Bruno would usually appear on the doorstep of 17 Alte Bahnhofstraße without warning. One such surprise visit was on Christmas Eve 1915. Piete and Willi, feeling virtuous from their duty attendance at church while their mother and grandma made ready for the celebrations, sniffed delightedly at the lovely cooking smells - there were still spices, even if the carp was missing - as they opened the door.

"I feel as if something special is going to happen this year. Perhaps the Kaiser will celebrate Christmas by saying the war is over."

Willi laughed shortly. "You and your feelings! How can he? What about all the fighting, with the Russians and the French and our cousins (scornfully) the English? Uncle Bruno is fighting the French at this moment. Oma said so yesterday, she had a 'forces mail' letter from him."

"They won't fight on Christmas Day. Everybody sings 'Peace on earth' at Christmas time. Last year they all stopped fighting and gave each other cigarettes in No Man's Land."

"You just wait. They'll fight if their officers tell them to. That is what soldiers do."

The argument was abruptly terminated as everyone was summoned to the Christmas Tree. Piete was allowed to light all the candles with a long taper, then they stood silently, brother and sister hand in hand, in the flickering light, breathing the warm resinous air - like incense, Piete thought. The first carol was always Heilige Nacht. Their mother sang the first note in her pure contralto. As they drew breath the door-bell clanged harshly. Piete and Willi looked at each other in the silence.

"Told you!" she whispered as they waited, while Frau Golz went to the door.

Soon there was laughter and joy as Bruno strode in in his great army boots, his arms full of the parcels he had pulled out of his kit-bag. Later, as they sat at dinner, he announced,

"Wait, all of you! I nearly forgot." He went out, and returned with two bottles of burgundy, real French wine in French bottles.

"And I paid for these at the wine shop, in francs. They are not stolen - what people try to call war booty."

Frau Golz nodded approval and smiled. She felt too full for words, with the shock of his arrival on top of her exhaustion from the Red Cross centre, together with Christmas preparations. Noticing that his mother was close to tears again, Bruno put his arm round her shoulders.

"Now think of this. Here we are, calling France the enemy, yet sharing their good wine. Should we not drink to them in their own creation? Piete, you are a big girl now, 13 is it? If your brother can join us in a drink, you can too, perhaps?" His mother nodded in response to his questioning look. Piete had never tasted wine. At the first sip she felt like spitting it out, but she was determined not to give Willi another chance for mockery, nor to offend her uncle. She tilted her head back and drained the glass in a single gulp.

Bruno laughed. "What a way to treat a fine vintage! Now let me tell you a good war story, for once." He made them all laugh at this tale of a lance-corporal in his company and a French prisoner. "I often chatted with Corporal Standtchen. He was older than me, and from Göttingen. Like me he was in the Reserve. In civil life he was a professor of Romance languages, a really nice chap. One day I put him in charge of a group of prisoners, but before he marched them off I saw him talking earnestly to one of them. I thought perhaps the Frenchman was disobeying orders. He was gesticulating wildly, and for his part Standtchen looked furious. His eyes behind his glasses were blazing. 'I had better put a stop to this,' I thought, so rode up between them. The French prisoner was in a sorry state, boots nearly falling apart and tied together with string. When they had calmed down I asked what the trouble was. It seems the Frenchman was a professor at the Sorbonne. The whole argument was about the frequency of the use of the subjunctive in the old provençal Minnelieder."

Later, when Piete was helping Bruno to unpack in his room, he said,

"Help me off with these clumsy boots, Piete. They weigh a ton. I think I'll leave them here; I don't need them now, I have managed to find a lighter pair." As Piete tugged at the boots an idea came to her.

"Don't you want the boots any more, Uncle? Can I have them?"

"What on earth do you want them for, Piete darling?"

She sat back on her haunches and looked at him, holding the great boot. "To dance with."

Bruno leaned back in his chair and let out a great laugh. "Dance! You could hardly lift them off the ground. Imagine a quadrille in these lumping things!"

"Not that sort of dance, Uncle." She tried to explain how she wanted to act out her feelings about the war by dancing. How she could show, by being a soldier in the dance, what a horrible waste it was to go to war. She was earnest and determined, but her thoughts were still unsettled, making her rather incoherent.

"Willi says that soldiers will always fight if they are ordered to."

"That is very true. We must obey orders."

"Well, I'll be a dead soldier, lying in a coffin. Then the bugle will sound and I shall rise up, wounds and all, to fight again." Bruno looked curiously at her, sitting there with the army boot in her hands, her face transformed as the scene started to come alive in her mind. He spoke quietly,

"Take the boots then, Piete my dear. I shall come to watch when your dance takes place."

Christmases were for Piete, like her birthdays, also on 25th but April not December, milestones marking the dreary path of the war. The "over by Christmas" of 1914 was forgotten as the fighting ground on and the casualties mounted. Schneidemühl was an important railway junction, so troop trains, with their cargoes of war-weary soldiers, wounded and prisoners, passed through from both the Russian and the Western Fronts. Frau Golz, reminded daily of the hazards from what she witnessed in her work at the Red Cross centre, spoke little of her son's danger, but he was constantly in her thoughts and was the first name in her evening intercessions. Piete would kneel with her grandmother as she had done since she was tiny. Although she said nothing, not wanting to distress Oma, she could never suppress the questions that kept rising in her mind like bubbles. 'We are asking God to protect Bruno and French mothers are asking Him to look after those trying to kill Bruno. How can God decide what to do?'

There were times, too, when Piete found it hard to maintain her rôle as the Golz grandchild, especially when she listened to the opinions aired by the Schneidemühl ladies. A group of them spent every Wednesday afternoon with Frau Golz at their house, knitting and sewing for the troops. On these occasions the tongues would wag as fast as the knitting needles. Fräulein Ella Gumbrecht, who taught at the Volkschule (elementary school), was one of the most voluble.

"Did you hear about the dreadful attack on Karlsruhe, ladies?" By dint of taking in the daily bulletin posted outside the newspaper office on her way to the meeting she usually arrived well primed. "Shocking, shocking it was, raining down bombs from the sky on defenceless people. Only those horrible Froggies would do such a thing."

This time Piete, who was helping her Oma to wind some wool by holding the skein across her stretched hands, could not resist putting in,

"But Fräulein, what about the Albatros aeroplanes being made here in Schneidemühl for our Air Force? They carry bombs too. Where do they drop them?"

Frl. Gumbrecht snorted. "On proper military targets, of course. You should know that, Elfriede. Don't they teach you at that fine school of yours about such things?" She did not wait for Piete's reply. "Yes, and on a school too, in Karlsruhe. What sort of a military target is that? More than a hundred children killed outright, little arms and legs everywhere." She could never resist embroidering her news items.

There were gasps of horror and Frau Golz, seeing the look on Piete's face, said,

"Hand the wool to Aunt Louise, Piete dear. I want you to ask Marie if the coffee is ready, to bring it in." Piete ran out of the room. 'I hate that Frl. Gumbrecht with her beastly gossip. Everyone knows the war is horrible, she doesn't need to rub it in like that.' After delivering her message she ran out into the garden and whistled for her friend Gretel.

Piete loved being out of doors. Even as a small child she had fancied how exciting it would be to live like a gypsy. Grandfather Golz allowed gypsies to camp on his land from time to time, and Piete had often watched them, the swarthy women crouching by their fires and the ragamuffin children with their shocks of hair. In one of her games then she had been a Hungarian gypsy, Joan Mihaly. With her companions, and also at school, to the chagrin of her teachers, she was a natural leader. She was always the initiator of their war games, and in her assumed rôle of Lieutenant Von Yellenic, Hungarian aristocrat and volunteer, she would direct her 'troops' in sundry daring ploys into enemy territory, either in the Golz builder's yard or in the back yard of the house, where the wash-house with its great mangle, the cylinder filled with stones, served alternately as HQ and prison.

On another of his surprise visits Bruno fished in his pack and brought out an unexpected item, a flat steel helmet quite different from the scuttle-shaped German ones that were now being used.

"Where did you get that, Uncle?" Piete, as usual, was all over her uncle, clinging to his arm and poking about amongst his kit and appurtenances.

"You have heard of Verdun, I suppose. Well, I picked this up on the battlefield, not far from Fort Douaumont."

"Fort Douaumont? That was a victory, wasn't it, when we captured the fort? We had a day off school for it, I remember. Thank you, uncle!" Piete made a mock curtsy.

"Victory!" Dr Golz pulled a face. "So that's how they presented it. Well, we took the fort, that is true. But the drawbridge was down and when we went in there were only about twenty Frenchmen inside, dead beat and fast asleep. Some victory! Two days later the whole place was nearly blown sky-high."

"Did they - had they mined it?" Willi had told her how, when enemy troops had to retreat , they often planted explosive charges which would be set off by the occupying Germans. But Bruno gave a short laugh..

"Nothing so simple! Some of our lads were brewing up coffee down in the cellars where the ammunition was stored. They even used gunpowder to make the fire burn, the idiots. A few of them were so blackened by the powder blowing up in their faces that when they ran out the others mistook them for French African troops and started shooting."

"How horrible, uncle!"

"That is war, my dear. Stupid, wasteful and pointless . ." Dr Golz sat with the helmet in his hands, teeth clenched on his pipe, gazing sightlessly at the portrait on the wall opposite, a heavily framed oil painting from two generations back.

"Can I see it please?" Piete took the trophy from Bruno. "It belonged to a Frenchman?"

"You can have it if you want. For your dance." He gave a short laugh, then stopped, seeing he had hit the nail on the head. "No, it is actually a Belgian helmet. But they are more or less the same, probably made in the same factory, out of useful things like iron railings."

Piete examined it curiously. It had two smooth holes on the front, and a deep indentation near the holes. The lining was made of leather, but was hard and brittle and heavily stained, like the strap.

"That is blood. It was lying upside down when I found it, like a basin of blood in a butcher's shop."

"What happened to the Belgian soldier?"

"Oh, the medics would have taken him away. Or if he was dead, they always tried to clear the bodies, because of the rats."

She shuddered, then started examining the helmet again. Inside there was a name scratched: van Glabeke, César. Suddenly everything started spinning round in her head, the name, the thought of the dead soldier - she was sure he must have died - killed by her own countrymen, his grieving mother, like Frau Schön, whose son had died on the Russian front. All the graves in the fast-growing war cemetery outside the town boundaries where she and Gretel went . . . Her uncle looked at her with concern.

"Sit down, sweetheart. Put it down. Forget about it."

"I don't want to forget! I am going to write to Mrs van Glabeke and tell her how sorry I am, and that I shall treasure her son's helmet. Where can I write to, Uncle?"

Bruno always spoke with her as if she was grown up. She loved him for it. He considered the question.

"Hm! It sounds like a Flemish name, van Glabeke. So she probably lives in Flanders. You could send it to Mme van Glabeke, Flanders, Belgium, c/o Red Cross, Paris, France. It just might reach her." Piete went straight to her room and, armed with a French dictionary, set to work. 'La guerre est un désastre; Dieu ne la veut, ma famille désire la paix.' There was so much more she would have liked to tell César van Glabeke's mother: how they had shot the two Belgian spies in Schneidemühl just after the war started, how she and Gretel looked after their graves and those of other 'enemies', how she felt as deeply for French or Belgian or Russian soldiers when they were killed or wounded as for Germans, how she and all her friends longed for the war to end . . . She sat for a long time thinking, but how could she say all that in French? So she just signed the letter 'Mmselle Elfriede Kuhr (14 ans)' and sealed it up as it was.

Piete was by now a tall,big-boned, lively 14-year-old. With her bold eyes, high cheek-bones - the Haber cheek-bones, like her grandmother - , budding breasts and hair in two thick plaits coiled decorously by her ears, she looked more mature than her years. The war, too, had made her, like so many, more aware of the precariousness of life. It had become part of the environment for the growing girl, living, like others of her age, in a timeless present for the most part. Some features of provincial life in Schneidemühl were unchanged, in spite of the war. There was still swimming in the Küddow river at the municipal bathing station, with its wooden bathing huts and springboards on the bank. The river had been dammed up to make it deep enough for diving, and the water was always ice-cold, tumbling over the weir. In the hot summer of 1916 it was a favourite spot.

The following winter was a hard one. A large flat water-meadow at the edge of the town was regularly flooded by the little Zgordalina, which flowed into the Küddow. The municipality would set up crude benches, long boards nailed to great logs, for people to put on their skates. It was February 1917 and the frost had held for weeks, the ground hard as iron and the ice firm and solid. Someone had brought out a gramophone, which broadcast a scratchy Skaters' Waltz from its bronze trumpet. Skating here was fun but hazardous, with the occasional tufts of grass setting traps for the unwary. There was a crowd of merry-makers, bear-like in their miscellaneous garments, mostly young people, high school boys and girls and conscripts on leave, looking not much older. There was even a sprinkling of young officers in their smart uniforms, much more interesting to Piete, now nearly 15, and her school-friends than the gauche schoolboys. The previous October one such man, a blond, blue-eyed Air Force lieutenant, had bought Piete an éclair at Fliegner's café in town, introducing himself courteously as 'Werner Waldecker from Bielefeld, at your service!' Seeing the uniforms, she thought 'perhaps he is here today.' Her skating became more daring, following the rhythm of the music in progressively wider curves. At the fastest moment of one curve her left skate caught on a grass-tuft and her feet flew from under her. She crashed down heavily on her backside, skidding three or four yards before coming to rest. The tuft had dislodged her skate, which vanished. Her friends laughed so much that they could not help her up. Piete, bruised and winded, laughed too as soon as she caught her breath. Someone shouted "Hullo, young lady!" and a tall officer swirled expertly to a halt beside her. Lieutenant Waldecker! He helped the girl to rise, looking really concerned at her evident pain, and led her limping to the benches.

"I'll fetch your skate for you." Piete watched him as he flew off, his officer's cap, which he had doffed as he came up to her, still in his hand, his fair hair shining in the sloping sunbeams. He skated well, with natural grace, and for the moment she forgot the pain in her ankle.

"Shall I screw it on again?" Piete nodded and made to hand him the skate-key, hanging on a bootlace round her neck. Her cold fingers fumbled with the lace, so the young man drew off a fine leather glove and carefully unfastened the key, smiling and winking as he did so. She flushed scarlet.

"No! I've had enough. Don't bother about the key. I want to go home."

"Not without me. If you insist I'll take you. But why don't we stop at Fliegner's for an éclair?" Her two school-friends Grete and Trude immediately responded, but the officer made it plain they were not welcome. He rapped out jokingly,

"Company, right turn! Quick march!" and the girls laughed and skated away, arms folded.

Werner Waldecker was very attentive as they made their way slowly back into town. Reassured by his courtesy, Piete began to enjoy leaning on his arm, a necessity as her ankle had swollen up and hurt a lot. It was almost dark and the street lights were bright in the frosty atmosphere. In the warm café he chose a corner table, hanging her skates with his on a hook nearby. Her bruised back and ankle throbbed painfully, but somehow it became part of her feeling of contentment. There were no éclairs left but he ordered sweet cracknels and some mulled claret. Piete enjoyed the sensation of its warmth all the way down as she sipped the spiced wine, and began to feel light-headed, almost drowsy and completely happy. He asked her many things about her family and the life she lived.

"So that is your Oma. She is a fine person, Frau Golz. I have spoken to her at the station. She does not spare herself, always helping some sick or wounded soldier and making sure the ladies know what to do. She is doing important war work. I am not surprised that you are proud of her." His hand, warm and comforting, rested lightly on hers as it lay on the table. She felt no urge to release it.

"What lovely hair you have." He was now idly twisting the end of one of her braids, which had come loose during the skating. "I should like to see it all loose. May I, some day?"

Herr Fliegner, coughing loudly as he pulled down the blinds in the window, prompted them to get up at last. Piete staggered as she rose from the table, and Werner Waldecker held her closely, letting his hand caress her neck as he helped her on with her coat.

When they stood in the lobby at 17 Alte Bahnhofstraße he put both arms round her and would have kissed her. 'But that's what all the officers do when they take girls home. Grete told me.' She averted her face, held his hand fleetingly then limped as fast as she could to the stairs, calling back from the turn,

"Thank you . . er, for everything."

Willi jumped up as she came in. "At last! Come and hear this, Piete. I've just learnt it." He tried to pull her towards the piano.

"Not now, I'm tired and my ankle hurts. I'll have to put something on it, or bathe it." She pushed him away and escaped to her room. Why hadn't she let Werner Waldecker kiss her? She had really wanted him to. Piete remembered the way the lock of fair hair drooped down over his forehead as he looked into her eyes, and the warmth of his hand, so firm yet gentle. What a fool she was! She sat on her bed in the dark for a long time, turning over all that had happened. It seemed an age since she had scrambled out of the same bed that morning.

1917 was the year when Piete grew up. This, at least, was how she saw it, looking back at the end of the year, after her fourth war-time Christmas with the family. Her isolation in school had persisted through the war years thanks to the episode of the 'forged' note. Only her present class teacher Fräulein Kutschelis, who taught her two best subjects, German and English, liked her enough to ignore her reputation. However, this had given her a certain cachet with her fellow pupils, enhanced by her natural rôle as leader in many of their activities. Piete was tall and athletic - though not particularly a sports enthusiast - , had natural musicianship and a vivid imagination. "Tell us a story, Piete!" was a familiar cry in the playground. Her emotions were deep but transparent, reflected in her clear-complexioned, mobile features and expressive eyes. She had a sharp sense of the ridiculous and was not slow in showing it, even in school. This did nothing to endear her with her teachers, many of whom were second-rate wartime substitutes replacing those in the Forces.

For such a teen-age girl, just becoming aware of her sexuality, her first love could not but be passionate and intense, marking her for life. Piete had listened to her friends' talk of their various affairs and flirtations, especially with the glamorous young officers so often seen these days in the streets of Schneidemühl. Their frivolous exchanges, while fascinating to hear about, seemed petty, even unworthy - for she had a strong sense of her virginity, a feeling, derived in part from her grandmother's deep religious convictions, that she must remain pure in herself. Werner Waldecker had responded to this with natural sensitivity and she loved him for it.

On a fine warm day in early September Piete and her older friend Trude, with Waldecker and a fellow officer from the Flying Corps called Lieutenant Leverentz, had made up a foursome for a day's excursion in the Königsblick Woods some kilometres out of town. After coffee at a popular café known as "The Little Castle in the Forest" they set off walking in high spirits, planning to return in the evening in the little 'rail-car' that plied between Königsblick and Schneidemühl. The weather was perfect, bright and clear, the sun glittering on the Küddow, which wound its way down through the wooded countryside. The ground was dry for walking and they soon split into couples, Piete and Werner walking ahead, hand in hand, while Trude and her partner dawdled behind. Waldecker encouraged Piete to talk more about herself. He laughed heartily at the bathing episode in Kolberg.

"Shh! Don't make a sound!" Piete squeezed his arm suddenly, and they both froze. A tall deer, his antlers gleaming white in the sunshine, strolled leisurely across their path less than four metres from where they stood holding their breath.

"The things I experience with you, darling!" he whispered in her ear, holding her close and kissing the lobe of her ear as he did so. When the others caught up with them they were astonished to hear of the deer, not having seen it at all. As the afternoon drew on they found a good resting-place on some rising ground near the memorial stone set up in honour of Kaiser Friedrich, who had visited the spot and given the woods their name. Trude and Leverentz embraced and kissed deeply, while the others sat a little apart from them. They were close and intimate, Waldecker respecting Piete's more chaste sense of her girlhood and refraining from any kiss on the lips.

From Schneidemühl station the couples went their separate ways. Waldecker accompanied Piete through the subway to her home. As they stood in the dark by the stairs he bent over her and spoke softly in her ear: "Darling Piete, do you know? I love you."

Overwhelmed, she could only stammer out "Th - thank you." before running upstairs to her room and burying her flaming cheeks in the pillow. Once again her diary had to be her confidante, as she tried to set down something of the day's experiences.

Two months later came news of the Russian revolution and Kerensky's surrender to Lenin, causing a great stir in a place so close to the border.

Lenin's exploits were hailed by some in Schneidemühl, including Piete's brother Willi and his friend Androwski, as a positive step towards the ending of hostilities. The majority were more cautious, suspecting anything 'Red' and seeing it as implicit support for the feared Spartacists and their leader Karl Liebknecht, who had been jailed the previous year after calling in Berlin's Potsdamer Platz for an end to the war.

Piete treasured her memory of the Königsblick outing. Once or twice afterwards she caught sight of Waldecker in the street, but not to speak to. One particular time he was walking down Posener Straße arm-in-arm with a handsome older woman reputed to be 'fast'. Piete did not want to be seen, so stepped back into a doorway. The lady, she considered, was very beautiful with her dark hair, red lips and bold eyes. 'They make a fine couple,' she thought, and wondered whether he ever bent over this lady to whisper "I love you." That evening she devised a short romantic tale in which Lieutenant Waldecker threw himself at the feet of the beautiful lady, who rejected him scornfully. He was comforted by a childhood friend who had grown to love him tenderly, but whom he thought of as "only a minor". These were the words Waldecker had murmured when they refrained from following her friend Trude's example in the Königsblick Woods.

A week or so later Trude approached her looking pale and shocked as soon as she arrived at school. "Have you heard . . about Lieutenant Waldecker?"

Piete suddenly felt sick. The faulty aircraft! She knew Waldecker was a flier, and there had been many accidents recently because of inferior parts in the aeroplanes.

"What . . what happened? Is he dead?"

"Yes. Crashed soon after take-off. He was due to go on leave to Bielefeld, where he lives, the next day."

Piete went numbly to her place, mechanically putting her books away and striving to keep dry-eyed and normal. Nothing was 'normal' any more. How could she make any sense of what happened? Why did God permit such things? How could she hide her feelings from Oma, from Willi?

Her schoolwork, normally well in the lead of her class, was seriously affected. Fräulein Kutchelis tried to fathom what was wrong. But how could she possibly tell her? Towards the end of term Piete carried some books back to the teacher's flat for her and was invited in. Gently the teacher tried to probe, but Piete resisted all inquiries. As Frl. Kutchelis persisted the room started going round and round. Piete came to lying on the sofa, with the teacher dabbing her forehead with Eau de Cologne.

"You are not getting enough to eat, Elfriede. You must be more careful. Remember, if you are worried about something, - anything!" She brushed the damp hair back from the girl's forehead and gazed at her, " you can tell me. I want you to think of me as your friend."

Piete thought wanly that this was the first time any of her teachers had said such a thing, had treated her as a fellow human being, indeed. But what was the use now? What was the use of trying?

After this her schoolwork plummeted, almost as though it were synchronised with the war, which also seemed to be disintegrating, in spite of the persistently optimistic official reports in the paper. Her attempt to re-take the school year in 1918 ended disastrously. Her new teacher, a Polish church minister, had disliked the insolent Kuhr girl, very noticeable amongst the younger class, from the start. On this occasion she had been ill - most children were by now quite seriously under-nourished - and brought a note from Frau Golz to the teacher. Ignoring it, he said,

"I know where you have been, Kuhr. Smoking and chatting with the soldiers instead of attending to your schoolwork. No wonder you get poor grades!"

Piete's temper flashed up. How dare he! All his innuendoes, his attempts to discredit her, boiled up in her. 'Why should I stand for this?' On impulse she picked up her school satchel and hurled it across the room in the direction of the teacher's desk. There was a gasp from the class and the teacher went pale. In the silence Piete marched over, picked up the satchel and left. Never to return, in fact. Her grandmother, hearing what had happened, did not scold her.

"People should not betray the innocence of children. I shall explain to the school authorities. We must find something for you to do."

6

Something to do! How was Piete to make sense of it all - the waste of war, the farewells, the violence on every side, the hopelessness . . . ! No, not hopelessness! Even in her darkest hours, even when she lost Werner Waldecker, there was always a spark of hope in the embers. She was alive, life was precious, and beautiful. In her musings she saw in her mind a child's face, a baby's face. Some time back she had visited the children's hospital with her mother - was it when she came on holiday at Easter-time? - to take small presents to the children. A nurse was carrying this infant, a tiny under-nourished little wisp of humanity with spindle limbs, small pot belly and big staring eyes. There were sores on its face, especially round the mouth. But those eyes!

"May I hold him?" Piete had taken the diminutive bundle - so light! She was scarcely aware of any weight in her arms. Yet here was life! She smiled at the little face and - yes - it opened in such a sweet smile, showing pink gums.

"I know what I must do, Oma. I want to be a nurse in the children's hospital."

She was too young to enter the nurses' training course, but Frau Golz made inquiries about unqualified assistants and soon discovered that they were desperately short-staffed in the Municipal Children's Home and welcomed help in any form. Sixteen-year-old Piete looked older than her years, and soon made her mark at the Home, over-crowded, under-resourced as it was. Many of the children were war orphans, many died. Everything was in short supply; it was "make do" with torn up sheets for bandages and dressings and even newspapers on the beds in cold weather to eke out the thin blankets.

Piete still confided in her war diary as the days wore on. Her brother Willi had at last been called up. Even the games with Gretel Wegner as Nurse Martha, in love with Lieutenant von Yellenic, had begun to pall, so she was much on her own. Once, on a free day from the Home, she set off to walk through the woods to the Sandsee. The path was unfrequented, so she was surprised, at first embarrassed, to meet Androwski, her brother's friend. However, he seemed pleased and joined her.

"So, you are to be a nurse?"

"No, this is just to fill in time. When the war is over Mutti wants me to join her in Berlin and help her to start the Music School again."

Detecting something in her voice, Androwski said, "Is that what you want?"

"Why shouldn't I?"

"Because you ought to be a writer."

Piete was astonished. The remark, from brainy Androwski, was so unexpected. But it emboldened her to say, "What I really want to be is a dancer, . . and a writer."

"What, a ballet dancer? Dying swans and all that nonsense?"

"It isn't nonsense, but no. Not that sort of dancing. Dances that tell stories . . ." Once again, as so often when she talked with clever people, Piete's words dried up. So she changed the subject abruptly.

"Oma thinks that I should be a prophet, like in the Bible. She found a quotation in her grandfather Haber's old Bible which said that was what I must be."

"The Bible!" Andrewski's voice was filled with scorn. "You don't believe all that superstitious rubbish about God and prophesying."

Piete felt intimidated. "Yes . . . no . . . I don't know. But I promised Oma."

The young man lapsed into stubborn silence. Piete wanted him to take her seriously. She held his arm and said, in as friendly a way as she could,

"Do you think I was wrong to promise? Don't you believe in God?"

"I believe in humanity, that is enough for me. God is only an invention of men. We have to save ourselves, like they are doing in Russia."

Piete had welcomed meeting Androwski, but his words and his hostility to her ideas had merely intensified her loneliness. On their return to Schneidemühl they parted coolly.

They did not meet again until November, in the bitter closing days of the war. Everything was falling apart. Sailors in Kiel had refused to go to sea and taken over the battleships from their officers. This acted as a signal. All over Germany soldiers were deserting, refusing orders, tearing off their uniforms. Revolution was in the air. Unexpectedly Androwski arrived on the doorstep of 17 Alte Bahnhofstraße, looking paler that ever behind his glasses. When Piete answered the doorbell he looked embarrassed and asked for Gil, Willi's Mexican nickname.

"He is still in the barracks. Come into the warm, you look frozen." Androwski was wearing his usual high-collared jacket, threadbare now and so much too small that his wrists stuck out from the sleeves. When they entered the room he threw himself into an easy chair.

"The war is dead! Long live the war!" He grinned crookedly.

"What do you mean?"

"When one war comes to an end the rulers and the generals look about for another one. That is what always happens."

"Not this time it won't!" Piete was indignant. "We'll stop them, you see if we don't."

Androwski's cynicism grated on her, but she did not feel able to counter his arguments, either then or later. As she sat up in bed with her diary she tried to put her feelings into words. If clever Androwski thought that she ought to become a writer this was her training-ground. She read over some of the pages. Such a stack of paper it had become! There must be some good things in all this! But the words now often seemed to her to be full of holes, like Marie's colander in the kitchen.

Once, when she was quite little, she was playing with sand on the beach. "Like silver!" she said as her hands felt the fine white sand. "Like silver! Some silver for Mutti!" she grasped two handfuls of the lovely warm sand to take over to her mother, on a deckchair nearby reading a book.

"Look Mutti, silver, silver!" She opened her fists to pour the 'silver' onto Mutti's lap. But her hands were empty. All the treasure had escaped through her fingers and was lost. As she perused the pages it seemed to Piete that here too the treasure, the real significance of what she had tried so faithfully to record, had slipped through her fingers.

'I must dance out my feelings.' The idea of making manifest deep emotions as well as a powerful message through dancing had crystallised slowly in Piete's imagination, its inception going right back to the acquisition of her uncle Bruno's great army boots in the early days of the war. Then there had been César van Glabeke's blood-stained helmet, and finally Gil's torn uniform, which she had insisted in taking off him when he was demobilised. Together they would make a strong impression, each item speaking directly to any in the audience who had endured the war years, as well as conveying a brutal image to others who might have escaped.

There was an inevitability about Piete's choosing to become a dancer and pursuing the idea so resolutely. Her most vivid or intense moments had always been associated with movement. In the interminable war games played with Gretel and other friends she had acted out not only the episodes she had dreamed up, but her feelings about the war and what it meant to those involved. In spite of living in what might have been dismissed as the quiet backwater of Schneidemühl she had acquired there a deep understanding of what war was, its indifference to human suffering, its futility and wastefulness. In the Red Cross centre at the railway station she had seen at first hand what it did to its 'heroes', the front line fighters, so many crippled in body and mind. Over the years she had watched the 'prisoners' cemetery' grow from a few unmarked graves to a great field, absorbing a large plot of land owned by her own Golz family. As well as Uncle Bruno, she had exchanged letters with other soldiers, met from the troop trains or responding to food parcels. She was acquainted with death and knew its ugliness, its uncompromising blankness.

During the latter part of the war Piete had managed to get dancing lessons, thanks to her grandmother. The dancing teacher, Herr

Kleinschmidt, had told her at the start that at fifteen she was too old ever to become a ballet dancer, but she had persisted. As the oldest pupil she had made herself useful to him by helping with the younger ones, and in return he had taught her the basic movements. By the time the lessons ended she had acquired both control and poise, which were to stand her in good stead later.

The end of the war also meant for Piete the end of her war diary. So much of it was associated in her mind with things now past. One of the more recent episodes had been her staging of the 'death' of Lieutenant von Yellenic. It had taken shape so realistically that 'Nurse Martha', alias little Gretel Wegner, had burst out crying, genuine tears, and couldn't be comforted. Piete too had felt strange, equating the carefully laid out dummy on the camp-bed in her brother's room with Lieutenant Waldecker, whose cortège, with flower-strewn coffin, she had witnessed on its way to the station. She had brought the chronicle to a fitting end with an account of her and Gretel's final visit, at the end of November, to the snow-covered prisoners' cemetery.

As she set down the closing words, copied from the grave of a French prisoner, in her rounded, still childish handwriting, "À toi mes pensées et mes larmes, tous les jours", Piete thought 'will anyone else read this?' She remembered her mother's words, 'It will be a valuable record to show to your children.' She could no longer show it to her mother, that was certain, since it now contained so much that she would disapprove of. For the early pages there were typed copies sent by her mother, but the rest was in her own hand, complete with occasional blots and crossings-out. 'I must bundle it up and give it to Willi as a present.' In spite of his jokes about her being 'a latter-day Pliny' she knew he had been interested in her writing. Perhaps he would show it to Androwski, too. She found one of the large brown paper bags stored in the cupboard under the stairs and stuffed the sheaf of manuscript into it, tying the bundle across and across with a long piece of tape. On the outside she wrote in black letters,

FOR MY DEAR BROTHER, FROM PIETE. Please keep it safe

The last words were an afterthought, in case he should mistake it for something more trivial. As she deposited the parcel in Gil's room she felt both sad and relieved.

Her work in the Children's Home occupied Piete until her eighteenth birthday, 25th April 1920. Her mother had arranged that on reaching 18 she should come to Berlin, with the joint aim of relieving her own mother, Frau Golz, who was now more frail, of the responsibility, and having Piete to help her set up the music school again. Piete had no alternative but to agree. Secretly, though, she kept in mind her ambition to become a dancer, and vowed that she would find another teacher in Berlin. Her grandmother, seeing how thin and lacklustre her dearest grandchild had become, thought the change of air and surroundings would do her good.

"You are such a ghost these days, Piete my love."

Piete was in one of her favourite attitudes, sitting on the rug by Oma's knees with her legs curled under her while the old lady stroked her head gently with gnarled, onion-smelling hands.

"I can't help being thin, Oma. I just don't feel like eating after seeing all those poor mites with their swollen tummies. And . . turnips, ugh! I hate the sight of turnips."

"Well, perhaps Grete has better food in Berlin now. I have saved some marks for you to take to her. There is always food somewhere in the city if you have money."

Piete looked up at her. Oma looked so old and frail! She remembered the shock she had had the week before, coming in unexpectedly early, to see an old woman crouched on the coal-box weeping bitterly. At first she had not even recognised who it was, her hair all dishevelled, her hands covering her face as she rocked back and forth. Oma! Realising she had not been heard, Piete crept out, then came through the front door again, whistling and making as much noise as she could, to give her grandmother time to collect herself. Now too the old lady braced herself to be cheerful.

"You will have a fine time in the city. Your mother will introduce you to all her friends; she has such a wide acquaintance, many distinguished families."

I must find work first," Piete jumped up. "I have been teaching my fingers the typewriter keyboard so that I can work in an office. I made out a plan on a piece of cardboard. I can find all the keys without looking, it's easier than playing the guitar."

Two days later came the time for departure. Another farewell! Piete felt remote, as if she was observing herself carrying the heavy suitcase through the subway, her knapsack, also heavily loaded, on her back. Willi could not bear the thought of seeing her off at the station and had said his goodbyes at home before going to meet Androwski. Frau Golz had managed to gather some foodstuffs for her daughter, fresh eggs from the rich family of Piete's school friend Irma Kenzler, some real sugar hoarded for just such an occasion and some home-made cakes. She carried them in a small basket covered with a clean cloth.

"There is a little for you too, my child, for the journey. It is a long tedious way to Berlin."

Her grandmother saw her settled in a seat by the window. The train was fairly empty, just a few others boarding it here and there down the long platform. The engine blew off steam noisily. When Piete kissed her Oma she noticed that her cheeks were wet. She felt strange, sad and apprehensive, with an emptiness beneath it. All the greetings and farewells she had witnessed or been part of in this station! She thought of the Red Cross hut, made from two old carriages pushed together, of the many times she and Willi had stood where Oma was standing now, waving goodbye to Mutti.

The guard signalled. A last door slammed shut, and with a clanking of couplings and strong puffs from the engine the wheels began to turn. Piete leaned from the window waving, as the figure of her grandmother grew smaller and smaller. Farewell, Schneidemühl!

III   Wolfgang

1

THE SENSE of relief when the Graesers finally reached Munich was palpable. Major Karl Anton Obenaus had bullied his way past the various road-blocks on the tedious 200 kilometre journey from Lindau. Again and again they passed men in tattered uniform trudging along, boots split, frequently with filthy blood-stained bandages. Some jeered at the official-looking car or spat in the road. Others tramped on, heads down, scarcely bothering to get out of the way in spite of the strident motor-horn. Consequently dusk was thickening as they pulled up outside the substantial Obenaus villa in Arcisstraße. Hans Graeser had been living with his grandparents since leaving school in the summer and was at the door to greet them. To eleven-year-old Wolfgang this tall, bespectacled college student seemed immeasurably older, and their reunion was almost comically formal, complete with handshake - the first time, Wolfgang thought, he had ever done this with his brother. At first he had to share his brother's room, a necessity that Hans resented, valuing his privacy. Soon, however, Hans found university accommodation during term-time and relinquished his claim on the room to his younger brother.

Lily's parents, both now in their seventies and with their children all grown and away, had managed to retain something of their free and easy pre-war mode of living in spite of rationing. Bavaria had been able to 'live off its fat' and to temper the harsh realities of the war economy more successfully than other parts of the empire. After the privations of war-time Naples and their hasty departure the Graesers felt the contrast strongly. Nevertheless Carl Graeser, now 61, felt ill-at-ease with their status as guests of his wife's family and agitated to find new employment and a measure of independence. His sense of identity as a German citizen prompted him to seek an army post now they were in the country.

"There are problems, Carl." His brother-in-law had something of the military mind-set. "To the immigration people you class as a foreigner."

Lily broke in. "What rubbish, Anton! Carl has been in German employment all his life. What about the hospital directorship? Doesn't that count for anything?"

"Then there is your age," Major Obenaus pursued doggedly. "You are well over normal retirement age for the army."

"I think that my record, as Lily says, should weigh in my favour. Surely the army cannot afford to bypass my sort of practical experience."

Lily's father, comfortable in a deep leather armchair by the fire, had been smoking a fragrant cigar while this post-prandial conversation took place. He tapped a length of grey ash into the tray on the arm of his chair before speaking.

"I see no problem at all, Anton. I know Major-General Schwitters well. He is not going to put any obstacles in the way of acquiring so experienced a man as Carl for the army. I shall call on him tomorrow."

So it transpired that Dr Carl Graeser, equipped by the Bavarian Legation with the necessary documents, was accepted for army service. Within a week of their arrival in Munich he was summoned to Trier, where he took over the post of Divisional Medical Adviser to the 8th Army Corps, with responsibility for the military hospital there, a tougher and more demanding job than his former post in Naples. Being more than 400 kilometres from Munich and beset by administrative and other problems, Carl had little time to spend with his family.

This was felt most keenly by Wolfgang, who now, thanks once again to his grandfather's influence, attended the well respected Theresiengymnasium as a day scholar. After the undemanding, relaxed little German school in Naples this strict academy, with its uniforms, its cavernous assembly hall and regimented routine was hard to take. Hans now spent nearly all his time away from the Arcisstraße house and his scientific preoccupations - he was studying chemistry - had little appeal for his young brother. Wolfgang made no close friends at school, so was very much on his own, apart from his mother. Their point of contact was music and he took refuge increasingly in this and his painting. For the latter, pursued partly at his father's insistence but also as a relief from school discipline, he drew on his substantial folio of sketches from Italy and Switzerland, one of the treasures conveyed by the 'illicit' cabin trunk. Gradually the new pictures accumulated, giving Carl Graeser once again the idea of mounting an exhibition once the war was over.

War weariness was everywhere evident - in people's demeanour, in the sparsely filled shops and ill-serviced streets, populated by out-of-work beggars and mangy curs. The Allied blockade, coupled with poor harvests and an acute shortage of manpower on the land, led to hunger strikes in both Germany and Austria. In the middle of January 1918 the Bavarian government, in response to a desperate plea from the new young emperor Karl in Vienna, sent trainloads of potatoes to Austria to help stave off a breakdown of authority and wholesale chaos. Malnutrition was rife in the army of both countries. Coupled with the appalling privations of trench warfare it made the men an easy prey to infection. By March nearly half a million front line troops were suffering from a particularly virulent strain of Spanish influenza, with another 80,000 hospitalised. At this point General Ludendorff, who had never abandoned his dream of marching into Paris at the head of his victorious Wehrmacht, decreed that it was time for a final major offensive on the western front.

Wolfgang was bewildered by the patriotic fervour in school. Noting his lack of enthusiasm, his fellow pupils soon classified him as an outsider, and he even overheard, probably intentionally, references to 'that Italian Jew-boy'. It was commonly accepted that most war profiteers were Jews, fuelling the latent anti-semitism rife everywhere, so 'Jew' was a term of indiscriminate abuse. Wolfgang's known musical tastes made the sneer more acceptable in the general school climate of philistine chauvinism. His only relief at the Theresiengymnasium came from his English teacher. Herr Max Oprecht, a younger cousin of the well-known Swiss publisher, had spent some years as a student in Cambridge before the war. He had singled out Graeser almost as soon as he arrived and was quickly aware of his abilities.

"This Herr Oprecht you are always talking about, Wullie. He sounds a rather unusual person."

"He is nice, Mama, really nice, unlike horrible old Schadow."

"You mustn't talk like that about your teachers."

"Well he is horrible. He has hair growing out of his ears and his beard is all wispy, like an old mare's tail." Wolfgang had just been playing the violin, with his mother on the piano, and he was elated.

"An old mare's tail, an old mare's tail!" It became a sort of chant, the time marked by slapping on his violin. Lily could not help laughing in spite of her disapproval.

"All right, that is enough. Tell me more about the English teacher."

"He has to go pretty slowly. You have no idea how stupid some of them are, Mutti. But he lets me just read as long as it is English. And he knows everything - Charles Dickens, George Eliot, Robert Browning, Carlyle . . . oh, all the good writers. He says I should go to England and see Shakespeare acted in English."

"I don't imagine that sort of talk goes down well these days."

"Oh he doesn't say this in class, only to me. You would like him, Mama . . Mutti. Could Grandfather ask him to dinner sometime?"

"I don't see why not. Your father will be home this week-end. I'm sure he would like to meet a fellow-countryman."

The dinner went well, in spite of marked differences between Carl Graeser's army-oriented views and those of his younger compatriot.

Wolfgang was in high spirits and kept them amused by his inadvertent lapses into Italian, mixed with slightly self-conscious remarks in English.

"Does the holiday mean we are winning the war after all, Papa?" Wolfgang was referring to a 'victory holiday' for schools decreed by the Kaiser the previous week to mark Ludendorff's initial advance.

"General Ludendorff is a fine strategist. In my view he may yet reach Paris. But," he added less confidently, "the troops are in poor shape, to judge from those we see in Trier."

"The Kaiser's holiday was typical of him," said Oprecht impulsively, "premature and stupid. The man is clutching at straws now. He deludes himself into thinking he is still Head of State and Supreme Commander, but Hindenburg and Ludendorff are actually running the country - into the ground." The last words were muttered sotto voce.

"Nevertheless, young man," Dr Obenaus said ponderously, "he is still the Kaiser."

"In name, yes, sir. But look at the way the generals got rid of Bethmann Hollweg last year. Theirs is the real power. That's why they supported that puppet Chancellor Michaelis."

Carl Graeser took this up. "I agree that George Michaelis has not the stature of Bethmann. But you can't dismiss the power of the throne so easily. I am encouraged by the reponse to Tirpitz's Fatherland Party launched on Sedan Day. I read in the paper that they already have more than a million members in six months."

"That is not good news, Doctor, not good news at all."

"Why not?" Graeser said sharply.

"More Germans burying their heads in the sand, that's why. Since America decided to join the Allies it has been evident that to all intents and purposes the war is lost. What they should be doing is negotiating a just peace while they can."

"What! On the basis of the Fourteen Points? President Wilson is an armchair peacemaker, an academic. He has no idea. . ."

Lily, sensing the cooling of the atmosphere, interrupted, laughing lightly. "We are not going to agree on this, I can see. Wolfgang, you have opened Pandora's box. Go to bed before you do any more damage."

Wolfgang was about to remonstrate, but his father nodded when he looked that way so he reluctantly rose from the table, shaking hands with the three men and kissing his mother before leaving the room.

"You have a very remarkable son, Doctor," said Oprecht. "I am finding it hard to keep pace with him in English. The boy is a voracious reader."

Lily welcomed the change of subject. "I hope he is not a trial to you, Herr Oprecht. He can be very demanding, I know."

"Not a bit of it, Frau Graeser, he is a delight to teach. English is not a popular subject these days. It is good to find someone not blinded by war fever."

Max Oprecht became a regular visitor to the Obenaus house. As the war dragged on to its ignominious end he was grateful for the relief of the more liberal atmosphere after the sombre Prussianism of the school staff-room. Soldiers, officially or unofficially demobilised, streamed back into Munich to join the thousands already unemployed and living from hand to mouth. There was much talk of "workers' soviets" in the working-class districts. In the more affluent quarters around the Herzogpark break-ins became endemic. Dr Obenaus had all the locks changed after one of the servants was dismissed for pilfering, and a new member of the family, a guard dog christened 'Wolf' by Wolfgang after himself, was installed in a kennel near the kitchen door. Wolfgang loved taking him for walks and the two became close friends, so much so that others had to ask the boy's permission before doing anything for the dog.

At last, in October came reports of the failure of Ludendorff's last desperate throw of the dice. He disclaimed all responsibility for the débâcle, cynically joining with Hindenburg in backing the appointment of SPD politicians before retiring. "Let them face the consequences of the mess they got us into." Prince Max von Baden, the new Chancellor, sent a note to President Wilson. In Italy General Diaz began a final assault on the Austrian line to mark the anniversary of Caporetto, but the demoralised, half-starved Austrian and Hungarian troops melted away before them.

"So we can say goodbye to the Alsace!" Dr Graeser heaved a sigh. "I suppose Prince Max had no choice. He is as level-headed as anyone, the right person for such a miserable task."

Max Oprecht was more detached. "It is a touch of low comedy, don't you think, to have an American professor telling us all what to do. I doubt if he even knows where Slovakia or Serbia are when he talks of 'Czechoslovakia' or 'Yugoslavia'. They keep out of the struggle until it is more or less over then step in and preach to the victims."

"Victims indeed! You may well call us that. Have you heard the talk about betrayal from within?"

"Oh yes, they are full of it in the staff-room." Oprecht shrugged. "Half of them think like Bismarck still. They can't see that it was his mind-set, his Prussian seal set on Germany, that led to the war and all this."

Dr Obenaus made as if to intervene, then fell silent. He had aged noticeably as the year drew to a close and there was little of his former ebullience. A tired, dispirited old man. His wife Ursula was by now something of a valetudinarian, spending most of her time in her own room. It was left to Lily, the daughter of the house, as so often, to try and lighten the atmosphere.

This conversation took place at the beginning of November. The "Democratic and Socialist Republic of Bavaria" was announced a week later, greeted by the new people's leader in Austria, Kurt Eisner. Normal services were disrupted all over the city. News was disseminated by posting placards. Twelve-year-old Wolfgang found it all quite exciting and had to be snubbed frequently by Hans, home from university. He reported great ferment among the students, many of whom were in sympathy with the socialists and were joining the revolutionary 'soviets'. In spite of posters forbidding it, looting was widespread. The great new Tietz department store in the city centre was emptied. Prompted by that and the cold weather, women raided all the main fur shops. One afternoon Wolfgang, accompanied by his faithful Wolf, asked a young cyclist what was happening in the city.

"I work in the station restaurant, in the kitchens, but I've been sent home. They broke in last night and took everything, all the wine, cheese, Wurst, everything! Wish I'd been there! Anyhow, it means a holiday." He laughed and rode off, ting-a-linging his bell cheerily.

Soon the news from Berlin came in. The Kaiser had fled to Holland in a ten-strong motorcade, with a "court" of generals. A red flag flew over the Royal Palace and Philipp Scheidemann, elder statesman of the SPD, declared a socialist republic from the Reichstag window, while Karl Liebknecht and Rosa Luxemburg attempted a communist takeover with the Spartakus League.

Nevertheless life went on. Order was gradually restored in Munich. There was much jockeying for position in the new 'Councils'; the machinery of the great city resumed its customary pace. The terms of the armistice, posted up everywhere, aroused horror and disbelief.

"They will suck Germany dry! They are vindictive, impossible!" This was the dominant note in the Herrenklub in Palais Preysing, where Obenaus and Graeser met other professional people.

"What choice have we? Those who agreed to the terms are now sitting in the Reichstag." Maximilian Brantl, a lawyer in his late thirties, spoke with precision. "My view is that they are quite unrealistic. It is just more French vengefulness, like Alsace-Lorraine. The Entente will find out soon enough that the terms can't be implemented."

"Without the army Ebert and the rest are powerless." Professor Marcks from the History faculty of the university said bitterly. "Germany is not the place for a socialist government. History shows us that."

A tall, spare, well-dressed man with a clipped moustache, who had been listening to the discussion, now spoke up:

"I disagree with you there, Marcks. My attitude toward the new German republic is more affirmative. It is something new, something appropriate to the German spirit. The positive result of our defeat - yes, we have to accept the word (this was in response to murmurs of objection) - is that it places Germany in the forefront of political evolution. Wilson's League of Nations is no more than an attempt to prop up the old bourgeois plutocracy of the West."

This led to a general buzz of conversation. Carl Graeser had found the comment disturbing. He turned to his father-in-law.

"Who was that?"

"Have you come across any of Heinrich Mann's writing, the socialist supporter? That is his brother Thomas."

"The author of Buddenbrooks? It is surprising to find him supporting the socialists. I heard that they were at daggers drawn, he and his brother."

"Thomas is a thinker, a writer really, not politically active like Heinrich. Thomas's wife's family live in our neighbourhood, the Pringsheims. Very well respected in Munich. And very well off." Obenaus added.

On 21 February of the following year all was thrown into turmoil again, as the news broke of Kurt Eisner's assassination by Count Arco. Wolfgang was at school. At the end of the morning the whole school assembled for a special announcement from the Principal. Studies would be suspended. The boys were dismissed with the advice to return home immediately. The obvious delight of many of the staff, especially older members, soon communicated itself to the students. For once Wolfgang felt able to join his classmates in the general euphoria. They formed a chain and danced across the courtyard to the main gate, shouting "Down with the Reds!" It was left to Herr Oprecht to reprimand them. He noticed Wolfgang and called him over.

"Graeser! What are you doing with this rabble? Off with you all, and if you value your skins keep your mouths shut when you are in the city."

The advice was timely. The murder sparked off a wave of violence and further looting. Shots and explosions were heard from the city centre, and sometimes closer to the Arcisstraße house. From time to time there was the hum of an army aeroplane, swooping over and sowing leaflets asking for calm until order could be restored. A strict curfew was imposed.

The assassination heralded months of turmoil and uncertainty in the Bavarian capital. In April the radicals proclaimed that they now controlled 'the Räterepublik (Soviet Republic) of Bavaria' and were in alliance with similar republics in Hungary and Russia. The Graesers became accustomed to hearing the sound of firing as different factions sought to gain power, and to the curfews from 11 p.m., sometimes even 9 p.m. On Palm Sunday 1919 Carl Graeser, on leave from Trier and emboldened by rumours of the imminent collapse of the rule of the soviets, decided to risk taking his sons to the Odeon to hear J S Bach's St. Matthew Passion. Lily declined, feeling that her parents should not be left alone. There were skirmishes in the city centre between troops supporting the soviet Council and German government troops. Many of the audience, nervous at the sound of gunfire, left during the intermission and Graeser contemplated doing likewise.

"We must not give in to the Reds, Papa. We can walk home afterwards, it is Sunday after all. And I really need to hear the rest of the story. (This is how Wolfgang saw the oratorio) We shouldn't leave it half way through."

Carl smiled at his younger son's pleading. "What do you think, Hans? Should we risk it?"

Hans was also enjoying the performance in his quieter way, especially as he had several college friends in the chorus. For once he agreed with Wolfgang. It was the twelve-year-old's first experience of the great work and he was stirred and excited by Bach's dramatic, architectonic realisation of the Passion story. On the homeward walk he was silent and withdrawn while Hans and his father discussed the performance.

A week or so later Wolfgang rushed in from his walk with Wolf, waving a piece of paper.

"Look, Mutti, look! The aeroplane was dropping these all over the town. They are going to knock out the Reds, you'll see."

Lily took the leaflet: "'People of Munich! We know what you are suffering. Hold out! Help is near!' I suppose this must be from the government forces at Bamberg. I hope it doesn't mean more shooting. I wish Carl was with us; but at least Hans is out of harm's way." Soon after the Bach Hans had set off on a hiking holiday with fellow students. Wolfgang, his head full of Bach's music, had asked his brother to borrow The Musical Offering from the university library and had been spending hours in his room poring over it, sometimes playing the theme or attempting one of the canons on his violin. Once he cajoled his mother into helping him in trying to realise the masterly six-part Ricercare.

"Isn't it amazing, Mama!" In his excitement he had reverted to Italian. "All out of one little tune, twenty notes. It is like a spider making a whole web out of his own insides." Before returning it Wolfgang transcribed the whole work in his own neat, elegant hand, to have his own copy at hand.

The death-knell of the revolution in Bavaria was sounded by a bloody event in the night before 1st May, which had been proclaimed by the socialists as a 'worldwide' holiday. Gradually the news filtered out that ten hostages held by the revolutionaries in Munich's Luitpold School had been brutally murdered. There was immediate spontaneous revulsion at the meaningless slaughter. In the streets all red armbands disappeared. The régime tried to dissociate itself from the act, posting placards 'abhorring and rejecting this bestial deed', but the damage was done. By the evening Munich was in the hands of German government troops.

"At last we are returning to sanity!" Carl Graeser was enjoying an extended leave from his army duties at the beginning of July. "I have brought you a present, Wolfgang. It is for you and your friend." He handed the boy a small package.

"What friend? I don't have any friends at school."

Dr Graeser smiled. "Open it and you'll see." Wolfgang tore off the wrapping. It was a finely designed little book with a picture on the front of a dog tied to a tree with his master beside him.

Herr und Hund   ein Idyll   by Thomas Mann

"Do you understand now?"

"It's for me and Wolf! Thank you, Papa. Is it a good story?"

"Well, I heard the author giving a public reading of part of it at the Neues Theater. It was fascinating, such a vivid picture of the dog going hunting. The only thing he ever caught was field-mice! It made me think of you and Wolf. Now," Dr Graeser put his arm on the boy's shoulder as he looked at the gift, "what about you going public?"

Wolfgang looked startled. "Me! I can't read in public."

"Not reading, your paintings. Before you object let me tell you. I have arranged for an exhibition to be mounted here in Munich next month. I showed the director of the art gallery some of your mountain landscapes and he was very impressed. And Johannes, your 'Uncle' Johann, says he will arrange the catalogue and write an introduction about your drawings and paintings."

Wolfgang was at first taken aback by the idea. The paintings were his, his own feelings about Italy, his beloved Napoli, and about Zürich and the mountains, their snowbound, inaccessible peaks. It would be like exposing himself to public gaze. On the other hand he felt proud of his father's praise and Uncle Johann's backing for the project. When his mother added her pleas he became reconciled to it and even agreed to help with arranging the exhibition.

This was the highlight of Wolfgang's time in Munich. The printed catalogue looked impressive, with its proud title: Bilder eines Knaben: Malereien und Handzeichnungen eines Zwölfjährigen. Admission cost 50 pfennig, proceeds for the benefit of the families of children who had died in the war. The exhibition created quite a stir in the school, which was not distinguished for its artistic creativity. For a short while 'Graeser' was something of a celebrity, greeted by the teachers in the corridors and treated with more respect by his fellow students, especially when they heard that a number of the pictures had actually been bought for substantial sums.

Shortly after the exhibition closed, Dr Graeser received his demobilisation papers and returned to civilian life in Munich, with a small army pension. He fretted at being out of work and dependent on the Obenaus family again, though Lily tried to persuade him he deserved a rest. There seemed no chance of his starting a practice in the city. Over the next 18 months he acted as a locum from time to time and made inquiries about a teaching post at the medical school. These proved fruitless, but by a lucky chance a visitor from Berlin to the school overheard him, and told him of a forthcoming vacancy in the fashionable suburb of Nikolassee, a growing practice, with opportunities for work at the university medical school.

Early in 1921 Dr Graeser took up the appointment and moved to Berlin with his wife and son.

2

The winter of 1920-1 was just beginning to release its fierce grip on Berlin when Dr Carl Graeser and his family arrived at the beginning of March. Thanks to his army connections and to influential Swiss friends in Berlin the medical practice was awaiting him in Nikolassee, out towards Potsdam. The lake that gave the suburb its name, fed, like the Wannsee, from the great Havel, kept the air fresh. Though no more than twenty kilometres as the crow flew from the Brandenburg Gate, Nikolassee seemed like countryside to fifteen-year-old Wolfgang, the only son at home. Hans was still at the university in faraway Munich, having changed his studies from chemistry to music.

Wolfgang had no regrets at leaving Munich. His three years at the grammar school had been, he felt, a futile, miserable period of his life. After the free and easy Neapolitan atmosphere - at least until their precipitate departure at the end of 1917 - Munich seemed to him stiff and artificial. At school he was constantly being reprimanded for behaviour that would have been normal in Naples. His fellow-pupils treated him like some strange animal, with his odd turns of phrase and unpredictable changes of mood, so he made no close friends. At home, as he was asked by his Obenaus grandparents to call their house, he had never felt comfortable either, knowing that all three of them, his mother, Hans and he, were really no more than guests. Until the year after the war ended his father had been away in Trier, rarely appearing in Munich and beset with worries and problems.

'Of course, there had been his exhibition.' Wolfgang was strolling in what was to become one of his favourite haunts, the sloping common land beyond the Evangelische Friedhof of Nikolassee, with its long vistas and the bubbling stream at the bottom. There were still workmen in the big house he must now call his home, number 17 in tree-lined Prince Friedrich-Leopold Straße, so he had wandered off to spend time with his own thoughts on this expansive, sunny Spring afternoon. Yes, that exhibition arranged by his father and 'Uncle' Johann had been a triumph of sorts. Wolfgang smiled as he remembered the looks of incredulity on his fellow-pupils' faces when Herr Langschrott the art master had congratulated him on it, urging them all to 'make sure and see Graeser's fine studies of Swiss and Italian landscapes.' But what had been the point of it after all? Seeing his work up there on the walls, with strangers staring into scenes that had been so intimate, had affected him oddly. To pad out the exhibition his father had persuaded him to include a series of sketches of hands which he had done before leaving Naples. Watching people peering at these had made him feel naked. And when his father, the day after the opening, proudly read out the comment in the Münchner Neue Zeitung, that 'here is a remarkable new talent, an artist who should go far,' he had gritted his teeth and vowed silently never to pick up a paintbrush or pencil again.

He kicked idly at a tuft. Some of the rough grass had been flattened by the recent snow, of which there were still a few soiled streaks on the upper slopes. By now the wheat around Naples would be a handsbreadth high. But this was Prussia, where everything was late, formal, regimented. As if to contradict his thoughts, a little dog ran past him, barking furiously and chasing a ball. Wolfgang looked round. A heavily built man in a loose raincoat had thrown the ball. He smiled at the boy as he came up, breathing heavily.

"Too much energy, that's his problem. And mine is too little." Wolfgang welcomed the distraction from his train of thought as the man groaned comically, putting a hand in the small of his back. 'He must be Papa's age - no, even older.' The boy was always guessing or asking people's ages, mentally dividing them by his own fifteen years.

"Is he a thoroughbred?"

The man laughed at the naive question. "By no means. Mixed ancestry, like the rest of us." He looked curiously at the boy. "Haven't seen you here before, have I?"

"No, sir." Something in the stranger's demeanour prompted Wolfgang to be respectful. "We only moved in a few days ago, in Prince Friedrich-Leopold Straße."

"Really? That's where I live. Wait a moment. Is it number 17, the doctor's house?" It transpired that the man lived almost opposite the Graesers and had planned to call that very day. Wolfgang took to him immediately, an unusual occurrence with his excessively prickly adolescence.

"Why not call now, sir? The house is a bit of a mess, but my father is at home. I 'm afraid I . . ." He wanted to ask the man's name, but was too shy. The stranger sensed his hesitation.

"Müller. Paul Müller. You had better call me Herr Professor when you introduce me. It sounds better, don't you think?"

"Oh! . . . yes, of course." Wolfgang's thoughts were racing ahead. What was he a professor of? Music perhaps. Or mathematics, or philosophy? Perhaps he, Wolfgang, could learn . . . His mind went back to the Munich grammar school, to rigid, unimaginative Dr Braunschmidt, to his blind frustration at leaving everything unfinished. To his voracious, undisciplined reading, in German, Italian, French, even English, thanks to Herr Oprecht - and poor Miss Jones. Some words floated into his mind: 'The web of our life is of a mingled yarn, good and ill together; our virtues would be proud if our faults whipped them not, and our crimes would despair if they were not cherished by our virtues.' In Naples he had been intrigued and fascinated by the flow of Shakespeare's language, even when he could not understand it. He suspected it was equally obscure to Miss Jones. Then this speech had suddenly shone out at him.

"A mingled yarn."

"I beg your pardon?" Herr Müller was looking at the boy in some puzzlement. They had just passed the cemetery and were crossing into Prince Friedrich-Leopold Straße. Wolfgang flushed and stammered.

"Sorry! I . . I was dreaming."

"Dreaming in English!" Paul Müller smiled. "I tend to dream only in German. But that sounded like a quotation. 'A mingled yarn.' Let me see, let me see. Shakespeare?"

The boy looked startled, but pleased. "Yes, it's from All's Well That Ends Well.We read it with our tutor in Naples. But Herr Oprecht - he was my English teacher in Munich - said one needs to see Shakespeare acted in English. Do you read Shakespeare, sir?"

"No sensible man can afford not to. Your teacher was right; it is a revelation seeing a good English production. Not even Schlegel can capture the magic of Shakespeare's English." He stopped walking, looked beyond and through his companion.

"'To die - to sleep,
no more; and by a sleep to say we end
The heart-ache and the thousand natural shocks
That flesh is heir to: 'tis a consummation
Devoutly to be wish'd. To die, to sleep;
To sleep, perchance to dream - ay, there's the rub:
For in that sleep of death what dreams may come,
When we have shuffled off this mortal coil,
Must give us pause - there's the respect
That makes calamity of so long life.'"

He paused, looking now at Wolfgang, not through him. "Do you know Hamlet?"

"No. Miss Jones said everyone reads Hamlet so she would avoid it, and we didn't study it in Munich either. But go on, sir. Please!"

Paul Müller was touched and amused by the boy's eagerness. He declaimed the rest of the soliloquy, Wolfgang standing with fists clenched and his intense blue eyes fixed on the man's face. When he had ended the boy let out his breath in a great sigh, but said nothing. Müller was about to speak, but decided not to. They finished their walk in silence and soon reached number 17.

The introductions were mutually satisfactory. Professor Müller even asked if he and his wife could register as patients, since they lived so close. Wolfgang had retired to his room - he had claimed one of the attic rooms as his own - but came down to bid the guest farewell, with a book in his hand. As he shook hands he showed Professor Müller the book, his rather tattered English copy of The Complete Works of Shakespeare, in painfully small print.

"Excuse me, Herr Professor. Could you show me where that speech is. Please!" Müller took the book, turning it over in his hands curiously.

"Quite a treasure, this. Here you are, young man, the beginning of Act III. It is often quoted out of context, but you really need to know the whole play to see what he is getting at." He handed the book back and said, turning to the boy's parents, "And even then one can't fathom it all."

For days after, Wolfgang's head was full of the soliloquy. It was like magic, Professor Müller was right. How could Shakespeare three hundred years ago have known so well what he himself felt? 'To die, to sleep, no more. And by a sleep to say we end the heart-ache and the thousand natural shocks that flesh is heir to. 'Tis a consummation (he mouthed the strange word slowly) devoutly to be wished.' But then, think of all that followed. "Ay, there's the rub." He spoke aloud to himself in the small looking-glass in his room.

"We have to find a private tutor for Wolfgang, Lily my dear. He simply must have that Matura if he is to get a place in the university. That was one of the penalties of moving here from Munich." Dr Graeser and his wife were by the fireside after their frugal supper. The workmen had gone home, the servants were not yet engaged and the air was redolant of Carl's cigar, almost his only personal extravagance in these thin post-war times. The boy heard his name spoken as he came into the room.

"Come, Wullie! You have been quite a recluse lately." His mother held out her arms and he went awkwardly to her, suffering rather than responding to her embrace. He looked at his father.

"What were you saying, Papa?"

"You need a tutor, my boy, to get you through the Matura."

Wolfgang straightened up, his eyes suddenly alert. "What about Professor Müller? Could you ask him? He's retired, isn't he?" Dr Graeser liked the idea and by the end of the month, their second in the new house, the arrangement was finalised. Wolfgang would spend four mornings a week with Professor Müller.

The meeting with Paul Müller was one of those so-called chance happenings that made Carl Graeser speculate about chance or . . what? Destiny? His mind went back to that other 'chance' meeting with Lily Obenaus all those years ago. Whatever the cause, accident or fate, the coming together of Professor Müller and Carl's wayward, brilliant son was a stroke of good fortune. Müller was only two years older than Dr Graeser, but Wolfgang could be forgiven for assuming he was more, with his bald crown and unruly fringe of thin grey hair, his tortoise-shell framed spectacles, heavy moustache and thickened, ungainly body. The Swiss doctor, shorter and slimmer in build, at 65 prided himself on his fitness and still kept his dark hair, streaked now with grey. If Carl Graeser's body was more supple than the other's, Paul Müller's alert, iconoclastic mind, wide-ranging culture and incisive intelligence left the other far behind, and sometimes threatened the harmony of their relationship, especially when the conversation assumed a political colouring. Müller's professorship derived from his last academic post, the chair in earth studies at the Wilhelm University in Berlin, but he was no narrow specialist. Like Goethe, whose writings he often cited in his sessions with his new pupil, Müller's geological studies were an adjunct to his other interests, especially in the humanities. He was a competent linguist, fluent in Russian and English and with a working knowledge of French and Italian. In his younger days, before turning to science, he had been a classical scholar and he still read Plato in the original from time to time, sensing a natural affinity with Socrates. Like many intellectuals in these post-war years, like the author of Buddenbrooks, he would often take refuge in irony. Unlike Thomas Mann, however, and to the initial disappointment of Wolfgang, Paul Müller was musically almost illiterate. He was aware of this and wryly apologetic about it to Frau Dr Graeser, with whom he had soon struck up an easy friendship.

"I love to watch you play." Lily had been trying through a Mozart violin sonata, with Wolfgang at the piano this time, just before they sat down to luncheon after the tutorial one day. When the session was held at number 17 he was frequently invited to stay on if Frau Müller was away.

"And you love also to hear the music I hope, Paul." Lily added, mischievously, "Can you remember a single note, in fact, I wonder?"

"Of course I can." Paul felt challenged. "It went something like this, the main theme." He gave vent to a tuneless moan in an attempted falsetto, tapping the time on the table with his finger. Wolfgang looked down at his plate, his mouth full, trying to keep a straight face. Then he exploded, spattering food in front of him and almost choking. Having started he could not stifle his giggles. His father frowned and thumped him on the back.

"Control yourself, Wolfgang!"

The boy sobered up momentarily at the severe tone, but as conversation resumed round the table he was overcome by another fit of giggles. Red in the face, he got up and rushed out of the room. Dr Graeser started to apologise, but his guest brushed it aside.

"Please, don't give it a thought. I should never have given tongue - not my strong point," grimacing at Lily, who had found the whole episode more entertaining than embarrassing. "He is highly strung, that son of yours. It is like training a race-horse, teaching him. Or rather, him teaching me sometimes. Our main problem is keeping our minds on the Abitur syllabus. But he will have no trouble with that." He turned to Dr Graeser. "When is the examination to be?"

"His age - or rather his youth - is the problem. There seem to be difficulties about his taking it so young as an external student. Fortunately we have been able to approach the minister responsible. He told us that Wolfgang might be permitted to sit the examination in the Mommsengymnasium early in 1924. Will that be time enough? You know it is normally a four-year course of study."

"Oh yes, we'll cover the ground easily before that." He added with a chuckle, "It will leave us more time for other topics, like Greek or mathematics."

The next two and a half years, culminating in the examination, which Wolfgang could hardly take seriously it seemed so un-taxing, and including - much more significantly - the fateful discovery in that treasure-house, Otto Haas's bookshop in Bernburger Straße, constituted one of the happiest times in Wolfgang's life, until the final dark three months. In Paul Müller he had for the first time come into intimate contact with an intellect and sensibility to match his own. Their study sessions, usually held in Müller's tobacco-scented, book-lined study with its threadbare Persian carpet and old leather chairs, were a delight to both. The older man was enlivened and stimulated by, and perhaps even a little in love with his lively, attractive and brilliant young pupil. In his turn Wolfgang, thrilled by the vistas opening up before him as their studies ranged ever wider and his questions became more and more searching, came to revere and love Paul Müller only a shade less intensely than he loved his father. The one cloud on his horizon was the evident mis-match between the personalities of the two older men, sometimes needing all Lily Graeser's tranquil diplomacy to deflect them from open hostility. Behind this, unacknowledged by either but exerting its baneful influence, lay a hint of jealousy, a certain rivalry for the boy's affection. Until Müller's advent Carl Graeser had been able to take for granted his prime place in his son's heart. For in spite of the fair hair, delicate almost girlish complexion - never marred by the adolescent spots and pimples of his peers - and intense blue eyes, all legacies from his mother, she had never been first in the boy's affection. Ironically, that place was taken by his older brother Hans, whose looks were so like his father's.

The summer of 1921 was glorious - weeks of hot, sun-filled days and cloudless skies. In the vineyards of Alsace the grapes burgeoned, preparing for what was to become an historic vintage. Berliners shared in the lifting of spirits. The Grunewald, its groves refreshingly cool after the city streets with their melting asphalt, and the shimmering Wannsee had never been so popular. Towards the end of August the Graesers and Müller combined to hire a boat for a day's sailing, Frau Müller excusing herself as 'a poor sailor'. Paul Müller was an experienced yachtsman and assumed the rôle of skipper on the rather unwieldy craft, sporting a peaked linen cap in navy blue with a prominent K (for Kapitän) "to hide my bald patch," as Müller said with a grin. On the boat he proved to be remarkably agile in spite of his bulk. There was just enough wind to fill the square mainsail with its broad horizontal stripes of red and yellow. Hans was away camping with college friends, so Wolfgang was the only young person on the expedition. He was in high spirits, plunging from the side of the boat and swimming after it with shouts of delight. Once, during a tack, a gust of wind caught Müller's cap and whisked it over the side.

"My cap, my precious cap!" he shouted in comic dismay. "Without it no-one will know that I'm the Kapitän."

Wolfgang had been lying at full length on the foredeck after a swim, soaking up the sunshine. He sprang up, dived neatly over the side and grabbed the cap as it began to sink. Müller and his mother cheered as he hurled the bedraggled object onto the deck before scrambling back. As Müller wrung out the water he turned to the lad.

"You make a good retriever, many thanks! This is an old friend, I'd hate to have lost it."

In the evening, prompted by Wolfgang's mathematical interests, they decided to take the bus out to Potsdam to see the new observatory which had been specially constructed to test Einstein's general relativity theory.

"What an extraordinary sight!" Lily was gazing up at the strange bulbous shape of the Einstein Tower, with its boat-like concrete base and four curved window embrasures, topped by the round telescope dome. "It looks like a boat, or . . or a submarine." Her voice had changed with the last words.

"It is beautiful!" Wolfgang had also been arrested by the exotic design of the observatory. He turned to Müller. "Don't you think so, sir?"

"Not my idea of beauty," said his father, nettled not to have been asked first.

The other replied, "Functional certainly, if that constitutes beauty. The thing is, will it prove Einstein right or wrong?"

"He can't be wrong!" Wolfgang was almost indignant. "Time and space are the same thing, and that means all the rest . ."

"Come, Wolfgang," his father interrupted almost querulously, "You are out of your depth. Don't talk about what you do not understand." Carl Graeser had been on edge for some time. He had submitted to Müller's leadership on the boat with an ill grace, and a conversation about Versailles and its consequences had foundered on marked differences in the two men's views. Wolfgang, hurt by his father's 'put down', relapsed into a sulky silence.

As they made their way in Potsdam towards a restaurant a newspaper seller passed them, shouting "Latest! Erzberger assassinated!"

Lily, already sensitive to the changed atmosphere in the party, voiced her distress. "Oh no! Will it never stop, this senseless violence? What a way to end such a beautiful day!"

Graeser had bought a copy of the paper and scanned it rapidly before handing it to Müller.

"Huh! not before time, if you ask me. He lost his libel case, remember. Erzberger was a traitor, for all your talk, Müller. One of the infamous Versailles gang."

"I can't accept that," Müller said shortly, looking up from the paper. "Matthias Erzberger was a man of integrity. Even in 1917 he had a clearer idea than most of the way things were going. What do you think, Lily?"

"I just hate the pointlessness of it. Haven't we had enough killing in all these years? Why can't it stop?"

A shadow was cast over the rest of the day. Wolfgang, uncomfortable at the hostility and upset by his father's dismissal, hardly spoke in the restaurant. Carl Graeser would have pursued the subject, but Lily vetoed it, seeing the danger signals.

That night, exhausted physically, Wolfgang's thoughts raced as he lay in bed. Einstein, the great tower, Erzberger's murder, Versailles and reparations, time and space, Paul's (he always secretly thought of his tutor by his first name) expert yachtsmanship which had made his heart swell with pride, his father's sombre mood, the feel of the water on his skin . . . At last sleep overcame him, but the warm night was filled with dreams. In one he found himself at the top of the Einstein Tower, which had assumed the function of a submarine conning-tower. He was wearing the cap with the K on it, and people addressed him as 'Herr Kapitän'. He felt the motion of the water under him as the great craft rounded the tall navigation mark in the Wannsee with its basket-like structure like a beacon. He knew the ship was sinking. It had to sink. The deck was now filled with refugees, all chattering in the Neapolitan dialect and running back and forth in panic. Someone was begging him not to sink the ship, someone he knew. Who was it? Nevertheless he said, "A Kapitän always goes down with his ship," in stern tones, ignoring the clamour and grasping the controls, which were shaped like the hand-grip of his father's army revolver. As the water began to close over the ship the cries of the drowning came to his ears, but faintly, as though through fog. He held fast to the controls, the water swallowed him up, he opened his mouth to breathe and breathed water, he had no regrets, he was coming home . . .

Wolfgang opened his eyes. The house was silent, there was a sliver of moon directly in his line of vision through the bedroom window. The distant roar of Berlin, ever wakeful Berlin. He lay still, letting the dream ebb away. The strange part was that there had been no fear of drowning, in spite of the screams and cries around him. The feeling of . . what? completion? fulfilment? still pervaded his senses. He turned on his side and slept dreamlessly until morning.

3

At Wolfgang's next session with Paul Müller, in his book-lined study, neither referred for some time to the Potsdam outing, as if by unspoken agreement. They were supposed to be covering the geography syllabus for the coming Matura - or Abitur, as it was better known here, - but this was particularly prone to digressions in the light of the travel experiences of both. Müller had, as he said, grown up in Bismarck's Germany with its ever-expanding trade and industry. The railway boom made the whole of Europe accessible when he was in his twenties and he was able to take advantage of it.

"I even visited your beloved Napoli, Wolfgang. A teeming, stinking, beautiful city like a great amphitheatre, with the bay for a stage. Your father must have seen it like that too, from the other side, when he was a ship's doctor."

"Yes, he has told me about it, and about the diseases that used to rage in the Lower City. You must have heard about the cholera in '84, when King Umberto insisted on going right into those stinking slums where it killed so many. That is how a king should lead his people, don't you think, sir?"

"You know my views on hereditary monarchs. Don't forget that Prussia had a madman on the throne when I was born. I agree that Umberto was courageous. Now what were we studying?"

He laughed as he turned their attention back to the European trade routes, which had brought them to Wolfgang's childhood home. Dr Müller found it necessary to keep his brilliant pupil on a very loose rein, so did not ever attempt too narrow a concentration on the subject in hand. He knew that only a hint was needed for Wolfgang to follow it up, first from his father's small library and Müller's much larger one, then from the university library, to which he now had access thanks to his tutor. The chief problem of the boy's academic guide was to convince him of the need to compartmentalise the different 'subjects' in line with the Abitur requirements. Wolfgang's mind was bent on finding and identifying pattern, connections. Like Goethe he constantly sought the Urpflanz behind the variety of the world around him.

Their best common ground was mathematics. Here Müller soon realised that he had nothing to teach his pupil. Instead they indulged in mutual stimulation, setting each other arithmetical and geometrical problems. The Einstein Tower visit prompted intensive mutual exploration of the general and special relativity theories, which led them in turn to philosophical speculation on the nature of reality.

"That is the task of our philosophers, Wolfgang."

"Hasn't philosophy now been overtaken - no, I mean taken over by science, especially the human sciences like physiology and psychology. But also mathematics." Wolfgang could never bear to leave mathematics out of their discussions for long.

"Well, I suppose Edmund Husserl might agree with you over mathematics. He is a fine logician who teaches in Freiburg now. He studied mathematics here in Berlin and I got to know him a little when we both attended Weierstrass's lectures - I must tell you about them sometime. Husserl approached philosophy through mathematics. In fact, here is a book of his if you are interested." Müller fetched down from the shelves behind him a small volume. "The Philosophy of Arithmetic. He has some good insights into the conceptions behind geometry, the way our thinking starts from the intuition of such essentials as point, triangle, line, rather than from empirical facts."

The boy had been listening intently. He took the book, adding it to a small pile already accumulating on the floor beside him. Dr Müller leant back in his chair, absent-mindedly sucking at his pipe.

"My grandfather, Johannes Peter Müller, was a physiologist. He was professor of physiology here in Berlin before I was born."

"Did you know him well?"

"No, alas! He died when I was four. I vaguely remember him - a shock of grey hair, big side-whiskers. He wasn't old when he died, not even my age. But to get back to your point: I don't think you can dismiss philosophy quite so easily. One of the best definitions of philosophy I know comes, as it happens, from another physiologist, a psychologist as well, a man called Wundt, Wilhelm Max Wundt. He died last year - a sad loss to German philosophy. Let me see . . ." He gazed at the ceiling, watching the smoke curling up from his pipe: "'the task of philosophy is the construction of a logically consistent world-view which shall bring all special knowledge into one general system of thought.'"

"That is good, very good!" Wolfgang was excited. "Let me write it down." He scribbled it into his dog-eared notebook. " Isn't that what Goethe and the others were aiming at, a logically consistent world-view? But I don't know whether it applies to that other book you lent me, The World as Will and Idea." Wolfgang had devoured the book in a couple of evening's reading at home. "'The principle of sufficient reason.' I like that, especially when he is talking about forms and the place of mathematics. He calls it 'form devoid of all content.' Do you accept Schopenhauer's approach, Dr Müller?"

"I like his style, so lucid and elegant. There is no denying the man had extraordinary insight, for instance in his anticipation of Freud's work on the unconscious. Nietzsche thought he was a fine educator." He reached down yet another book from the shelves. "Here you are, Schopenhauer as a Teacher. But my answer is no. I can't stand either his clinical views on love or his pessimistic outlook on life. I fancy that the term 'pessimism' only came into general use because of his influence."

"Isn't there plenty to be pessimistic about since the war? Father finds it hard to be an optimist these days."

"Your father had a difficult time in the war. Leaving everything he had built up in Naples must have been a bitter blow to him. But at least," Müller spoke with unaccustomed feeling, "he had - and still has - the security of the love of your dear mother, Wolfgang. Which is more than Schopenhauer had, the old misogynist."

The boy had bridled and flushed at this last remark. He blurted out, "Let's not talk about love."

Müller looked at the boy quizzically then turned to his desk and directed the talk back to the more neutral territory of trade routes. He had noted such sensitive spots before. Wolfgang seemed peculiarly vulnerable at these times, so that the older man's heart went out to him. Müller had no children; more and more he was, as it were, adopting his pupil as a 'proto'-

son, a rôle which Wolfgang both liked and shrank from. There were times when he felt he was 'pig in the middle' between Paul and his father - an English expression from Miss Jones, who taught Hans and him the game on the beach at Posilipo. Wolfgang still remembered his blind frustration - he was nearly always the 'pig' - rushing about and jumping up while Hans and Miss Jones lobbed the ball over his head and mocked his inability to catch it. He never managed to get Hans in the middle, but there were occasional triumphant moments when Miss Jones threw carelessly and had to take his place. But now there was no Miss Jones.

Because of his ever-widening intellectual and musical interests, Wolfgang was already, at 16, a prolific letter-writer. One of his chief correspondents on music matters was his godfather and uncle, Ludwig von Hofmann, who lived in Dresden. He was a keen amateur musician and had always been interested in his talented nephew, sharing his enthusiasms and helping him to find copies of music to feed his latest interest. Herr von Hofmann occasionally came over from Dresden on business and stayed with them at Nikolassee. For Wolfgang, Uncle Ludwig was also a link with his Swiss and Italian childhood. He had happy memories of the 'three men', as Ludwig used to call the nine-year-old Wolfgang, himself and his brother-in-law, off on walking or boating expeditions after Hans had gone away to school in Switzerland. One such expedition, to Capri, almost ended in disaster when their small coach overturned, crushing Carl Graeser's stomach with a projecting angle of the coachwork. The doctor made light of his injury, but could not disguise his pain, which recurred from time to time in later life.

Wolfgang could always expect an interesting Christmas present from Uncle Ludwig. The one for 1921 was a book to feed his growing fascination with baroque music, thanks partly to brother Hans, who had switched from science to music at Munich and was studying Telemann for his degree. On 8 January Wolfgang sat down to his 'thank-you letter', covering page after page in his rapid, fluent hand. He had just acquired a great collection of old editions of baroque music: Corelli, Tartini, Leclair, G.F.Händel, Locatelli, Veracini, and was excited by new discoveries - the 'pure and noble' vocal music of the 16th century, his 'idol' Leclair. . . With characteristic assurance the 16-year-old sketched out what he saw as the three 'high points' of Western music: Italian vocal music of the 16th century, the music of J.S.Bach a century later, finally the period of Mozart and Haydn, with Beethoven providing the synthesis.

'what has now come and is coming is merely a combination of what has already been achieved. I am not talking about all the great industry of Herr

Schönberg and his like in Vienna, which I consider to be pure fraud. In my opinion it is not possible for our ears to hear atonally; a revolution like that would take centuries and Herr Schönberg wants to do it in a few years! In any case, his Gurrelieder are quite 'Wagnerish' and tonal. By the way, I recently read a witty epigram by Reger: 'Half Wagnered is half won!' (Halb gewagnert ist halb gewonnen).'

In the Spring of 1922 came Wolfgang's admission to the Hochschule für Musik, for which his father had been making strenuous representations ever since they arrived in Berlin. Thanks to her Leipzig music contacts Lily Graeser had an introduction to the recently appointed deputy principal, Herr Professor Dr Georg Schünemann. In January Wolfgang and his mother were invited to the Music School to meet him and discuss the possibility of admission. Dr Schünemann was a big, ponderous man with receding hair slicked back with rather pungent hair-cream and a large, fleshy nose. Wolfgang found himself staring at the nose as the professor and his mother exchanged greetings.

"So this is your young genius, eh?" Dr Schünemann spoke jocosely, patting Wolfgang on the head in a manner he resented. "I hear you have made yourself familiar with Das Musikalische Opfer. A great work, a great work." He sat down at the piano; they were in his spacious office with its heavy ornate writing-desk, crystal chandelier and dark velvet curtains suspended on rings from the polished mahogany rail. All in keeping with the occupant, Wolfgang thought. But as the professor played the three-part ricercare with poise and delicacy, the boy at once responded.

"Come, my boy, take the left hand. Let us do homage to Johann Sebastian together."

Dr Schünemann could not have chosen any better way to break through Wolfgang's reserve. Soon they were deep in talk about the structure of the work, the fascinating complexity of fugues and canons, all derived from the king's twenty notes.

"Now why did Bach not accede to King Frederick's request to improvise a six-part fugue on the theme? There's a poser for you, my lad."

"He was quite right not to do so, sir. The theme is flawed and he recognised that straight away."

Schünemann laughed. "But couldn't say so to his Prince, eh? You may be right. But he did compose the six-part ricercare later. And what a sublime work it is."

"Ah, but that . . ." The boy became more animated as he sought to unravel the great fugue, illustrating his points on the piano and sometimes intoning a superimposed phrase. The Deputy Principal listened attentively, but eventually had to call a halt.

"No question, Frau Doktor, no question at all! Your son must join us here."

Lily got up. "So his age will not . . ?"

"Leave that to me. I shall talk to Professor Schreker this-afternoon. He must join as a violin student, of course. This will mean an audition with Professor Klingler. We shall arrange that too. I do not anticipate any problem."

It was as well that Wolfgang had Dr Schünemann's support. The audition did not go well. Karl Klingler was a technician, precise in manner, fussy and meticulous. He found fault with Wolfgang's stance, his bowing arm, his fingering, even his intonation, grimacing with exaggerated disgust however slight the inaccuracy. Consequently the boy played badly. The worst part was when the professor made him play a movement from a Mozart sonata that was a special favourite with him and his mother. Dr Klingler hammered out the piano part, playing it too fast, faking the runs and shouting advice to the boy, now nervous and intimidated and seething with suppressed rage. Klingler did not want him but could not override Schünemann. The experience coloured Wolfgang's early days in the Music School. He felt at first once more like a new boy, his alienation reminding him of those miserable first weeks at the Theresiengymnasium in Munich.

The pattern of life changed as he began to settle down to his new routine. Days were spent at the Hochschule für Musik, Joachim's famous conservatoire, where the easy good fellowship of the student population gradually helped him to overcome his shyness. Amongst them he had teamed up with another of Klingler's students, the Bulgarian Leo Alkalay; then there was the friendship with Grete Hanauer. Professor Klingler's lessons were his main trial. It was always: 'Take my copy and transfer all the markings to your own copy, all please, phrasing, bowing, fingering." Then Klingler would insist on a slavish adherence to every detail. He was a good practical musician and the method worked with most of his students, particularly the girls, who were readier to take it on trust, but Wolfgang found it a constant irritant. His own conception of the works studied was often at odds with his teacher's and in any case he felt he understood the music better than his teacher did.

He was fortunate to find a kindred spirit in Leo, who was six or seven years older than Wolfgang. They became aware of each other when working together at J.S.Bach's concerto for two violins for one of the student concerts. Leo was an exceptionally brilliant player who had won a scholarship in Sofia to attend the prestigious Berlin Music School. He had a similarly instinctive grasp of music and the two students shared a hatred of the cut and dried method of 'Kunstfertigkeit (technique) Klingler', as they christened their teacher. They abbreviated it to K3 and it became a shared private joke. In spite of his seniority Leo was not at all intimidating to Wolfgang. His German was somewhat halting, so they often conversed in French. Professor Klingler was no linguist and was suspicious, not without grounds, of their chatting together, but could do little about it; Leo was his best student and did what he could to reconcile the professor to the other. Later in the course Klingler off-loaded Wolfgang to his second in department, Professor Andreas Moser. Moser was an older man and a fine scholar. He was more relaxed than Klingler and took to his new young student from the first, appreciating his instinctive musicianship and recognising that there was more here than a potential run-of-the-mill orchestral player, probably not primarily an executant at all.

The sessions with Paul Müller, across the road from the big, empty-feeling house in Nikolassee, were now less frequent, but still full of interest for the adolescent boy. He loved to share his college experiences with the older man and Dr Müller took pleasure in the affection of this lively, brilliant, beautiful young man with his clean Teutonic looks. Paul's wife rarely made an appearance; Wolfgang gathered that the union was very different from that of his own parents, much more a mariage de convenance, each of them leading their separate lives. He made no comment, but his acute sensibility soon recognised that his tutor was strongly attracted to Lily, his own mother. Their open camaraderie filled a gap in the older man's life and Wolfgang was the vicarious beneficiary.

It was always one of his chief regrets that he could not talk about music with his tutor. Some time after the interview with the Deputy Principal he mentioned to Müller how Schünemann had introduced their playing and discussion of The Musical Offering.

"It is your kind of music, sir. Do you know that?"

"Now you are mocking me, young Graeser. My kind of music! You know my limitations in that direction." Müller picked up a book. "This is my kind of music, differential calculus. Now if music had this sort of satisfying symmetry . . ."

"But that's just it! It has, it has!" The boy jumped up in his eagerness. "The Musical Offering is like a mathematical puzzle - or rather, a set of mathematical puzzles based on the king's theme. Bach even wrote, before two of the canons, Quaerendo invenientis, Seek and ye shall find!

The player had to find where the theme was to enter. Just like our teasers, Dr Müller."

In spite of himself the tutor was interested. He listened as the boy started to expound the mathematical patterning of the sequence of fugues and canons, illustrating them with scribbled diagrams. Müller tried to follow, then asked,

"But didn't Bach write another collection of fugues just before he died?"

"Yes, of course, Die Kunst der Fuge, a sort of text-book on fugue writing which he didn't live to finish. I have never seen it. Nobody plays it these days and no-one took any interest in it when it was published. His family didn't even make enough money to pay for the plates, so they had them melted down. Copper was valuable!" Wolfgang laughed.

J S Bach was always central to Wolfgang's musical life. He responded in particular to Bach's formidable intellect, so evident from his phenomenal grasp of counterpoint. Like the Thomaskantor, Wolfgang delighted in the mathematical challenges of fugue and counterpoint, appreciating to the full the elegance with which Bach converted maths into music.

Margarete Hanauer's aria in the cantata on St. Stephen's Day went well. Frau Kuhr-Golz had taken a liking to Wolfgang, treating him almost like a younger brother of Elfriede's. He respected her professionalism and felt flattered by her interest, and came to enjoy his visits to the small apartment in Steglitz, its precise neatness reflecting the character of both female occupants, but especially the mother. After one of the last rehearsals Frau Kuhr-Golz asked to hear some violin music.

"Play us something now, Wolfgang my dear. I should like to hear you play without having to do anything or to criticise." The two girls joined in the request. He turned to Piete, saying shyly,

"Will you play for me, please?"

"What do you want to play? My sight-reading is not as good as it was since I started bashing a typewriter for a living." They settled on Mozart. Wolfgang fetched some well-thumbed sheets from his music-case.

"I used to play the piano part of this one for my mother ages ago, so it can't be too hard."

Wolfgang never considered himself a soloist; at the college he always played second violin in chamber music. His one solo appearance, with Leo in the Bach Double Concerto, had been imposed on him by his first teacher. The performance with Piete was musical, but far from note-perfect. It collapsed in laughter when they were interrupted by heavy thumping on the interior wall communicating with the next-door flat.

"That old man, he's impossible!" Piete explained that they had agreed on certain times for music with their fractious neighbour. "I think he sits there with his watch in his hand. Come, Wolfgang, tell us about when you were living in Naples. I have always longed to go to Italy."

"What a request!" Wolfgang paused, bow in hand. "Do you have all night to spare? I lived there for eleven years, you know."

Grete broke in: "We visited Milano once before the war when I was ten. We travelled by train, of course, from Zürich. St. Gotthard, all those tunnels and waterfalls! And Milan is beautiful, great wide streets and so full of life!"

"That is Piedmont - well, Lombardy. The north is not like the south." Wolfgang was quite indignant. "Naples is the real Italy, the bay shimmering and sparkling, old Smoker over there to the East - Vesuvius, you know. Mama - my mother used to call it our link with the underworld. Life in Naples was . . oh, I don't know how to put it, expansive, full of colour . . ." For a moment the boy was transformed, ecstatic. Then his face darkened. "When we had to leave in 1917 it was horrible. They all hated Germans after Caporetto. Even our friends, the Italian ones, stopped talking to us. As if we were lepers, or - or cholera victims."

"Cholera!" Piete sounded shocked. "They cured that ages ago, surely, in the last century."

"Not in Naples. My father had some cases in the hospital when I was about five - that would be 1910 or 1911. I think the authorities tried to hush it up because they had made such a public affair of having cleaned up the city. But of course, you can't hide that sort of thing from doctors." Wolfgang could not be drawn to say more about Italy, the last topic having touched off one of his lightning changes of mood.

4

The promised visit of Piete to Wolfgang's home in Nikolassee came a few weeks after Christmas 1922. Their friendship veered between coolness and warmth on both sides, but Wolfgang's mother was keen to meet Piete as well as wishing to return Frau Kuhr-Golz's hospitality to her son and urged him to firm up the invitation. The Saturday morning was bright and clear as he set out to walk the eighty or so metres to meet Piete at the S-Bahn station. Wolfgang stamped on the frozen puddles, taking the cold fresh air in great gulps. The sun sparkled on trees rimed with frost. At the station a small boy was swinging himself round and round one of the iron stanchions supporting the roof, ignoring his more decorous older sister when she said, "Your hands will be filthy, Conrad. Come away!" Wolfgang stood outside the waiting-room with its white and green vitreous tiles, immediately under the station name-plate. He grinned at the boy, who smiled back and went on swinging. People were muffled up against the cold, but Wolfgang had left his jacket open and his shirt unbuttoned, relishing the keen freshness. He was looking forward to seeing Piete, but felt some underlying apprehension of the visit. What would his father think of this outspoken, anti-militarist girl with her free and easy manner? Would she hold back from her unpredictable, passionate outbursts? Would Mutti like her? His parents had met Grete and Leo once or twice at events in the college, but he felt more uneasy about their reaction to this outside friend.

The tracks sounded the approach of the train and Wolfgang stepped forward, scanning the windows as they passed him and the train shuddered to a halt.

"Wolfgang! You must be frozen!" Piete had jumped from the carriage behind his back. She embraced him quickly, their breaths steaming in the cold air. "What a marvellous day! You are really in the country out here, aren't you?" Once again he felt his breath almost taken away by her suppressed energy. Piete was cheerful, voluble, lively. And so beautiful! It was good to be with her. They made a striking couple as she took his arm and they walked down the platform, both of a height, he with his straight fair hair, blue eyes and slim build, Piete full of animated talk and gesture, her dark hair smoothed back from her forehead, accentuating the strong bone-structure of her face with its high cheekbones. The warmth of her arm in his communicated something of her excitement as she looked about with keen interest.

"You are lucky to live out here. The air is so much fresher. And all these trees!"

"You wait!" Wolfgang was infected by her high spirits. "We'll go for a walk later over the common. It is only a step from our house, a great wide grassy valley with a stream at the bottom."

The introductions when they arrived at number 17 went well. Piete was impressed and a bit awe-struck by the imposing-looking house with its steps and big front door, but she took an instant liking to Frau Dr Graeser with her ready smile and warm welcome. Wolfgang's father was a little more intimidating, but Piete appreciated his formal courtesy - he called her Miss Elfriede. His old-fashioned correctness took her mind back to her Golz grandfather in Schneidemühl. As there were some hours before the meal and the day was bright and clear, Wolfgang took Piete to his favourite haunt, the common land beyond the cemetery. The cold weather had deterred most casual strollers so they had the place almost to themselves, apart from one or two determined athletes in running shorts.

"Come, I'll race you, Wolfi! To that post over there, see?" Before he could reply Piete was off, covering the frosted turf in long strides. Wolfgang was fit. He loved the outdoors and ran in this stretch of open ground regularly. He soon overtook the girl. She put on a spurt and they reached the post together. As she touched it Piete stumbled. Wolfgang put out his arms and for a moment they were close together, their breath mingling in the frosty air. His bright gaze met her smiling eyes and their lips touched in a fleeting kiss.

"Oh! I wasn't expecting that!" Piete had blushed, and moved away to sit on a bench next to the marking post. Wolfgang too seemed confused. He remained standing until she patted the bench beside her.

"Come on, Wolfi. Let's get our breaths back."

"Why do you call me that?"

"Don't you like it?"

"It's not that. My godfather - he's my Uncle Ludwig - used to call me Wolfi when I was little. Mutti still calls me Wullie sometimes. Otherwise people always just use my name." He smiled, laying his arm gently on her shoulder as they sat together. "I like you calling me that. It matches your name Piete. Or should I call you Elfriede?"

"God forbid!" Piete laughed. "It's only when people are cross they do that - except your father, of course. He is nice, such a gentleman. He reminds me of my grandfather Golz, Mutti's father. He died long ago, when I was quite small, but I remember him vividly." She started talking about her Schneidemühl childhood, describing the ballet lessons and how she helped the dancing master with the beginners.

"Is that when you decided to be a dancer?"

"I can't remember when I first thought of it seriously as a career. My mother still thinks I'm crazy. Come on, let's walk, I am getting cold." Piete jumped up, pulling Wolfgang to his feet. They set off along the open valley, sometimes holding hands or arm in arm. Wolfgang felt very happy.

Piete took deep breaths. "The air is so good out here, not like stinking Steglitz."

"But Berlin is exciting, don't you think? So much going on, so cosmopolitan! In Kurfürstendamm you can hear ten different languages in half a kilometre, English - mostly with the Yankee twang! - , Russian, Chinese, even some French now."

"It is fun living there as long as you can survive. There are thousands of beggars, prostitutes, down-and-outs; lots of them with what's left of army uniforms. And things will get worse now. Have you heard about the Ruhr?"

Wolfgang was roused by this. "The French had no right! They are trying to start the war all over again. My father says . . ."

"Don't let's spoil our walk by talking politics, Wolfi. I'm sorry I started on it. Tell me your plans. You are not going to be a violinist, I know."

"No. My mother is a very good violinist, we don't need two in the family. In any case, I haven't the patience - all those scales and arpeggios! It is the symmetry that appeals to me, like mathematics. Music and mathematics are cousins, blood relations." Wolfgang went on to his interest in The Musical Offering and in Bach's mastery of counterpoint. "It is like your dancing, Piete. Symmetry in motion."

"I am not so sure about that. For me dancing is a form of expression, a special language in which I can say things I can't say any other way. I want to bring home to people what the war was really like, the waste, the pain, the futility. That's why I kept that helmet and Gil's old uniform, remember?"

Wolfgang laughed. "Oh yes, and your uncle's army boots."

Piete's mind was still on the war. She shook herself, then went on,

"But one needs real physical control, like in athletics. Or like your scales and arpeggios," smiling at him. "That is why people have set up these new schools of dancing. One of Mary Wigman's pupils is going to start one quite near here, did you know, in the Grunewald."

"Dancing, dancing! We keep coming back to dancing. My tutor here found me a poem the other day, an English poem, all about dancing."

"Really? What was it like? I can read English a bit. Have you got the poem?"

"It is an old poem, quite old-fashioned English, like Shakespeare. Orchestra it's called. That's why Paul thought I would like it. He lent me his copy. It is quite a valuable book, too, a limited edition. An English friend sent it him last year as a birthday present. Paul - I don't call him that to his face, of course! - has a great library, I am always borrowing books from him." Wolfgang stopped walking and turned to her. "Wait a minute, I learnt one verse by heart. It is all set in ancient Greece, gods and goddesses. The speaker is one of Penelope's suitors.

Dancing, bright lady, then began to be
When the first seeds whereof the world did spring,

The fire air earth and water, did agree
By Love's persuasion, nature's mighty king,
To leave their first disordered combating
And in a dance such measure to observe
As all the world their motion should preserve."

Piete had listened closely. When Wolfgang came to the fourth line they exchanged a glance and he flushed deeply, stumbling over the next few words.

"It is beautiful, Wolfi. Can you show me the book?"

"Certainly. Come up to my room when we get back."

The room was right at the top of the big house, its sloping ceiling directly under the roof and its small window overlooking the houses opposite. Piete looked about her with interest. So neat and well organised!

"If I had been brought here blindfold Wolfi, I think I would know this was your room."

Wolfgang was looking amongst the books stacked round his small writing-desk under the window. "You are the only female to set foot in it apart from my mother. Here's the book."

She took it, a slim volume bound in leather, the title tooled in gold leaf.

"What a lovely book, such thick paper! I hardly dare open it."

"Here, I'll show you where that verse comes." The two heads, one dark, one fair, bent over the book. Piete began to read the next stanza, but was hesitant, losing the rhythm. Wolfgang took over.

"Since when they still are carried in a round
And changing come one in another's place;
Yet do they neither mingle nor confound,
But every one doth keep the bounded space
Wherein the dance doth bid it turn or trace.
This wondrous miracle did Love devise,
For dancing is love's proper exercise.

"You see," he closed the book carefully, "his idea is that the whole universe is in constant motion, held together in a great dance."

"And held together by love," Piete added. "I like that. That's what I think too."

At this moment a gong sounded from the house below, summoning them to dinner. Wolfgang, self-conscious at Piete's comment, jumped up.

"I'll race you to the next floor." He took the narrow attic stairs two at a time and waited at the top of the main staircase. "Now, let's make a proper entrance." He took Piete's arm formally and they walked sedately down to the dining-room. 'Such a child he is really!' she thought, laughing at his game.

The meal was a friendly affair, marred only by some sombre comments on the Ruhr occupation from Dr Graeser.

"They want to ruin us, the French. Sheer vindictiveness, after those appalling Versailles reparations."

"But, excuse me, sir," Piete could not help herself saying, "isn't it because we are not conforming with the terms of the treaty we signed that they occupied the Ruhr?"

Carl Graeser looked at her in surprise."The terms are impossible. They want to bleed us white." He spoke peremptorily and there was an awkward silence. Piete's mind went back to Verdun, to all the blood soaked into the ground there, to van Glabeke's poor blood-stained helmet . . . She was roused by Wolfgang's mother saying,

"What are your plans, Elfriede? Wolfgang tells us you want to be a dancer."

"So your mother won't have your help in her singing tuition?" Dr Graeser took it up. "I have heard that her method of voice production is very highly thought of."

"No sir, I just know it is not my kind of life. My mother is a fine teacher, you are right. I would only let her down." She went on to describe her dancing lessons, then with a mischievous smile added, "I have a plan to surprise my mother soon with a demonstration. She thinks I could never be good enough as a dancer and says that I am wasting my time and my wages on it. I have to prove her wrong."

"You young people always think you know best," Dr Graeser said jocularly, but with a hint of bitterness. "Wolfgang here has all kinds of plans too, mathematics, Greek, philosophy, Chinese, I don't know what!" He looked indulgently at his son. "He still has the Abitur to get through, though."

Wolfgang shrugged impatiently. "That's nothing, Papa, really. Dr Müller says I could pass it now if I wanted, and it is not for a year."

Piete's visit came to an end soon after the meal. The two young people retraced their steps to the S-Bahn station, neither speaking for a while. As they waited for the train, Wolfgang said,

"When will you give up the office work, then?"

"As soon as I can. Hans Gérard - he's my dance tutor - thinks I could earn at least as much as a dancer as I do now."

"In Berlin?"

"Not necessarily. It may be better to go on tour round the smaller towns."

"Will you do your soldier's dance, the one with the helmet and the boots?"

She smiled. "Perhaps, I don't know. I shall certainly perform it one day, 'By love's persuasion, nature's mighty king'. Isn't that what your poem says?"

As she spoke the train rolled in. They embraced hastily, Piete holding the boy close for a moment, with a kiss on both cheeks. Wolfgang felt stirred up inside and tongue-tied. As the train moved away he called out, "See you soon!" The words were swallowed up by the rattle of the wheels, but Piete smiled and waved.

5

After watching the train out of sight Wolfgang trailed back home slowly, turning over in his mind the day's experiences. Everything was so vivid! It was as if Piete had transmitted an electric charge, as if he had absorbed some of her vital energy. He thought about that kiss, putting his hand to his mouth. "Wolfi!" He smiled as he remembered her very intonation. He usually hated anyone to shorten his name, even at times resenting his mother's tender 'Wullie', but from Piete's lips . . . He stopped suddenly, lifting his face and sniffing almost like a dog at a new scent. The recollection of her closeness on that bench, the faint, warm, perfumed breath so special to Piete. "Piete!" he said it aloud and felt his face go hot. Was he in love?

The thought sobered him and he strode out more firmly, running in quickly at the side door and up to his attic fastness. Paul Müller's book still lay on his desk. It opened on the same two stanzas and he read them over. The music of the spheres in a dance! The concept appealed to him on many levels. It was like that definition Paul had given him. He found it in his notebook: 'a logically consistent world-view . . one general system . . .' But Piete's idea of dance was not consistent with this; her need for a new language, for self-expression was almost anarchic. He remembered his father's curt response to her suggestion that the Ruhr occupation might be justified. She was German, wasn't she? More German than him or Papa, for that matter. Yet she seemed to feel no shame at the ignominy of Germany's position and the infamous Versailles conditions being imposed on her. He closed the poetry book with a snap, threw open the windows and took deep breaths of the chilly air before settling down to his studies.

At his next session with Paul Müller Wolfgang handed back the poetry book.

"Ah, the music of the spheres, the universal dance! It's a lovely idea, isn't it, Wolfgang?"

The boy did not respond immediately, busying himself with his books and papers. Eventually he said,

"I was thinking of that definition of philosophy you gave me, sir. I suppose the Almagest, Ptolemy's earth-centred system, which is what this poet is celebrating, was a logically consistent world-view. But now, well ever since Copernicus, it seems just fanciful. And now there is Einstein."

"Isn't Einstein seeking his own Almagest? Aren't you too, with your love of symmetry? What about Bach?" The sessions with his tutor often began like this before they started work. This time Wolfgang found it harder to leave the topic, worrying it like a dog with a bone.

"Alright, what about Bach? Perhaps there is a universal pattern. Perhaps Bach had a vision of it but never managed to realise it fully. Did I ever tell you what Dr Schweitzer, the great Bach scholar, says about the subject for Bach's unfinished text-book on fugue-writing?"

"Die Kunst der Fuge? There is a manuscript copy in the State Library here, did you know? They call it the Berliner Autograph. The librarian told me once that it is one of the collection's most treasured manuscripts."

Wolfgang, following his own train of thought, was hardly listening. He said,

"There is something intriguing about Dr Schweitzer's description of the theme. Wait a minute, I have it here." He fetched out the notebook he always brought with him to the tuition sessions:

"'The theme . . opens up to us a still, serious world. It lies there desolate and rigid, without colour, without light, without movement. It neither delights nor distracts, yet one cannot escape from it.'"

"Hm! It sounds your sort of thing, Wolfgang. Why don't you ask to have a look at the Berliner Autograph when you are next in the State Library?"

The idea took root, and some time later Wolfgang, armed with a letter from Dr Schünemann and a recommendation from his courtesy 'uncle' Dr Johannes Wolf, did succeed in gaining permission to see the precious manuscript. The writing was very hard to decipher and he soon realised that he would need to study it closely for many hours to make any sense of it. Before handing it in he looked again at the twelve note foundation on which the fugues were based, that subject which 'could not be called a stroke of genius but which nevertheless one could not escape from'.

As if to verify the truth of Schweitzer's dictum the theme stayed with him as he walked away from the library, running through his head like - like - he could not put a name to it. Like pure water? Like a cool wind? Like the clean smell of his freshly laundered bed-clothes? Like silver sand running through his fingers at Posilipo? Like Piete's clear complexion? Or like all these together? Wolfgang was hardly aware of where he was going until he found himself at the Potsdamer Platz. Near the clock tower a man in a grubby white coat with an apron tied over it was rolling a barrel across the paving-stones. The air stank of petrol fumes. He turned down Bernburger Straße to get away from the noise and smell and found himself outside a small, rather exclusive-looking shop. In the window was an open book displaying music. Obviously a specialist antiquarian shop, a survival from pre-war days by the look of it. He glanced at the name: Otto Haas. Something impelled him to look again in the window and he went suddenly cold as he read a title on one of the two or three select books set out there: Die Kunst der Fuge. Like an automaton Wolfgang pushed open the door and went in. The bookseller sat on a high stool, poring over a dusty-looking leather-bound volume. He peered over his gold-rimmed spectacles at the intruder, then eased himself off the stool. He was much shorter than Wolfgang so had to look up as he spoke.

"Good-day! Is there something I can interest you in, young sir?"

Wolfgang asked to see the copy of Die Kunst der Fuge and the proprietor - for it was old Otto Haas himself - reached it in from the window, smoothing the pages down with his gnarled hands and turning the old volume about.

"Ah, a fine copy for its age. No foxing, and the leather, you see, is hardly faded. Handle it with care, young man, if you please." Herr Haas seemed reluctant to part with the book. Wolfgang looked at the title-page for the publisher's name: Nägeli, Zürich.

"My birth-place! When was it published?"

The old man adjusted his spectacles and pointed. "There, sir, you see. MDCCCII, 1802. More than a century ago. So you are also from Switzerland, the country of mountains."

Wolfgang looked up. "Have you been there?"

"I travel to many places in search of my stock. Yes, I found this and more in your home city, with its green Lippat and the lake." His tone changed. "Might you be wanting to purchase this rare book, sir? It is something of a specialist interest." He took the book out of Wolfgang's hands, saying regretfully, it seemed to the boy, "Who writes or studies fugues today? I have heard that some composers are abandoning harmony altogether. You are perhaps a musician?"

"I study music," Wolfgang said shortly. "Can you name me a price?"

"In Swiss francs?" Herr Haas said quickly. "I could let it go for fifty francs."

"Fifty!" Wolfgang's face fell. "So much? And in marks?"

"Ah!" The old man hesitated. "We have some problems just now, Herr . . . ?"

"Graeser, Wolfgang Graeser."

"Herr Graeser. Today . . . one moment." He consulted a paper on his desk. "Ten thousand marks. I cannot guarantee that price tomorrow."

Wolfgang asked him to reserve the book and left the shop. He must have it! What could have guided him to the shop in Bernburger Straße, with the very theme running through his head? It was part of a pattern: The Musical Offering, the symmetry of his mathematical work with Paul, Husserl and his Philosophy of Arithmetic, Schweitzer's 'still, serious world', the Berliner Autograph with its rapid, almost impenetrable script and notation . . . Two days later Wolfgang carried the precious find up to his room. His father had demurred at the cost, but Lily, responding to the urgency of her son's tone, for once overruled her husband and insisted that Carl should release some of his diminishing supply of francs.

For days Wolfgang could hardly be persuaded to eat. He would rush up to his room as soon as he returned from the Music School, immersing himself in the fugues, canons, mirror canons, covering pages with his neat, rapid script and with diagrams. At night he would throw himself on the bed, tossing and turning, Bach's subject filling his dreams.

'There is something wrong!' Wolfgang raised his head from the Die Kunst der Fuge copy, pressing his fist to his forehead and staring out at the patch of sky. 'This is not Bach's idea. He could not have created the theme just for this.' He soon realised he must consult the Berliner Autograph again, with its confusing assortment of loose sheets, in order to get at the master's true intentions. As if on a screen, or like a pattern in water, like the symmetrical circles from a dropped pebble, he would catch glimpses of a great airy structure spun out from those magical twelve notes. Then the curtain would fall again as he pored over the Nägeli edition.

Dr Johannes Wolf, now a respected musicologist at the university, was one of Lily Graeser's friends from her student days in Leipzig. In Munich Wolfgang had taken to him and he, in turn, had happily adopted the courtesy title of 'Uncle Johann'. He had been a frequent visitor at the hospitable Obenaus house as well as helping with Wolfgang's exhibition. Wolf had always been interested in Lily's brilliant, multi-talented, moody son. Lily enlisted his help in gaining permission for Wolfgang to study the Berliner Autograph, a major concession on the part of the library authorities for one so young. Professor Wolf knew Dr Schünemann at the Music School, and Wolfgang was given considerable freedom, attending or skipping classes more or less as he wished. His violin spent most of the time in its case, but Uncle Johann had loaned him an elegant little clavichord, which joined the sparse furnishings in Wolfgang's attic study and became indispensable as he began to tease out the complex strands of Die Kunst der Fuge.

Dr Carl Graeser, beset by money worries like most professional families, expressed concern at the time Wolfgang was devoting to his Bach studies. The tuition fees at the Hochschule für Musik and Professor Müller's honorarium took a large slice out of his earnings as a General Practitioner and with inflation exacerbated by the French occupation of the Ruhr his meagre army pension was losing value steadily. One Sunday morning Dr Graeser found himself alone in the house with his son. Lily had gone to the service in St John's Protestant church; their one housemaid was at her own home. After his early morning run and sparse breakfast Wolfgang had as usual incarcerated himself upstairs with his papers. The doctor had made it a principle not to disturb him at his work, convinced by Johannes Wolf's obvious respect for his young protegé's musical skills and penetration. But on this occasion he broke his rule, labouring slowly up the bare attic stairs to his son's room. Wolfgang was poring over a sheet of paper covered with what looked like sequences of horizontal brackets. He looked up in surprise, smiling and clearing papers off his bed so that his father could sit down.

"How is it progressing, my boy? Wolf has told me that you are delving into Bach's consciousness to a remarkable extent."

Wolfgang blushed with pleasure at this unexpected testimonial. "Papa, it is really exciting. I think I am the first person to understand what Bach was doing. Not even his amanuensis, not even his own children realised it. Nor from what he says about it has Dr Schweitzer grasped the scale and stature of the work. I wish I could meet Dr Schweitzer to talk about it with him."

"Not much chance of that , Wolfgang my dear," Carl Graeser said with a smile. "He is in the heart of Africa, ministering to the natives." Then, with a change of tone, "Are you sure you can spare all this time and effort just now, though? You still have the violin course, and the Abitur is not all that far ahead. You must pass that."

How lined Papa's face looked, how troubled his eyes! Wolfgang realised he had hardly looked at his father since he and his mother had talked him into buying the Nägeli edition of Die Kunst der Fuge.

"Don't worry, Papa. Please believe me, the Matura is child's play. I could do it in my sleep now if I had to and it's not for almost a year. It is because there is so much time before it comes that I can get on with this. Uncle Johann thinks that the Bach Yearbook will print an article of mine about it."

"What about Latin and Greek? You were always complaining about them in Munich."

"Latin is nothing. One reads it like German, or English, and I know all the set texts already. As for Greek: look, Papa." Wolfgang picked up a book and some sheets of paper. Carl Graeser took them: a Greek edition of the Odyssey. "That is as far as I've got so far, the first eight books. But Paul - Dr Müller only lent me the book last week. It is good fun translating Homer, his stories are so lively and fresh."

His father was scanning the sheets of paper covered with Wolfgang's neat rapid script. "How on earth do you find time for this?"

"Dr Müller suggested it as a way of revising Greek and to stop me getting stale." The boy laughed. "You know what he's like about music. He is right, though, it does wake me up after all this sort of thing." He held up the page he had been working on, diagrams of Bach's fugal patterns. "I realise now how much our culture is rooted in the classics, as Spengler describes in that amazing book. He can see where we are going in the Western world."

The conversation did something to relieve Carl Graeser's anxiety about his son's future. There seemed to be no limit to the boy's intellectual energy. Gazing at Wolfgang's bright face and sensing his sheer vitality, Carl was taken back to his own student life in Bonn, to his ambitions to be a research biologist and to the heady early days at the Naples hospital. How different Napoli then from Berlin now!

The Berlin of 1923 was a city of paradoxes. On the one hand, beggars, many of them crippled, destitute ex-army conscripts in tattered uniforms, at almost every street-corner and ragged, malnourished children playing in the evil-smelling courtyards or scavenging in the gutters. On the other, new glittering department stores like the Kurstadt on Hermannplatz with its great column of light, used as a navigation mark by aeroplanes coming in to Tempelhof, or like the Berlin "Harrods", Wertheim's. The capital costs of these and of the new factories springing up in Moabit and other districts were met by loans from the international money market, the entrepreneurs who took them out, many already enriched by war profits, happy to contemplate the diminishing burden as the value of German currency sank and sank. Berlin nevertheless remained a magnet for foreign wealth, especially from America. An exciting, dynamic cosmopolitan metropolis. For Russians, both displaced aristocrats and new socialists, Berlin was a Mecca, with its cafés, theatres, cinemas, cabarets and concert halls. In the Wilmersdorf district not far from Wolfgang's home in Nikolassee it was more common to hear Russian than German spoken in the streets and even the litter of discarded newpapers revealed Cyrillic script.

Socially and culturally, Berlin was a melting-pot. The downward pressures on the old middle and professional classes were relentless as savings vanished and fixed incomes shrank. The embittered losers, former factory managers - some even in the dole queues - , the old officer class, professional men and women like Dr Graeser and Frau Kuhr-Golz, provided a rich soil for right-wing anti-government propaganda. The democratic socialists in the Reichstag, for all their idealistic new constitution, were thought by many to be tainted with the infamous Versailles agreement, and remained powerless without the help of the old army corps - some of them reconstituted as Freikorps - and big business, both of whom had their own separate anti-socialist agenda.

At the same time artists, playwrights and directors, musicians, cabaret and film stars flocked to Berlin. In the year that Wolfgang Graeser joined the Hochschule für Musik the famous Moscow Art Theatre on its first post-war and post-Revolution tour, under its veteran director Konstantin Stanislavsky, was given a royal reception and played to packed houses. At the Academy of Arts Feruccio Busoni gave master-classes and promoted Bach's music, succeeded on his death in 1924 by Arnold Schönberg. Even the young radical Bavarian Bertold Brecht was drawn to the Prussian capital, attracted in part by the anarchist Dadaists. He found many like-minded, iconoclastic writers, actors, directors, dancers and cabaret artists.

To Wolfgang the welter of new ideas and influences was stimulating and exciting. The city was full of young people, no longer shackled by the pre-war conventions or moralities, engaged in sport, athletics, swimming, camping or merely bummelnend. In one way he felt himself to be a part of this great experiment in urban living. On the other hand his Italian, Swiss and Bavarian background set him apart so that, while conscious of and responding to it, he remained detached from the wider influences of the city and absorbed in his studies. The work on Die Kunst der Fuge, close and exacting as it was, nevertheless acted as a release from the tedium of the Music School routines. Surrounded there by aspiring, mainly young executants and their uncomplicated ambitions, he felt himself to be an interloper. Out of a sense of duty to his mother and to justify his father's fee-paying Wolfgang did his statutory half-hour of violin practice, but was always glad to turn to his desk and immerse himself again in the thought-world of the great Johann Sebastian with its order and symmetry.

"You must write to your godfather, Wullie, if you want him to find out about the Hellerau concerts for you. He will surely be interested in these new studies of yours, too. Don't forget to remember us to your Aunt Elli." Lily was constantly having to jog Wolfgang's memory these days over such tasks. On his mother's prompting he pushed the Die Kunst der Fuge papers to one side and reached down a clean sheet.

'Dear Uncle Ludwig' Once the ice was broken his pen almost ran away with him:

Litterae non scribuntur, nisi - if one has a request. . . I've heard that on 22nd to 26th April in Hellerau Professor Gurlitt from Freiburg will be presenting a series of historical concerts. Last year he did a similar presentation for the opening of the Kunsthalle in Karlsruhe (mediaeval music, mixed with readings of mediaeval poetry . .) I would be so interested that I might well come to Dresden for those three or four days. This is a big favour I am asking of you, dear Uncle Ludwig, to find out more details of the performances; they will certainly interest you as well. . .

I am still very very busy - it will go on for years! - so can't find time for letter-writing or anything else. I have to take the Abitur a year earlier than I would have done at school. It is the most unpleasant of exams, the subjects have no connections with each other yet one needs to know them all thoroughly. Everything interests me, but it is hard to find time for it all. . . I try to 'make a virtue of necessity' so I'm now reading all Homer through in Greek, for my own interest. The first twelve books of the Odyssey took me 14 days - great fun! It helps not having to study it in school, I can form my own judgments more easily. I used to be absolutely negative about Greek, but now I'm convinced that our culture is so deeply rooted in hellenic culture that one cannot ignore it. Nevertheless the old idea that antiquity is the only true culture, the only source of the good and the beautiful - that is pure madness! Spengler has helped me towards a more objective and historical view.

Last autumn I busied myself with Chinese culture. I have also rummaged around in whatever sources I could find about Indian, Arabic, Babylonian, Egyptian, American etc. Chinese culture attracted me so powerfully that I firmly intend to learn Chinese and Japanese and travel to East Asia after completing my studies. I have got to know the director of the East Asia museum and his researcher, W. Cohn and somebody Kummel - forget his forename - , so I have had a glimpse of the fabulous treasures in their museum, which will be open to the public next winter . . .

The Music School involves enough work alone, over and above the Abitur, so you can see how much I have to do.

I played in a house concert with Frau Ellers, an excellent harpsichord player, French music, one of a series of chamber music concerts . . . also in a Bach cantata, an aria obbligato, and with a little chamber orchestra. That was last year. Nowadays I hardly ever get round to music-making - just quartets and early music occasionally. Frau Ellers is on tour in Italy with her harpsichord and two Swiss women singers. It is possible that my song cycle will be performed in Turin, so I have the tempting prospect of travelling to Italy - possibly after the Abitur.

How is Aunt Elli? Does the little Chinese doggie still do his tricks when he is eating?

Lots of thank-yous in advance for what I hope you can do for me.

My parents send their best wishes, as does your

Wolfgang Graeser

A few days later Grete Hanauer came up to him in the canteen of the Music School:

"Where have you been, Wolfgang? We hardly see you these days. I have a message for you from Piete."

In spite of himself Wolfgang found he was blushing at hearing the name which had been so much in his thoughts. To cover his confusion he turned away and picked up a big folio.

"This is what I've been doing, a re-discovery of one of Bach's greatest works."

"Oh, Die Kunst der Fuge. Piete told me about you finding the book in one of the old shops here, then getting permission to see the Berliner Autograph. Sounds fascinating." Grete, no scholar, sounded the reverse of fascinated. "Anyhow, she has an invitation for you. Something to do with a dance display. Are you interested in dancing?" She registered surprise, then added with a chuckle, "or just in Piete, I wonder."

"Piete is nice." He could now control his response and looked straight at her. "And, yes, I am very interested in dance. Not dancing, the Charleston and all that American nonsense, but dance as rhythmic expression, as a creative, gymnastic art-form."

The invitation was to see Mary Wigman's dance group from Dresden, who were appearing at the Theatre in Nollendorf Square. At first Wolfgang refused, pleading pressure of work. He was not sure of his relations with Piete, who was in so many ways more mature and at the same time unpredictable, disturbing.

"You must come, Wolfi, please. Look, I have been given two tickets by my dance teacher and I thought of you straight away, after our talk, remember? '. . every one doth keep the bounded space / Wherein the dance doth bid it turn or trace.' You see, I got it by heart."

She was hard to resist. To his surprise he found himself captivated and impressed by the 'Scenes from a Dance Drama', presented by twelve young women with discipline and intensity, a controlled emotionalism that reminded him in a strange way of the fugal patterning he was so absorbed in. He remembered his abstracts in the Munich exhibition, how the lines and colours were a transference from musical forms to visual shapes and colours. The draped figures in the dance sequence moved with liquid grace, assuming sculptural tableaux, their white hands and coiffed faces combining in abstract yet emotionally charged patterns. The audience seemed stunned into silence for much of the performance. Applause at the end was spontaneous and prolonged.

"Wasn't that tremendous!" Piete hugged the boy in her excitement. "What about it, Wolfi? 'This wondrous miracle' - that's what your poet says isn't it?" She did not wait for a reply. "Hans Gérard has given me an introduction to Mary Wigman. Come on, let's go round to the stage door."

The famous dancer was younger than Wolfgang expected, with the same clean-cut features and fluid, tiger-like movements as Piete's. She had heard of Piete's ambition and was positive and encouraging. The two dancers were immediately deep in conversation, leaving Wolfgang standing in the cluttered dressing-room rather at a loss until Piete said,

"Oh, sorry! This is my friend Wolfgang Graeser from Nikolassee. He is much cleverer than me. Tell Miss Wigman what you are working on, Wolfi."

Wolfgang resented the hint of patronising. He said curtly, " Miss Wigman won't be interested in such dry academic stuff." Realising that this might sound rude he added, "The discipline and beauty of your dancers has left me speechless, Miss Wigman. May I congratulate you?"

Sensing his unease, the dancer drew him out gently about his work and soon also discovered his interest in physical fitness and outdoor pursuits. Wolfgang became more and more at ease with this vital, beautiful woman. On impulse he said,

"When my edition of Die Kunst der Fuge is complete I want to write something about body culture, about the discipline of dance and gymnastics, relating it to the whole culture of the Western world. Could I ask you to write a Foreword for it, Miss Wigman?"

She laughed. "That would depend on what you say, of course. It sounds very ambitious. Thank you for asking me, I should certainly like to see the work." She went on to recommend him to Steffi Nossen, whose new dance school "on similar lines to my own in Tauentzienstraße" was being established in the Grunewald. "You can reach it easily by bicycle from Nikolassee - good exercise for you. I shall tell her about you and your work."

Wolfgang and Piete parted at the S-Bahn station. There was tension on both sides. Wolfgang had felt excluded from the conversation about dance and unable to respond to Piete's excitement, his own feelings more complex, less on the surface. For her the performance confirmed her in her determination to make a career in dancing, having just 'burned her boats' with her mother by telling her so. Her affairs seemed far from the desk-bound scholarship of this clever youth, attractive though he was.

She told him her intention of leaving Berlin. This came as a shock, but he felt a certain sense of relief, a lifting of pressure. His own ideas and plans were in full flood: the Bach project in the forefront, with material accumulating for a bigger work, The Later Bach, on the whole of the master's output in those productive final years before his death in 1750. Piete's ideas on dance had also begun to germinate in his mind, and although he had many reservations about her advocacy - as it seemed to him - of uncontrolled, perhaps uncontrollable freedom of expression, Wolfgang was quick to recognise the creative potential in Mary Wigman's team-work. It linked with his own sense of form as well as his pursuit of physical fitness, mens sana in corpore sano, the tag his father liked to use. He would certainly take up Miss Wigman's suggestion about the school in the Grunewald.

As they embraced their eyes met, Piete's dark lively looks, Wolfgang's searching blue, always with an unspoken question in them.

"Come Wolfi, let us part as friends." She leaned forward and kissed him on the lips, then with a little laugh turned away to find her bus-stop outside the station.

6

Paul Müller was interested to hear Wolfgang's account of the 'Scenes from a dance drama'. He asked about his pupil's 'dancer friend' but soon realised that the boy was not to be drawn on that topic, simply saying, "Oh, she has left Berlin," and turning the conversation.

"My father used to say mens sana in corpore sano. Isn't that what people are all after nowadays, with gymnastics and sport - those six-day bicycle races! I love cycling. Miss Wigman's dancers were certainly fit. Their control was amazing."

"Don't make me feel my age, young Wolfgang." Müller sighed. "Did your father tell you where that Latin tag comes from?" Once again he had recourse to his library, bringing down this time from an upper shelf a dusty leather-bound volume. "Here you are, Juvenal, the old cynic. You can brush up your Latin for the Abitur. It is in his prayer to the gods at the end of the tenth Satire. See if you can make me a translation of the whole passage. Frau Müller and I are coming to dinner tomorrow to meet some friends of yours. You can give it me then. If it is elegant enough you can read it to the assembled company."

Wolfgang realised that the last comment was half in jest, but decided to take it as a challenge. His favourite Uncle Johann would be at the dinner and he wanted to impress him and Aunt Gisela. When he started reading the Satire at home he was surprised to find himself drawn into its theme of the vanity of human wishes: the mad pursuit of wealth and power, the fickleness of the mob, rending the mighty Sejanus and desiring no more than 'panem et circenses'. How like 1920s Berlin it was! When he reached the passage on the misery of old age, with its toothless gums, deafness, forgetfulness and loss of friends, he looked up from the book. 'I shall never let that happen to me.' He read on rapidly to the closing prayer and quickly scribbled out a rough translation. There was just time to versify it before the guests arrived. Another half-hour of concentrated work and he wrote the final couplet rejecting man's deification of Fortune as the front door bell sounded in the house below. Wolfgang clattered down the attic stairs three at a time and slid down the banister rail to the hallway below, waving the sheet of paper at Paul Müller, who was greeting his parents.

"Frau Müller sends her apologies. She has a headache and has gone to bed." Lily made suitable condolences, but without much enthusiasm as she had expected something of the sort. She confided sotto voce to her husband that 'perhaps it was just as well, because Paul was more forthcoming when his wife was not present.' Professor Wolf and his wife arrived as Paul was looking over Wolfgang's hasty translation.

"'O Thou, who know'st the wants of human kind,

Vouchsafe me health of body, peace of mind.'

(That is neat, very neat! Almost as good as the original." Wolfgang flushed with pleasure.)

"'A soul prepared to meet the frowns of fate,

And look undaunted on a future state;

That reckons death a blessing . . . . .'"

Müller looked quickly over the rest of the passage. "H'm. Well done, my lad. Are you going to give us a recitation, then?"

"Certainly, sir, if you think it's all right."

"What's this? Construing Latin?" Dr Johannes Wolf had overheard the exchange. "I have something else for you, Wolfgang. I was talking about you to Ambassador Lüfenacht at the Embassy the other day and he has asked you to a party next week. There will be many musicians there: you know Frau Lüfenacht is a great music-lover. And she loves parties." He turned to Carl Graeser. "They want to know more about Wolfgang's Bach studies. He could make some useful contacts."

"Come now!" This was Lily Graeser. "We must not spend all our time out here, the food is waiting."

The dinner was a lively affair. Müller and Wolf had met professionally before but this was their first at a social gathering. Wolfgang was interested to see the contrast between his two friends: Paul a bit overweight and lumbering, Uncle Johann, twenty years his junior, slim and dapper with his trim moustache and black beard, cut imperial-style. Intellectually they were a good match, and he was happy to listen most of the time as the discussion ranged over music, philosophy, science, psychology. Lily had banned politics: "It will spoil all our appetites." At the end they called for Wolfgang's Juvenal translation, which he read out, rather self-consciously. He finished to applause and 'bravos!'

"Come, Gisela. Let us leave the men to their cigars. I have something to show you." Lily took Frau Wolf into the sitting-room. There was a general sense of well-being as the friends exchanged brands and lit up. Wolfgang did not smoke, but liked the rich tobacco smell, with all its associations.

"It is good to forget the outside world for a short while," Johannes Wolf pushed his chair back and crossed his legs. "How are you faring, Carl, with the money problem?"

"It gets worse by the day. They even tried to make me pay Wolfgang's fees at the Music School as a foreigner. After all my military service in Trier, not to mention the Naples hospital. I wrote a strong letter to the Director about it. Are we or are we not Germans? I sometimes wonder."

"Nationalism is a strange phenomenon." This was Müller. "Germany remains a federation in spite of Bismarck, in spite of the Hohenzollerns." He laughed. "Even in spite of Goethe. We still think of ourselves as Bavarians, Saxons, Prussians first, don't we? Perhaps even Berliners - or Brandenburgers. What are you, Wolfgang, tell me that?"

"Italian!" That caused a general laugh, but his father took it up more seriously.

"There is a need to assert one's national identity today, especially in Berlin, swarming with Russians, Americans, East Europeans - Jews especially. Have you ever set foot in the Scheunen Quarter? It is almost entirely an East Jewish ghetto now. I was talking in the Klub to Moeller van den Bruck. He has a new book out, The Third Reich? One moment, I have it here." He opened the book and read:

'When the revolution overwhelmed the war, burying all hopes . . amidst all the insanity we found a meaning in the thought that the German nation would be driven into becoming political. . . . Today we call this resolution not conservative but nationalist. The nationalist wants to conserve all that in Germany is worth conserving. Nationalism has the will to preserve Germany for Germany's sake. The nationalist looks to the future, knowing that there can be no future that does not have its roots in the past.'"

There was a brief silence. Then Dr Wolf spoke. "He is one of the Juniklub set, isn't he, like Spengler? I find them a bit extreme. We heard Spengler in Munich, do you remember, Carl, talking on Goethe? At about the time your exhibition was on." He smiled at Wolfgang. "Spengler was impressive, I will say. A fine historian, prophetic and very influential. What do you think, Müller?" He was aware the older man had fallen silent. Müller tipped his ash off before speaking.

"Spengler has an extraordinary breadth of scholarship. I found his book stimulating, but also disturbing. There an extreme form of nationalism implicit in it, combined with a determinist, almost nihilistic attitude. We must accept the pattern of history, he seems to say, and cannot change it. And I am uneasy at his projecting the past into the future as he does. All a bit glib. There was a good piece in the Tageblatt last autumn by Thomas Mann."

Carl Graeser broke in: "He admires Spengler, I know. I heard him in Munich just after the war and he was warm in Spengler's praise."

"Well, yes, Mann does admire his erudition and his style. But this article was highly critical, accusing Spengler of being anti-art, anti-culture, of misleading youth with his fatalistic advocacy of power. Wolfgang and I have argued over this, haven't we?" He turned to the boy with a smile. Wolfgang said impetuously,

"History has a pattern. Life, existence has to have a pattern or it is worthless. Spengler understands that because he can see the whole. Our great thinkers have always tried to express it, Leibniz with his monads, Goethe, Schopenhauer. Bach was expressing it in music when he died."

"Ah, Die Kunst der Fuge!" Dr Wolf was glad to change the subject. "How are your studies going, Wolfgang? Can you make any sense out of all those loose pages in the Berliner Autograph? They have driven some scholars to despair."

"Yes, it is very confused, Uncle. But I can see what Bach was aiming at. It is tragic that he could not complete the great edifice." Wolfgang's eyes were shining. "All spun out of those twelve notes. What a vision!"

Johannes Wolf pursued the topic, questioning Wolfgang about his method, and when the boy tried to explain his need to set out Bach's schema in diagrammatic form, asking to see some of them. Wolfgang went to fetch some samples. When he came back his father was holding his hands to his stomach, his face white and distorted with pain. Müller had gone to fetch Lily.

"Papa, what is it?" Wolfgang dropped the papers and ran to his father, kneeling by his chair.

"The old trouble, my boy, Capri." Carl spoke with gritted teeth. "It will pass in a moment."

Lily ran in. She tipped one of the tumblers of water onto a napkin and held it to Carl's forehead, saying,

"Please, don't worry. He has had this before. It is from an accident in Italy many years ago."

The incident put an abrupt end to the evening. Lily persuaded her husband to go to bed; he was for seeing his guests out, but when Wolfgang added his pleas to his mother's Carl agreed, taking the stairs slowly, leaning on his son's shoulder. He helped his father into bed and stayed with him for a while, holding his hand and saying nothing. When he left to go to his own bed, for a long time he could not sleep. Suddenly his world had become more precarious. He thought of Juvenal's desolate depiction of old age, of the pain in his father's eyes . . .

Another dark tunnel! The train was thundering towards the black hole in the mountainside, he tried to scream but no sound came out. Now the tunnel was the bubbling crater of Vesuvius, with toothless old crones beckoning him down. Their open mouths, ringed with black gums, were like holes, like the entrances of small tunnels, like a row of great swollen crotchets. "Jump!" they seemed to be calling, "Jump! Jump!" He could see the shape of the word but could not hear for the roaring in his ears, louder and louder, increasing in pitch and intensity. "The theme! I must find the theme!" The line of notes danced before him, they were strung together, a lifeline. His arms stretched out, he tried to clutch the line. Must he jump to reach it? . .

Wolfgang woke with his fists clenched tight, the knuckles white in the moonlight filtering through the dusty panes of his window. He sighed, swung his feet off the bed and padded over to the clavichord. His fingers picked out the first eight notes of Bach's 'still and serious world.'

Fürst-Bismarck Straße 4, Swiss Embassy and Ambassador's residence, at first felt intimidating to Wolfgang, who went there alone on a grey, overcast, chilly day. The imposing front door opposite Moltkestraße, named after the old general who had led Germany into the war in 1914, stood before him, its black panels decorated with heavy brass bosses. The wide road, its asphalt dark with rain, was deserted but for a closed carriage with two black horses outside one of the big buildings further down. Wolfgang felt a stirring in the pit of his stomach. What would come of this visit? He felt small and it was a few moments before he could summon up the courage to tug at the antique bell-pull. There was no answering sound from within. After a long minute the door opened noiselessly and he gave his name to the footman, who consulted his list before stepping back and ushering him in and towards the great staircase. He could hear a buzz of voices as he mounted slowly, fascinated by the wrought-iron balustrade with its succession of iron figures, each within a swirling double circle of metal. A uniformed servant standing by the open double doors of the reception room called out his name, so that for a second he felt like turning tail. The ambassador, chatting in a small group nearby, turned immediately with a smile and hand outstretched.

"Herr Graeser! So glad you could come. My wife and I have been wanting to meet you. Madeleine my dear," he rested a hand on the arm of a lady, younger than himself, who was in animated discussion with two or three other young people, "this young man is our great Bach scholar, Herr Wolfgang Graeser."

Ambassador Hermann Rüfenacht had a way of putting people at their ease. With his bushy moustache, wing collar and casually tied cravat he stood out from the more formally correct diplomats and professional men. An alpen rose on his lapel shed a petal from time to time in the dry, heated atmosphere. He led Wolfgang over to a group of three people, two women and a man he immediately recognised as a conductor from the Opera. The ladies were both singers and one of them knew Wolfgang's mother "from Leipzig days". He was soon being questioned about his Bach studies. A small group gathered round to listen as he warmed to his theme, expounding his views on Die Kunst der Fuge and its relation to Bach's other late works.

The evening was much less formal than he had feared, thanks to the warmth and lack of ceremony of the Lüfenachts, and Wolfgang soon began to enjoy the animated scene. A few musical items interrupted the flow of conversation from time to time. Frau Councillor Lüfenacht asked him if he wished to perform, but he declined.

"I am not an executant, Madame, merely a musicologist."

"Merely? You must not say that, Herr Graeser. We know something of your remarkable Bach discoveries, don't we, Hans?" She turned to a slim young man beside her. "Do you know each other? Pastor Zurlinden, Herr Graeser, the Bach scholar. Hans is almost one of the family here. We rely on him, especially in these difficult times."

Wolfgang liked the newcomer, who he estimated must be about twice his own age. Zurlinden asked many penetrating questions about the Bach, prompting Wolfgang to ask,

"Are you a musician, pastor?"

"Ah, no, alas. Nor a pastor in fact any more." He smiled, a little ruefully, Wolfgang thought. "I love music - which is the meaning of amateur, is it not? I play the piano a little and sing in a choir. Just now I am studying law and jurisprudence in Berlin, in preparation for the diplomatic service. And I try to help our people, Swiss people, who are suffering from the financial troubles. Bach has always been one of the 'gods of my idolatry' ever since my parents took me to hear the St Matthew Passion when I was twelve. I was astonished to hear you say just now that the Die Kunst der Fuge is as great a work. How can you justify such a claim?"

"Twelve? That was when I first heard the St Matthew Passion. My father took me and my brother to hear it in Munich." Wolfgang began to try to answer the question, but they were interrupted by the ambassador.

"Herr Graeser, this gentleman is keen to make your acquaintance. Dr Andreas Speiser, a countryman of ours. Is it Bern, Professor?" The man nodded and Rüfenacht went on. "Professor of Mathematics at Bern University, just here on a visit. A philosopher too, I think."

Wolfgang's eyes lit up at the word 'mathematics'. He was soon engaged in an involved discussion with the new arrival about the mathematical structures of fugues and canons. Before the evening ended Wolfgang had arranged both to show Hans Zurlinden some of his work on Die Kunst der Fuge and to try and arrange a meeting between Speiser and his tutor in Nikolassee.

"Did you say Paul? But I know Dr Paul Müller, we have met more than once. You are fortunate to have him as your tutor, Herr Graeser. A man of wide culture, quite a renaissance man."

In spite of this the proposed meeting never took place. It transpired that Professor Speiser had to leave Berlin in two days' time and Müller was away until after then. However, Wolfgang did take a folio of papers and diagrams to Fürst-Bismarck Straße the following evening and spent several happy hours with Hans Zurlinden, playing the subject and parts of the canons and fugues on the grand piano in the great music salon of the Embassy before retiring with Zurlinden to his own rooms in the living quarters for supper and more talk. The two were soon on first name terms as they found more and more points of contact, mutual interests. Zurlinden was almost fanatical in his love of the outdoors. He rode a powerful motor-cycle and had the use of a paddle-boat on the Havel. He ran as regularly as Wolfgang and shared his love of swimming and mountains. Since Wolfgang's brother, the other Hans, had left the family Wolfgang had never been able to share this part of his life with anyone; the friendship soon became important, both to the 31-year-old pastor and to his brilliant, gifted young friend.

"Whoever is that trying to destroy the tranquillity of Nikolassee?" Lily had just carried up to Wolfgang's room a drink of hot milk and a slice of cake. He would forget to eat when he was immersed in his Bach studies, so she was in the habit of interrupting him in this way. She opened the window but it was too high for her to see out. The motor-horn sounded again, accompanied this time by the noisy revving of a powerful motor. Wolfgang looked out then laughed, throwing down his pen.

"Hans being idiotic! He said he would show me his motor-bike."

"You won't be tempted to ride on it, will you?" Lily said anxiously.

"Why not? He has been all over Europe with it, Mutti. Hans is a good mechanic."

"He may be able to put a machine together, but he can't put you together if you fall off."

"Papa has no objection."

Lily sighed, but said no more, recognising the finality of the words. Wolfgang craned out of the window and waved to the goggled figure straddling the machine. He took a few sips of the drink, stuffed his mouth with cake and took the stairs in his usual impetuous fashion.

"I thought we might have a test-run on the Avus," Zurlinden said. "She has just had a tune-up and she's running like a bird. Listen!" He put his weight on the pedal and the motor roared into life in a satisfying manner. They had to shout above it. Wolfgang had scrambled into a thick pullover and wound a scarf round his neck and chin. They set off, Hans swivelling the machine round with flamboyant assurance, Lily shaking her head as she watched before returning to the house. 'I just hope they don't kill themselves.'

The ride was exhilarating for Wolfgang, in spite of . . no, partly at least because of his feeling of terror as their speed mounted and the wind whistled in his ears, drowning even the sound of the engine. The great new motorway, the first of its kind in Brandenburg, built for speed, was almost empty. An open two-seater overtook them and Hans shouted back,

"Hold tight! We're not allowing that." He opened the throttle to its limit and the motor-cycle forged ahead, past the motor with its two muffled-up riders. Wolfgang waved as they passed and the driver grinned, pulling over to let them by. The day was mild and sunny. When they turned off the Avus they made their way more soberly to a lakeside café on the Wannsee.

"Mmm!" Hans snuffed in the hot oily stench of the machine as they dismounted. "There is something intoxicating about that smell, don't you think?" He patted the tank. "Bucephalus I call her - though I suppose I should say 'him' with that name."

"Come on, Hansi, I'm dying for a drink." The familiar form of the name had slipped out involuntarily, the first time since his brother had vetoed it all those years ago. Zurlinden peeled off his goggles as they entered the café and placed their order.

As they lingered over their weak coffee and semmeln the conversation became more personal. The ride, with its hint of danger and its physical closeness had brought the two young men more intimately together. The friendship was valuable to both, to the older man, who had arrived in Berlin only shortly before they met and had no other close friends, and to the brilliant youth, brimming over with ideas and needing an advocatus diaboli to bring him down to earth from time to time. Hans Zurlinden was not as widely cultured as Paul Müller, but he was so much closer to Wolfgang's age and tastes, more like an older brother.

"Do you really believe all that stuff about Jesus and sin and rising from the dead?"

Zurlinden smiled. "That is a loaded question, isn't it? When one goes through the theology mill one tries to suppress thoughts like that."

"No, but do you, Hans?" the boy urged, his eyes burning into the other's face. "You don't seem to me like a Pfarrer."

"It is because of that that I am in Berlin. When it came to the point of settling into a parish as their resident pastor I realised I just couldn't face it, and all the faith baggage that goes with it. I have always wanted to work with - and for - people, but as an equal, not a 'man of God' as they call them. What about you, Wolfgang? How do you see your future?"

"Future! I hate the word." He looked out to where the motor-cycle was propped against a tree. "When we were flying along the Avus just now . . what speed? 100 kilometres? . . That was being alive, being in the 'now'. That is how I want to live my life." He stood up, stretching his arms as though wanting to embrace the air. "There is so much to find out, so much to grasp. Chinese, now," he sat down again, leaning forward, "Do you realise how much their philosophers understood, thousands of years before we in the west . ." he gave a scornful laugh, "the sinking West - Untergang des Abendlandes Spengler talks about - were even civilised. As soon as Die Kunst der Fuge is finished I shall learn Chinese properly so that I can begin to make sense of the Tao, Confucius, all that."

"What about that idea you were talking about the other day, athletics and dancing?"

"Dance, not dancing. That's another thing . . ." he took up eagerly, then laughing at himself, "Yes, I know, I know. My main problem is this wretched 24-hour day. If only we could stretch it to 36 or 40."

"Perhaps you should consult Einstein!" This set the boy off on another tack; they discussed the philosophical significance of overturning Newton's static universe, and Einstein's conclusions being questioned in their turn by Max Planck's quanta.

7

The visit to the dance school in the Grunewald took place later in the year , as the leaves were falling. The new, specially designed building was not yet built, but the site on the corner of Caspar-Theyß-Straße and Bismarckallee had been cleared and the foundations laid. Meanwhile the school subsisted in wooden huts, using the open lawns as much as possible. Wolfgang fixed an appointment by telephone and cycled up there from his home, winding along beside the lakes, Schlachtensee, Krumme Lanke, Grunewaldsee, to Bismarck Square. There was a roughly painted, laconic "Nummer 1/ Tanzschule" on a wooden board hammered onto a stake at the corner of the site. Wolfgang propped his bike against it and picked his way through the turned earth and heaps of bricks to the wooden buildings. Always sensitive to atmosphere, he paused for a moment, breathing in the scent of the pine-trees. There was something special about this place. As he approached the huts he was aware of girls' laughter and one firmer voice. The sight when he rounded the corner was a delightful one: a dozen or more loosely robed girls on the grassy sward, bare necks, arms, legs, bare-footed, most with the usual bubikopf bobbed hair. They were following an intricate sequence of flowing movements to the sound of a gramophone, led by a slightly taller, fair girl. The teacher stood near the gramophone, occasionally calling a name or clapping to reinforce the rhythmic movements. Steffi Nossen - for it was she - wore knee-length white shorts and a close-fitting singlet which emphasised her trim, lithe athlete's body. She looked hardly older than her pupils. Wolfgang watched in fascination, with an unaccustomed warmth of feeling whose origin he couldn't place. Was it Piete influencing him from afar? The drama teacher soon felt the presence of the stranger and turned.

"That's enough, girls. Break now! We have a visitor." She smiled, approaching with outstretched hand. "You must be Herr Graeser. Steffi Nossen." They shook hands. Wolfgang was aware of a strong, mannish grip. "Mary has told me about you. Your project sounds very interesting. We shall do what we can to help you."

Wolfgang listened with half an ear, his attention still caught by the leading dancer, who had come nearer and was looking at him with frank curiosity. Steffi Nossen noticed and beckoned her over.

"This is Brigitte, one of our stars. She leaves us next year, alas! just as the new building is completed. But you must come back, Brigitte."

"Surely, Miss Nossen. I love it here. My home will seem wet and flat after all this, a home for frogs!" She laughed lightly, gesturing to embrace the grass and woodland. Wolfgang was conscious of brimming vitality, unusual greeny-grey eyes set far apart, short tousled fair hair, a wide mouth. There was no regularity in her features, yet the whole impression was pleasing, delightful even. She seemed full of fun.

"This is Herr Graeser, Brigitte, Wolfgang Graeser. He is planning to write a book linking athletics, sport and dance. Is that right?" She turned to Wolfgang, whose attention was still on the girl. He flushed slightly, saying abruptly,

"Oh . . yes, yes. I want to make a synthesis, to establish the philosophical relationships between dance and other physical manifestations. To define the essence of body culture, Körpersinn, and its spiritual roots in our post-war Western society and its culture." As usual with Wolfgang, the ideas took over as he went on, referring to what he called the metaphysics of body-culture, the hierarchy of the world of the senses and their shaping of the perceived world. The girl looked at him in surprise, an amused expression in her eyes and mouth.

"It sounds very . . very intellectual. Are you a dancer, or perhaps a philosopher?" Brigitte's tone and the expression on her face made him realise what he had sounded like.

"Sorry! I let my tongue run away with me. No, I have never danced. I should love to dance like that. You all looked beautiful." He paused then looked straight at her. "I like your name, Brigitte. I have a cousin of that name in Zürich."

"Thank you, kind sir," she said archly before running to join the other girls, who were drinking milk and munching biscuits near one of the hut entrances.

After some conversation with Steffi Nossen it was agreed that Wolfgang might come and observe from time to time. He discovered that the loose flowing costumes were for a particular dance scena. Normal dress for the pupils was simpler: dark shorts or knickers, bare legs, a loose blouse. Freedom of movement was essential, as with all teaching stemming from the famous Frau Palucca of Dresden, whose pupil Steffi Nossen had been. Wolfgang stayed until the end of the day's tuition before cycling back home. To his surprise and pleasure he was joined a few metres down Bismarckallee by the fair-haired dance leader. She cycled beside him,

"Hullo, where are you heading for? I live in Zehlendorf."

"Nikolassee."

"Mind if I join you? It's on your way."

He discovered that she was living in a students' hostel while at the dance school. Her home was in Holland.

"Are you Dutch, then, Brigitte? Sorry, I don't know your family name."

"Van Schaer. But I'm happier with Brigitte. Can I call you Wolfgang?"

"Of course. It's my name." This prompted a playful swerve from the girl which nearly tipped him off his bike. They were soon on easy terms, exchanging details of their homes and background. Wolfgang had never met anyone like her before. Others of his own age usually seemed too childish. At school in Munich his fellow-pupils had been put off by his studiousness and left him alone. Even at the Music School he had made few friends, all older than himself. And now Piete had left Berlin. This girl - how different from Piete! Brigitte had none of Piete's intensity, nor her volcanic temperament. She seemed to find life constantly amusing, with her casual manner and laughing eyes. They discovered that she was almost exactly his own age, their birthdays just two days apart in September. She said,

"A pity we didn't know each other last week. We could have celebrated together."

He asked about her family.

"I'm the third in the family. Wim is the oldest, he's away now, studying in Göttingen. Then there is Anna,she is nineteen, still living at home. She works in my Dad's office in Delft. Then there's me, and Maarten, he's ten." She went on to talk about her home. "I sometimes think we really do live like frogs. Our house is right by a canal and below water level. We can watch boats going by from our downstairs windows, almost as close as I am to you. When we want to water the garden we just siphon water out from the canal with a bit of hose-pipe. We grow lots of our own food." She was interested to hear of his Italian background. "I want to go to Italy. It sounds like my kind of place."

By this time they had reached the student hostel. "I had better not ask you in. Frau Schwartz, the warden, is a real dragon. She goes into a rage if she spots any male on the premises, apart from her snotty-nosed little Herbert."

They parted amicably, with an un-specific agreement to 'have a bike-ride together sometime.'

As Wolfgang made his way home he realised that for the first time in . . how many weeks? - Die Kunst der Fuge had gone right out of his consciousness, ever since reaching the dance school.

The new friendship was overshadowed by worry about his father. The stomach pains had begun soon after the Graesers arrived in Berlin. Carl Graeser, thinking back to the Capri accident the year before Wolfgang was born, after which he had had internal haemorrhages, decided to 'grin and bear it.' Even after the dinner party incident he refused to consult anyone about it, though the pains increased in frequency, forcing him repeatedly to retire to bed and cancel surgeries and other engagements. He was also losing weight, so that even Wolfgang, preoccupied as he was with the intensive Bach studies, noticed the change in his father's appearance. He joined Lily in urging Carl to see a specialist, but he steadfastly refused.

"I know my own body. Let me decide such things please. It is bad enough for all of us trying to survive at present. I cannot justify paying a consultant's fee as well."

The hyper-inflation, or Billionenkrankheit (billion-mark sickness) as Wolfgang called it in a letter to his uncle, hit middle-class families especially hard. Savings had become practically valueless, so the Graesers had increasingly to either use their scarce Swiss francs or resort to barter. When Wolfgang arrived home after the visit to the dance school he found his mother in tears.

"There is no sense in it. I went down to the shop for bread just now - one can't trust Trudy (their one remaining maid-servant) to do the shopping. Frau Gombrecht wanted three and a half million marks for a loaf of bread. Look at this stuff!" She pointed to a cardboard box full of notes. "They go on printing money, but it is no longer worth the paper it's printed on. I had to persuade Frau Gombrecht to take my beautiful Meissen tea-pot in exchange for bread." A month after this outburst a loaf was valued at 500 million marks.

Dr Graeser was off work again. To avoid disturbing his wife at night he had taken to sleeping, or at least spending the night, alone in his dressing-room on a spare bed. On 13th October, the day after seeing Brigitte again, as Wolfgang was pulling on running shorts for his early morning run he heard a cry from his mother. Her tone was so strange that he flew down the narrow attic stairs to his parents' room.

"Wullie, your father! Come quickly!" He found her in the dressing-room, in her nightgown, bending over the bed. His father lay with a face the colour of putty, his mouth open, his breathing uneven, snoring and shallow. On the table beside him were an empty hypodermic syringe and three separate folded papers, each labelled in the doctor's precise hand: LILI, WOLFGANG and HANS, LUDWIG and ELLI.

Wolfgang took it all in instantaneously. He realised with a sinking heart that he had known this was a possibility. Suicide was in the air in Berlin, and he had exchanged looks with his father in the last week or so that had conveyed a message he had tried not to acknowledge.

"We must call an ambulance, Mutti. His heart is still beating. There may be a chance."

While they awaited the ambulance Wolfgang sat with his father. He read the note addressed to him: ' . . . I have observed my symptoms closely. My intestine is almost completely destroyed by a cancer. I choose this way to save your suffering and my own . . .' The familiar handwriting blurred before his eyes. Soon he heard the ambulance pull up outside and the door slam below. Wolfgang choked back his sobs. As the men came into the room with a stretcher, Carl Graeser opened his eyes.

"No, no, no!" He kept mouthing the word and shaking his head, but could not resist as he was gently lifted and taken downstairs. Wolfgang, suddenly in command, told his mother to stay at home and contact Hans and Dr Wolf. "And Paul Müller; he is so near. He will help us." He travelled to the hospital sitting beside his father and holding his hand. He was dry-eyed now. He felt immeasurably older. This was a defining moment in Wolfgang's young life. He had often thought of death, had even dreamed of it - the dark tunnels, the Napoli 'link to the underworld' - , but now he realised these had been little more than fantasy, play-acting. The grey face and spasmodic, stertorous breathing and those three deliberate messages so coldly set out, that was the brutal reality of it. His father's 'No, no, no!' as they had set about clutching him back from the grave haunted him for days afterwards. What right had they to do so? As the immediate horror of the event diminished, Wolfgang began to see a kind of heroism in his father's act. Why should one not set one's own seal on the striving, the pain, the cares and frustrations of life? Why should one have to struggle against the odds, to persist to the final ignominy, Jaques' seventh age, 'sans teeth, sans eyes, sans taste, sans everything'? The questions hung in the air. And yet, and yet . . . Wolfgang knew he could not have done otherwise. All his life Papa had been the ultimate authority, the arbiter, loved and revered in equal measure. How could he not try to rescue him from that dark abyss? Yet in a way he had not done so. By his deliberate act Carl Graeser had relinquished his previous rôle. It was as if he had said to his son, 'You are on your own now. I no longer wish to be in control.'

The operation, by Consultant Surgeon Rise, was successful. To Wolfgang and his mother it seemed like a miracle. After a week Carl Graeser had colour in his cheeks and could take nourishing liquids and talk rationally. In November Swiss friends and relatives arranged for him to convalesce in Lugano. Hans was now back home, so Wolfgang accompanied his father on the long train journey and saw him settled with friends before returning to the empty-feeling house in Prince Friedrich-Leopold-Straße.

"We must let Elli and Ludwig know what has happened." Lily spoke plaintively. The event, following hard on all the money worries, had almost shattered her and she relied increasingly on her two sons. Wolfgang immediately agreed.

"Uncle Ludwig is owed a letter by me. I never thanked him for his birthday greetings before all this happened to us."

The letter covered six sides in Wolfgang's rapid script. It was a relief to tell his godfather everything, knowing he would understand and sympathise. After detailing the attempted suicide and miraculous recovery - "We have been given a new father" - he tried to give a brief picture of his own immediate plans.

. . . I have still been working harder than ever. The five days in Switzerland, when I took my father, helped me through a crisis. In February comes the Abitur, which should at last open up university entrance. The private preparation for it permits me to miss this term at the Hochschule. I don't yet know whether I shall be able to attend any more . . . For the last nine months I have been working on a comprehensive historical / critical analysis of J S Bach's Die Kunst der Fuge, which is now ready. My studies extended far beyond music and aesthetics, into mathematics, acoustics and physics. My knowledge of higher mathematics made it possible to work on a new type of analysis which could have incalculable results. The fair copy of my work is now with Dr Wolf . . . At the university I shall concentrate on mathematics, musicology and Sinology (East Asia) . . .

When he read through the letter before sealing it he was surprised at one sentence which he could not recollect having written: 'I am not under control. An obstinate force drags me along over rocks and stones, I do not know whither, but I must follow.'

Wolfgang sat for a long time, staring at the paper. Should he cross the sentence through? At last he shrugged his shoulders, sealed up the letter and took it to the post-box.

All over Germany there was unrest. Resentment at the ineffectual socialist government grew, together with renewed talk of revolution. In November a right-wing group in Munich led by the 'war hero' General Ludendorff and an agitator calling himself Adolf Hitler staged a putsch and attempted to follow it up with a 'march on Berlin', emulating the successful fascist march on Rome the year before led by Benito Mussolini. To cope with the dangerous situation Chancellor Ebert vested General Hans von Seeckt with full emergency powers. He was only too conscious of his weak position: three years before, when he had asked the same man to put down the putsch led by General von Lüttwitz and the notorious Hermann Ehrhardt, Seeckt had refused bluntly, saying, "Reichswehr does not fire on Reichswehr". It was left to the workers to oust the hapless Wolfgang Kapp through a general strike. This time Ebert, with considerable courage, asked Seeckt to choose between 'putschism or the republic.'

"Either put me under arrest or defend your country's legitimate government." Fortunately for the Weimar Republic Seeckt chose the latter and the danger was averted.

Military power: economic power. The close of 1923 revealed starkly that these were the true dynamics behind state policy. Faced with the imminent collapse of the economy Hjalmar Schacht, president of the Reichsbank, declared the currency, now 'valued' at over four thousand million marks to the American dollar, obsolete and instituted the Rentenmark, backed by business throughout Germany and American money. The following year the American financier Charles Gates Dawes devised his 'Dawes Plan' to rationalise the currency and the reparation payments which had been partly responsible for the financial collapse.

After completing the Bach article and coping with his father's crisis Wolfgang was thrown increasingly on his own resources. His musicological research had made him realise that his days at the Music School were numbered. The Abitur would gain him admission to the university, where his ambition to go more deeply into mathematics and oriental studies could be realised. He was fortunate to have the guidance of Johannes Wolf in his father's absence. Wolfgang was always impatient of officialdom. Dr Wolf reminded him of the need for a leaving certificate from the Hochschule der Musik as well as his Abitur, to ensure his university place.

"As a non-German and in view of your age you will also need two sponsors. I can be one. Can you ask Dr Müller to be the other?"

Wolfgang, not much given to self-appraisal, was naively impressed by the two testimonials as he read them, first his tutor Dr Müller's:
'Wolfgang Graeser has been working under my supervision in history and languages towards his Reifeprüfung at the Mommsengymnasium . . His work in Latin is particularly noteworthy. . . His intellectual grasp is truly extraordinary . . his interests, which embrace so many heterogeneous areas . . the world of scholarship may expect great things from him.'

Wolfgang smiled at the reference to Latin. 'So the Juvenal was worth the effort!'

'Uncle' Johann's was equally flattering:

'Wolfgang Graeser has been known to me for several years and we have formed a close relationship through his keen interest in musicology . . His intellectual breadth and seriousness and his profound grasp of problems has astounded me ever since our first meeting . . His work on J S Bach's Die Kunst der Fuge would be a credit to a mature scholar . . . I believe that in this case it is entirely right that the age regulations should be waived . . .'

Was this really him, Wolfgang Graeser, Italian-Swiss-Bavarian-German . . what? Musicologist? Mathematician? Philosopher? Athlete? He laughed to himself at the last two, with Brigitte in mind, put the testimonials aside and dashed off a letter to the Music School asking for the certificate, before settling down to answer the response from his godfather in Dresden to his previous letter and thank him for his Christmas present. (Knowing Wolfgang's interest in the East Ludwig had sent his nephew a book on India and its culture.)

. . . there is no chance of my coming to Dresden at present. I must keep going until the Abitur in February. After that I hope to see you in Dresden after so many years . . . My special friend and benefactor Johannes Wolf wants me to give a talk about my Die Kunst der Fuge work to the German Music Society in the Spring . . . More good news from Lugano. Father's weight has gone up to 78 kilos (from 56!) and he needs now only to build up his muscles and heart. His disposition now is so much better . . . Give Aunt Elli greetings from me and all of us . . .

The friendship with Brigitte had taken a step forward just before all these troubles overtook Wolfgang. He visited the Dance School twice more, and each time had her company as he cycled home afterwards. The second time, the day before his father's failed suicide, was on one of those rare days of autumn sunshine, so they extended their journey to include a visit to the café by the Wannsee jetty.

"I saw you scribbling something when you were watching us do that dance sequence. Can I see what you wrote? What are you going to make of it all? I don't connect dancing with books."

Wolfgang laughed. "If I could dance like you I don't suppose I would." He tried to explain his plan for Körpersinn. "But I can't begin it until my work on Die Kunst der Fuge is out of the way." Brigitte asked about this and he described it, going on to his plans for a bigger work on 'The Later Bach' and his interest in mathematics and Chinese philosophy.

"You are such an intellectual, Wolfgang. It really frightens me. I am not at all clever like that."

"You don't need to be. It is a lonely life, and anyhow, I like you as you are. What will you do when you leave the Steffi Nossen School?"

"I have no idea. Go home. Travel. Find a job. Find a husband perhaps." She made a face. "It would have to be someone more down to earth, less head in the clouds than you." She spoke flippantly, but became aware that her casual words had gone deeper than she intended. She put her hand on his, adding impulsively, "No plans in that direction I promise you. One just says these things. No-one in their senses gets married before they are 25. Come on, let's go for a walk while the sun is out. It is so lovely by the lake and I adore dragging my feet through fallen leaves."

Brigitte recognised that this lively, brilliant, blue-eyed and fair-haired youth, so Teutonic in his looks and surface attitudes, concealed a deeper, more enigmatic persona. She was intrigued by the contrast, the hint of a split personality, but was happy to accept their friendship on the basis of their mutual physical attraction and shared love of movement, activity, the open air. Wolfgang could be such good fun! Before she left Berlin that year to spend Christmas with her family they exchanged addresses.

"I'll send you a Christmas card from Holland."

The friendship was a new experience for Wolfgang. For once he was able to give his restless brain a holiday when he was with Brigitte. She was so easy to be with - a bit like Grete Hanauer at the Music School, but quicker on the uptake, more lively, and refreshingly free from the driving ambition which seemed to motivate all his fellow students. Wolfgang felt none of the complexity he associated with his feelings about Piete Kuhr. Brigitte was just as good-looking . . . Well, no, perhaps not by conventional standards of beauty. As he thought back to the walk by the Wannsee - he was back at his desk, but for once Bach could not hold his attention - , to their synchronised steps, arms round each other's backs, laughing just for the sake of laughing, he warmed, and was aware, with a frisson of excitement, of a stirring in his loins. "Good-looking to me anyway!" He was surprised to hear himself saying it aloud. He took a sheet of paper and quickly sketched a face, Brigitte's squarish face, with its big mouth. The first time he had picked up a pencil for ages! What would his father say to this? The sound of the dinner-gong from the house below recalled him to himself. The next day all thoughts of the girl had been brutally expunged by what happened.

Christmas that year in the big house at number 17 was a quiet, sombre affair, with Carl Graeser away and the chronic shortage of money. Lily still attended church on such occasions, but Wolfgang and Hans, home from Munich ever since his father's crisis, had both rejected christianity.

Wolfgang's intensive work on Die Kunst der Fuge and his daily familiarity with older people: Johannes Wolf, Paul Müller, Andreas Moser his violin teacher, and more recently the East Asian specialists at the museum, had narrowed the seven-year age gap between the two brothers. They were able to relate to each other and to talk more freely than ever before. Hans Graeser, who was due to submit his doctorate dissertation on Telemann the following year in Munich, even helped with the 'tables' for Wolfgang's Bach article. Wolfgang was delighted:

"We must have a celebration to mark the completion of two great works by the Brothers Graeser - like the Brothers Grimm." Lily, now in her fifties but looking older, her hair almost wholly silver-grey, said,

"Until your father is with us again we cannot talk of celebrating anything."

1923 came to an end at last - it had felt interminable to many in the metropolis. Nevertheless there was a new optimism afoot in the new year. The indomitable resilience of Berliners, tested to the limit in the previous decade, showed itself everywhere: in the ever-changing boat-life on the Spree, in the lively bustle of the courtyards, in the street musicians, cinemas and cabarets. Following the currency stabilisation, foreign - mainly American - capital was once again pouring into Berlin. New buildings with clean Cubist lines appeared all over the city and its environs, one such being the new dance school going up on the corner of Bismarckallee, with its airy main hall, one side a great window looking out over the lawn to the pine-trees beyond.

The proofs of Wolfgang's Bach article had been checked by Dr Wolf and despatched to Breitkopf and Härtel in Leipzig for printing in the Bach Year-Book: six detailed chapters, 21 diagrams of the contrapuncti and six large sheets of musical examples which he had called Tafeln (tables). Wolfgang had spent the following weeks sorting out his studies for the Abitur. He took them lightly enough, but the ponderous imperialistic architecture of the Charlottenburg Mommsengymnasium with its dark arched entrance and rows of gleaming windows gave him a momentary qualm when he arrived for the first examination on a cold February morning. It was so like the Munich grammar school of unhappy memory. As he entered the big hall, with its ornate chandeliers, heavy panelled dado and serried ranks of desks, their surfaces showing signs of past boredom in scratched doodles, even the smell was reminiscent of those dark wartime days. The older boys around him looked curiously at this young, fresh-faced stranger in their midst. He found his name quickly and settled down. Once faced with the printed examination papers he was oblivious to his surroundings. As his tutor had assured him, there was nothing in them to cause him any uneasiness. He covered the pages with his neat rapid hand, and was finished always well ahead of the other candidates.

Over the three days he had much time to look around or stare out at the trees, once bearing glistening fringes of snow on their bare branches. Increasingly his thoughts turned to the dance school, to his plans for the gymnastics book and, of course, to Brigitte. They had exchanged correspondence over the holiday, the promised christmas card from Holland and a hastily scribbled reply from Wolfgang. The Spring semester was Brigitte's last at the school. They quickly resumed their open, casual friendship. Their mutual physical attraction remained undeclared, but revealed itself in the occasional intimacy of looks exchanged, hands held, fleeting embraces. To the girl this fresh-faced boy sometimes seemed not much older than her young brother. She even called him inadvertently Maarten once or twice.

"I'm not your brother."

"Wny not? We're almost twins, aren't we?" she said playfully. They were sitting together on the wall of the dance school, dangling their legs and eating brötchen. On impulse Wolfgang put his arm round her and kissed her on the cheek.

"Twins then. Now you kiss me." He turned her face towards him with his hand, smiling and looking straight at her. They kissed. He tasted a faint saltiness on her lips and was aware once again how she stirred him. She blushed and stroked his cheek.

"Nice! That was nice, don't you think?" Brigitte did not seem as disturbed by the contact as he felt. He did not reply. Instead he jumped down off the wall and busied himself pumping up the front tyre of his bike, propped against the wall beside them.

"I hope it's not a puncture. It seems a bit soft." So are you, she was thinking, but decided not to say it.

"Wolfi!" He looked up, startled at her use of the diminutive - Piete's word. "There is a new UFA movie about dancing, which might help you with your book. It is a documentary called Ways to Strength and Beauty. Why don't we go and see it?"

"Sounds good. Have you heard what it's like?"

"Steffi thinks we should all see it, so it must be good."

When they did go, the day before Brigitte's departure for Holland, Wolfgang was at first taken aback - and in the girl's company rather embarrassed - by the nudity of the performers. She took it more matter-offactly, and he was soon captivated by the dancers' mobile or statuesque beauty, skilfully - and totally un-erotically - photographed. They were like moving Greek sculptures, smooth and graceful. When the two emerged into the Spring sunshine Brigitte wanted to talk about the individual dancers and their muscular control, but Wolfgang was at first silent or monosyllabic.

"Did you not enjoy the film, Wolfi?"

"Of course! It was a marvellous demonstration of the beauty of the human body. Sorry not to be more communicative. It has given me lots of ideas for Körpersinn. I really want to get the book written now, before settling down to mathematics and oriental studies at the Wilhelm University. Did I tell you I've gained admission?"

"Oh, I can't keep pace with you and your intellectual projects." She sounded slightly piqued. "Will you say anything about Steffi's school in your book?"

"It's not that kind of book. More a general survey. I am trying to put gymnastics and dance into a proper contemporary context, to relate them to this sport and athletics that are so popular nowadays, as well as to the whole of Western culture-patterns."

Brigitte decided to change tack. "I hate all the competitiveness in sport nowadays, relay races, all that sort of thing. And the big athletics rallies, hundreds of people all doing the same thing at the same time."

Wolfgang agreed enthusiastically.

"That's our mechanised age for you. Men and women aren't machines. Whatever Hamlet says," he added with a laugh. Brigitte looked puzzled.

"Why Hamlet?"

"You know, when he signs his love-letter to Ophelia 'While this machine is to him, Hamlet'." He quoted in English.

"Please don't sign your letters like that then - even if they are love-letters," she said mischievously.

Instead of increasing their intimacy the film seemed at first to have cooled the relationship. For her it had been simply a delightful demonstration of controlled movement, a perfection to be aspired to in her own dancing, whereas it had set off for Wolfgang an intellectual chain reaction, as so often happened for him with a new stimulus. They parted in friendly fashion, embracing and kissing with a brief resumption of the wall episode and a promise to keep in touch by letter.

8

Wolfgang's father spent the remainder of the winter in Lugano. The news was progressively better and Wolfgang, mentally occupied first with the Abitur then with his new interests in Asiatic culture, mathematics and 'body culture', and socially with Brigitte and Hans Zurlinden, allowed himself to believe that a full physical recovery might be possible - he did not choose to take the thought further. Dr Graeser was trying to persuade the Swiss state authorities that he and his multi-talented son deserved some financial support. Lily Graeser said with a sigh,

"It is always the same. One has to push and push. I remember how hard it was to get them to support the Naples hospital before the war, even though it was more Swiss than German. The Swiss never like to release their money."

"Perhaps I should send Papa my testimonials from Dr Müller and Uncle Johann. They seem to have helped here in Berlin." Wolfgang and his brother had been reading their father's latest bulletin. Their mother agreed.

"They are no more than you deserve, Wullie darling. But what will you do if Carl manages to arrange for him and me to return to Naples? You see what he writes about applying to the German hospital again now that it is free from state control."

"Don't fret for me, Mutti. We can deal with that when it arises. I have lots of friends here, Hans Zurlinden for one. He'll certainly help." He turned to his brother. "What about you? Are you hoping to continue with the Telemann studies?"

Hans Graeser, with his dark military-style moustache and straight hair already beginning to recede from the temples, looked more than ever like his father in the old days, his mother thought. Even the same lines of worry on his forehead and around the eyes. She put her arm round him as he spoke:

"If you go back to Italy I shall too. I'm fed up with Munich. And music, for that matter. There's no way they will give me a grant for musicological studies as well as Wolfgang. You deserve it, Wolfi. That Bach work is far beyond anything I could achieve, we both know that, don't we?" Wolfgang had to agree so said nothing. His brother went on, "I have been making inquiries about banking. There is a chance I can get a post in a Swiss bank in Rome, and they have a branch in Naples as well now. As long as one has the title 'Doctor' they don't care what you are a doctor of."

After his initial surprise Wolfgang laughed. "At least you will be where the money is. I shall probably be applying to you for financial support once you are established."

Although Hans did go to Rome, Carl Graeser's Neapolitan plans came to nothing, so with some reluctance he re-joined Lily and Wolfgang in Nikolassee in the Spring of 1924. The reunion was an emotional one. All three were conscious of so much that must remain unspoken about the dark days of the previous October. They had left their mark on Carl Graeser: his hair was now white, and to his son he seemed smaller, diminished. Wolfgang's love for his father now was mingled with pity rather than deference, together with an inarticulate sense that he needed to make amends, that his own intellectual and other pursuits had played some part in draining his father's vitality. He began to show a new, tender solicitude, fetching things for him at home, anticipating his needs, whenever he could relieving him of anxiety. Carl was touched by these attentions, in spite of an occasional querulous irritability which he found it hard to suppress. He was intensely proud of his son's achievements and happy to bask in reflected glory.

One such opportunity was the talk, arranged by Johannes Wolf, which Wolfgang gave on his Die Kunst der Fuge studies at the highly respected Berlin Music Society. An immediate consequence was an invitation as guest speaker to the International Congress of Musicologists in Basel the following September, where he renewed his acquaintance with Professor Andreas Speiser. After their first meeting at the Swiss Embassy Speiser had sent Wolfgang a copy of his newly published book on geometry, The theory of series of finite system. The 39-year-old mathematician travelled over from Zürich, where he now taught at the university, for Wolfgang's talk and they spent some happy hours together discussing mathematics and philosophy.

"I have an ambition," Speiser confided to his young friend, "to visit Egypt one day and make an intensive study of Theban geometric patterning on tombs there. I have seen some archaeological sketches and I am convinced they have a geometrical significance that has not yet been deciphered."

He could not have found a surer way of engaging the boy's interest. Wolfgang asked question after question about the tombs. Before they parted he had made Professor Speiser promise to take him if the trip to Egypt ever materialised.

"I could be your assistant. I'll learn to use one of these new 'Leica' cameras. Have you heard of them? They are a firm in Wetzlar, Ernst Leitz, and the cameras are apparently something remarkable. They are not on the market yet but soon will be. None of those great plates and clumsy apparatus."

Like others who had come into contact with this lively, brilliant youth, like Johannes Wolf, Paul Müller, even dry old Professor Schünemann, Andreas Speiser was captivated by Wolfgang's enthusiasm. It would be more than three years before the Egypt project matured, but the meeting in Basel marked the beginning of a fruitful friendship by correspondence.

So much of Wolfgang's time now was spent with a pen in his hand. Spengler's ideas about the creative 'thinking hand' often came into his head as he sat at his desk in the attic room, looking over the roofs at the church spire, with its quiet Friedhof beyond. As a relief from his studies he would pen long, discursive letters to Brigitte in Holland, receiving back short scrappy ones in her characteristic, rather childish hand, always concluding with 'Ich umarme Dich' and rows of x-es. His only other non-academic correspondent was Uncle Ludwig in Dresden. After the Abitur he had fulfilled his promise of a short visit. Herr von Hofmann and his wife lived very simply in a small apartment in the suburbs of Dresden. The inflation year had hit them hard and his salary from the municipality - he was a local council official - was meagre. Wolfgang's Aunt Elli, Carl Graeser's sister, had her brother's facial looks but there the resemblance ended. She was short, plump and normally smiling and cheerful. They were a childless couple, but she doted on her pet chiuaua dogs - she had a succession of them, each inevitable demise prompting a shower of tears and a vow 'never to have another.' Ludwig would usually wait a month or two before seeking a replacement. Wolfgang disliked the yapping, rat-like creatures, but hid his feelings so as not to hurt his aunt's susceptibilities.

"Look what we found the other day, Wolfi! I was clearing some drawers and this came to light." She held up a yellowing post-card with an Italian stamp. "What beautiful hand-writing you had! Such a dear little boy you were. And so brown, with all that sunshine. No wonder you made your Teufelchen into black men."

Wolfgang took the card: five black golliwogs diminishing in size, with cloaks and staring eyes and his name 'WOLFI' in the corner of the picture. It took him back with astonishing vividness to pre-war Napoli. He read the date on the postmark: 28.XI.13. He laughed as he handed it back,

"I remember drawing that. How old was I? Just seven. That was after Hans went away. Miss Jones didn't want me to send it, she said it was rude to send devils to my godfather and quite unsuitable."

Elli was anxious for news of her brother. "Has he really recovered from that dreadful time, Wolfi dear? We were so shocked by your letter just before Christmas." Wolfgang had done what he could to reassure her, but could not disguise his own residual anxiety. His father tired so easily these days and events seemed to weigh on him. He had procured a small pension from Switzerland to supplement his army pension and, thanks to some family jewellery of the Obenauses, Lily could still rely on a modest private income for the occasional luxury. Both parents lived for their remarkable second son almost more than for themselves, with the result that Wolfgang felt himself increasingly driven. His mind often went back to that involuntary sentence to Uncle Ludwig: 'An obstinate force drags me along . . . I must follow.' He had drawn his father back from the grave; it was as though his father was saying 'now you must justify that action.'

His friendship with Hans Zurlinden acted as a useful escape-valve from this and his academic pressures. Soon after his return from Basel there came a late mild spell of weather. Wolfgang thought back to his walk in the woods with Brigitte the year before and suddenly had a longing for the open air. He threw down his pen, ran downstairs to the telephone.

"Hans! Can you take some time off? A couple of days? Good! Is the machine running well?"

The two set off on the motor-bike well muffled up and heavily laden with back-packs, to cover the 200 kilometres to Halberstadt and the Harz mountains. Before going Wolfgang had re-read Goethe's poem and copied out some lines.

"Do you believe what Goethe says in his Harz poem - 'A god has pre-ordained for each person his path'?" Wolfgang turned to Hans questioningly. They had negotiated the little lanes through the fir-trees up to the tiny hamlet of Torfhaus, just beneath the summit of the Brocken, obscured now by cloud. Hans had rested the machine against a tree and they were sipping hot milky coffee from the forester's wife as they stood by the door of the wooden cottage.

"Do I detect the influence of Spengler again in that question? You know we shall not agree about his view of human destiny."

"No, but do you?" Wolfgang was insistent.

"I'm not sure that Goethe meant it like that. When you take it out of the poem it sounds fatalistic, negative, but the poem as a whole is far from that. If you want an answer, mine is no, I don't agree."

"Look, it is clearing." Wolfgang was gazing up at the Brocken, its summit now gleaming in the sun. "Let's climb it while we can."

They thanked the forester and his wife, who would not take any money, and set off. It took them three hours of hard climbing to reach the top. The wind bit through their clothes, but the exertion had kept them warm. As they stood, breathing heavily in the thin air, the wind scattered the trailing mists and for the first time they could see beyond the trees to the land stretching away far below until it was lost in haze.

"This is what it is to be alive!" They took great breaths of the icy air. Wolfgang went on, with a carefree laugh, "There you are, Hansi! The Devil's Pulpit! Preach me a sermon. You know you keep telling me I need you to act as advocatus diaboli."

Hans decide to humour his whim. He scrambled up the rock then stood precariously, throwing out his arms in a wide gesture.

"Here, young man, I offer you all the kingdoms of the earth! Look about you." To reinforce his words he quoted some of Goethe's closing lines:

"'Du stehst mit unerforschtem Busen
Geheimnisvoll offenbar
Über der erstaunten Welt
Und schaust aus Wolken
Auf ihre Reiche und Herrlichkeit'"V

Wolfgang struck a pose, one foot forward:

"What must I give you, mighty one, for all this magnificence?"

Hans laughed and jumped down. "Your soul, my child, your immortal soul!"

"Hm! Give me some time to think it over. Meanwhile, what about something to eat. I'm famished!"

"Do you want me to turn the stones into bread?"

"No, I'll put up with our sandwiches."

The break in the cloud was short-lived. As they munched their snack the mists swirled up again, obscuring the view. Their high spirits made light of the descent from the summit and soon they were threading their way through the narrow lanes back to Halberstadt, where they spent the night at an inn.

As they drove through Potsdam the next morning, the sight of the Einstein Tower reminded Wolfgang of that other expedition

---

V 'You stand there revealing the mystery of your impenetrable heart, above the astonished world, gazing from the clouds over its kingdoms and splendour.'

three years before. Of a sudden his elation was dashed as his thoughts returned to his father. He could not stifle an obscure feeling of dread. It was as if a cold hand had clutched his heart. When his friend suggested stopping to look at the tower he said,

"No, I must get home." Hans looked at him strangely.

"Are you all right? Is something wrong?"

"I hope not." It had been just such a carefree outing with Brigitte at this time last year, the day before 'it' happened. He had not told Hans about the attempted suicide. What if . . . He did not allow himself to pursue the thought.

When they pulled up outside number 17 Wolfgang jumped down and ran into the house. Lily met him at the door.

"Is Papa all right?"

"He is resting. Have you had a good trip? Is Hans coming in?"

The normality of his mother's tone pulled him up. He beckoned to Hans before going into his father's study. Carl had been reading. The book, Der Zauberberg, had slipped from his lap and he was asleep, breathing with his mouth open. The horror of that other time overtook Wolfgang and he shook his father awake.

"Papa! Papa!"

"What is it?" Carl Graeser stirred and sat up. "I must have dropped off. Wolfgang, you're back. Good, good!"

In spite of his relief on this occasion it was as if Wolfgang had had a premonition. Christmas saw an intensification of the stomach pains and by the New Year it was impossible to disguise the deterioration of his father's condition. He rallied briefly in the Spring with the election of Field-Marshal Hindenburg as Chancellor:

"At least we have a true German in the seat of power now." Paul Müller, who was sitting with him, kept his own council, not wishing to worry the sick man. He was more outspoken with his ex-pupil when they were together later.

"If it had not been for the communists splitting the vote Hindenburg would never have been elected. Look at his supporters: the old die-hard Bismarckians of the Fatherland Party, Hitler's National Socialists, Jew-baiters and imperialists. It is a bad day for Germany."

"I don't agree." Wolfgang was indignant. "My father is right. Hindenburg is a true German. I know he's old, but he is a symbol, a sign that our nationhood is restored. No-one else could have attracted votes from so wide a constituency."

"We'll see." Müller saw no point in pursuing the topic. "At any rate, Stresemann is still in the Reichstag. He is a statesman, and more far-sighted than most."

Carl Graeser died on 26th July 1925. Almost his last conscious act was to take from his son's hands the newly published Bach Year Book for 1924, just arrived from Leipzig. As Wolfgang gave it to his father the sombre twelve-note subject of Die Kunst der Fuge sounded in his head. 'It does not give solace, yet one cannot escape from it.'

IV   Piete / 'Jo Mihaly'

1

THE TRAIN slowed down with a clanking of couplings as it made its way through the straggling eastern suburbs of the great city - Hellersdorf, Lichtenberg - to pull in amidst clouds of steam at the cavernous Schlesicher Bahnhof. Piete felt both excited and apprehensive. It was fourteen years - what momentous years! - since she had been in Berlin. She could just remember the trip with her mother to see her new Music Conservatoire, the big empty rooms with their shiny black pianos and ornate carved music-stands - all sold and scattered now. The sheer size of the city and its grime scared her after cosy Schneidemühl. As she picked it up, her grandmother's careful basket of provisions with its cloth brought a lump to her throat. Would she ever see dear Oma again? Oh, there was Mutti! Piete dashed the tears from her face with a sleeve and waved furiously from the window. Her mother was as elegant as ever, so upright and alert amidst this cosmopolitan crowd. But so thin!

"Mutti, darling! You are so beautiful!" Piete clasped her mother, aware as she did so of the thin shoulders, the deeper lines in her face. But still the same lovely perfume she remembered so well!

"Your cases, child! Point them out to the porter. I have a taxicab waiting."

They both enjoyed the unaccustomed luxury of the taxi as it made its way past the site of the new Tempelhof airport to Steglitz. Once at the block the driver, a war veteran with a great scar down the left side of his face, insisted on carrying the heaviest case into the apartment, toiling up the dark stairway with his limping gait. When he saw the bareness of the small rooms he refused the lady's proffered pfennigs.

"Buy a small cake for the Fräulein! My daughter loves sweet things, so perhaps you, Miss?" Piete smiled and thanked him. They watched him limp away down the stairs before closing their door.

Almost the first thing Piete set eyes on was a sheet of newspaper, Neue Berliner Zeitung, 13 März 1920, with a heavy black headline:

Fall of the Government! Kapp Reich Chancellor!

Her mother gave a short laugh. "That was six weeks ago, I kept it as a souvenir. Chancellor for three days! But it was a terrible time, no lights, no water, shooting in the streets. Berlin has not yet recovered. I think Herr Kapp was a good man, but weak, weak!"

"Let's not talk of him, Mutti." Piete and her brother had followed the reports of General Lüttwitz's attempted putsch and the strike which ended it. She knew she and her mother would never see eye to eye on such things. She picked up the paper: "This will be a curiosity in a few year's time. A piece of history."

Mother and daughter were very alike in looks, enhanced now by the thinness of both. Piete had lost her childish bloom in the dark days and months following Werner Waldecker's death. Her illness after the nursing had finished the job. There were dark shadows under her eyes and the strong facial bones stood out. Her mother studied her face anxiously.

"Elfriede my dear, are you still unwell? You look so tired and wan. Where are the roses?" She stroked Piete's cheek.

The girl smiled sadly. "You too, Mutti." She shook herself, and said more brightly, "I am well, just a little tired from the journey." She busied herself with unpacking the basket. "Oma has sent these for you, look! She made them herself. Now we are together I shall get work and we shall eat like pigs and grow fat. How many singing pupils do you have now?"

"It is building up slowly. I am known at the Hochschule für Musik, so they send people to me sometimes for special training. My cantilena style for singing in German is unique. Even Richard Strauss has heard of it, I am told. It suits the music of his operas."

Piete's self-education in typing soon found her an office job, poorly paid, but more than enough to support herself, so her arrival did help both women. She sat in with her mother's singing lessons when she was not working, and was soon helping with one or two younger pupils, children of her mother's rich friends, who liked to support her in this way. She was too proud to accept any more direct financial help. The sitting-room of the flat was now almost wholly given up to teaching. They called it 'the studio' and lived mostly in the cramped little kitchen. The winter following Piete's arrival was long and cold, to be followed in 1921 by a more than ordinarily bright and bloom-filled Spring.

"I have a treat for you, Piete my dear, a birthday treat." This was her mother's greeting as she came in from work towards the end of April. For her 19th birthday her mother had, through the parents of a pupil, succeeded in getting two tickets for the ballet at the Scala Variety Theatre, an unheard-of indulgence for them.

"I know how you love ballet. This is a new company under a French ballet master, of whom I have heard good reports. Let us enjoy ourselves for once. I shall wear my old fur again."

Piete was entranced, overwhelmed by the evening. She insisted on dragging her mother round to the stage door afterwards to get the dancers to sign her programme, "for a birthday souvenir, Mutti, please!"

As the girls gathered round her to sign, M.Gérard, the ballet master, came out.

"Qu'est que c'est? An enthusiast?" He smiled at Piete. "You enjoyed our performance?" He noticed Frau Kuhr-Golz standing by and made a deep bow. "Pardonnez moi. Madame? Votre fille . . ou peut-être votre soeur . . .?"

Frau Kuhr-Golz flushed slightly, a mixture of pleasure and embarrassment. "My daughter, sir. She has liked dancing since she was a child."

The ballet master surveyed Piete coolly. "She has a good figure, Madame. She will perhaps be a dancer one day." The lady did not respond, so M. Gérard scribbled his name on the corner of the programme, saying to Piete, "Vous aimez le ballet? You like to dance?" Reading her response in her eyes he went on, "You can find me here at the Scala."

Piete was thrilled and excited by the evening and the encounter, her first with a true ballerino. The next day was Sunday. She woke early, scrambled into her clothes and, picking up paper and pen, ran down the stairs and took an early tram to the Tiergarten. There was hardly anyone about. The chestnut trees were in full bloom, the birds singing. She found a bench, sat down and wrote her letter asking M.Hans Gérard for lessons, giving her work address. 'I shall not tell Mutti until I know I can dance properly.' As for paying . . . The ballet master responded to her burning eagerness. When she tried to explain that she could not afford his fees, he waved it away.

"You shall pay me from your wages when you are a ballerina."

It soon became impossible to hide her lessons from her mother. She had to fit them in after work and would arrive home on the point of exhaustion. Frau Kuhr-Golz disapproved, but knew her daughter better than to try and prevent them. Piete's lessons with the dancing-master in Schneidemühl had given her a useful grounding. Hans Gérard soon realised that this slim, vital girl with her lithe movements and nervous energy, like a coiled spring, was something exceptional. She was not a good team member; her dancing was dynamic, arresting, very individual. She told him of her ambition to create an anti-war dance drama.

"Ah, this modern dance! Von Laban has much to answer for. All who dance need to train and to tame their bodies. Only ballet can do that."

"I understand, Monsieur. To train, yes, but my body will never, I think, be tamed."

Hans Gérard laughed. "You are right, ma petite. You are a wild animal. But we shall make you a circus animal."

Piete was to remember those words two years later. In the meantime she forced herself to submit to the ballet discipline, practising steps and movements whenever possible, even when walking from the office to her tram, or on the rare occasions when she could wander round the main streets window-shopping, or just surveying the mass of humanity in the great metropolis. Piete missed the friendly street life of little Schneidemühl at these times. Here people walked with downcast eyes, except for the male and female prostitutes, whose bold looks and the despair or emptiness behind them scared her. Her mind went back to her schoolfriends, those who had dressed up to attract the young air force officers. Had some of them ended up on Kurfürstendamm with these painted faces and artificial smiles? 'Only a minor!' She remembered Waldecker's words and blessed him as she looked in distress at the kids - they were no older than she had been then - mincing along and touting for custom.

When Margarete Hanauer came to her mother for singing lessons in 1922 the two girls immediately struck up a warm friendship. They talked endlessly, and Grete soon persuaded Piete to call at the Music School and meet other friends. Later in the year, with her office job nearby, the two would share coffee and gossip, go to movies or exhibitions. One such was a 'first' in Berlin, the Exhibition of (Russian) Soviet Art in Van Diemen's Gallery on Unter den Linden. Piete said excitedly as they came out,

"Russia is the country of the future. Don't you think so, Grete? How vital these pictures are, so full of hope and life and action!"

"They are exciting, certainly. We have many Russians in the Hochschule. They are an artistic race. But most of our students are exiles from the Bolsheviks. There was much killing in the Revolution, much hatred. We Swiss don't like revolution any more."

Piete thought back to Androwski, her brother's Polish friend, and his callous acceptance of the Tsar's murder with all his family. "You are right, Grete. Nothing is worth killing for. Look what the Kaiser's war has brought us to." As they stood on the steps of the exhibition entrance they found themselves next to a man sitting in tattered clothes. His cap, an old army forage cap with the label torn off, was by his side, and a pair of crudely made crutches leant against the wall. His legs were both amputated above the knee. Piete scraped together some pfennigs from her thin purse to drop in the cap. The man nodded, saying nothing. 'But perhaps worth dying for,' she thought to herself, then said,

"I once tried to kill myself."

Grete looked at her in amazement. "You! Are you joking? I can't believe it, Piete. You are so full of life."

Piete told her how as a fourteen-year-old she had convinced herself that God wanted a willing sacrifice in order to bring the war to an end.

"So I waited until Oma and Willi, my brother, were out, then shut the doors and window and turned the jets of the gas-light full on and lay on my bed."

Grete was staring at her. "How awful! What happened?" She looked so horrified that Piete could not help laughing.

"Well, I'm still here as you can see. My grannie came back unexpectedly, so I jumped up - I felt really queer! - turned off the gas, opened the window and flapped the door to and fro to get rid of the smell. I had bolted the front door, so Oma had to wait."

Grete looked relieved. "Didn't your grandma smell the gas?"

"Yes. I pretended I'd left it on by mistake when warming a cup of coffee. She said 'You might have died.'" They both laughed at that. Piete added, "That's religion for you. Do you remember how we prayed for victory? I used to wonder how God could possibly make up his mind with prayers coming from both sides at once. At least I did it out of love, not hate. In war people are taught to hate. Otherwise how could they bring themselves to kill each other?"

She had cause to think of her words a week later, with the news of Walther Rathenau's murder, stark evidence of the growing anti-semitism in Berlin. The music students, many of them Jewish, were all angered by the assassination and staged a massive demonstration with placards and banners, causing chaos in the busy thoroughfares round Charlottenburg. Grete and Piete marched with the others. When her mother advised her 'not to get mixed up with such socialistic activities,' Piete showed her a cutting from the Vossische Zeitung, a message from Rathenau's mother to the mother of the murderer:

'In unspeakable pain I offer to you, the most poverty-stricken of women, my hand. Tell your son that, in the name and spirit of the murdered man I forgive him, as God may forgive him, if he makes a full and open confession before our earthly justice and repents before God. Had he known my son, who was one of the noblest people on earth, he would rather have turned the murderous weapon on himself than on him. May these words bring peace to your soul.'

Frau Kuhr-Golz read it silently. She handed it back without a word, her handkerchief to her eyes.

Later that year came Piete's meeting and friendship with Wolfgang Graeser. Soon after visiting his home the following Spring she decided the time had come to prove her dance skills to her mother.

"Do you remember, Mutti, how you gave me a birthday treat two years ago? Now it is my turn to give you one. Don't look round until I say, then play me a waltz tune." Her mother half guessed what might be coming, but humoured this whim and closed her eyes. Piete quickly wriggled into her home-made ballet bodice and skirt, bound on her pointed ballet shoes - which hurt like fire! - and called, "Now play!" Her mother improvised a waltz on the piano as her daughter tripped in on pointed toes and pirouetted to the music. Her mother took her hands off the keys, shaking her head.

"Piete dear, you have convinced me. That was lovely, so polished and graceful." Piete, who had been nervous of her mother's response, ran over to her with tiny steps and did a full ballerina's curtsey. Then she knelt down, put her arms round her mother and laid her head on her lap.

"That is what I must do, dear darling Mutti. Monsieur Gérard says he can find me work now and I can earn far more than I do thumping a beastly typewriter."

Her mother heaved a sigh of resignation. "You are 21, Elfriede, your own mistress. One thing I do ask, though. You must get my mother's assent before you take any dance engagement. She is so proud of the Golz name, and everyone in Schneidemühl knows you."

Piete's grandmother was not happy at the decision. It took several letters to persuade her to relent, and then only on condition that Piete adopt a professional name as a dancer, a pseudonym. After first resisting it Piete came to like the idea. It took her mind back to the elaborate 'let's pretend' games of childhood, and this provided her with her new persona. She would become a gypsy, join the outcasts, like those she befriended in her grandfather's builders' yard. From that moment Jo Mihaly, dancer and writer, was born.

2

It was as if the new name gave Piete a new life, a new sense of freedom from her former bourgeois world. She remembered how as a child she used to take the gypsies' side in Schneidemühl. Coming across the border from Poland, they had to park their tented wagons in the Golz builders' yard, for which she had the key, sometimes for weeks on end, while the Prussian authorities checked their papers. It was the handsome gypsy girls who caused fights between their men and the town officials when the latter tried to buy their favours. That fight, when she used the frying-pan her grandmother had sent her with to get mended as a weapon against a clerk and got a bloody nose for her pains! She laughed as she recalled it. The name Mihaly, borrowed from one of the Hungarian gypsy families, revived her feelings of solidarity with wanderers and the dispossessed.

How far away now seemed her visit to that posh doctor's house in Nikolassee! She met Wolfgang once more, briefly, just before leaving on a tour with a ballet troupe arranged by M. Gérard. Piete had come to say goodbye to Grete Hanauer, and the two girls were enjoying the sunshine on the steps of the Music School when Wolfgang hurried out from his violin lesson on his way to the Prussian State Library.

"Wolfgang!" Grete held his arm as he passed them.

"Don't stop me. I have an appointment with a researcher at the library." Then he noticed Piete. "Oh, Piete! I hadn't seen you."

"Take a good look, Wolfi! It is the last you will see of me for some time. And my name is Jo now, or Joan if you prefer, Jo Mihaly, dancer." This did make him stay, as she told him about Hans Gérard and her ballet work. "I have written out those verses of yours about dancing. Do you remember?" She quoted them in English:

'Dancing, bright lady, then began to be
When the first seeds whereof the world did spring,
The fire air earth and water, did agree
By Love's persuasion, nature's mighty king,'

They are pinned up in my room next to Armin Wegner's human rights, where he also talks about earth, air, fire and water. Wish me luck with the ballet tour, Wolfgang!"

He held out his hand rather self-consciously, but Piete ignored it, giving him a warm hug and a kiss on both cheeks. The two girls watched him jump onto a street-car, swinging his violin-case.

"Too clever for me, that one," said Grete. "He is absolutely obsessed now with that obscure Bach work Die Kunst der Fuge. Apparently they are letting him work on the precious Berliner Autograph, so he must be clever."

"He's a nice boy, but he has some crazy ideas. His father is ex-army, very conservative, and I get the impression Wolfgang takes after him." Piete shook her head, then added with a chuckle, "That's why I told him about Wegner just now."

Grete looked puzzled. "I didn't understand that. Who is Wegner?"

Piete - or Jo as she wanted to be called - told her about the poet Armin T Wegner's manifesto on human rights, published two years before in the Syndikalist, which had been condemned as scandalous by the more reactionary newspapers and magazines.

"All the fuss was because he says that love between two of the same sex is as precious as between men and women. People are such hypocrites! Wegner's rights are what I believe: the right to freedom, to earth, air, fire and water, to our own life and our own death, our own thoughts, to sleep and the right to choose our own partner of whatever sex."

Jo enjoyed the new life with the ballet troupe in spite of - or perhaps because of - its hand-to-mouth, gypsy-like existence. The six dancers, half of them Russian, were led by a Russian ballerina. They travelled westwards across Germany, appearing wherever they could get an engagement, Magdeburg, Hannover, Osnabrück - always short of cash, their pay in this inflation year scarcely paying for food and board. They crossed over into Holland, in the hope of more lucrative work in Amsterdam, and were engaged with a circus. Jo was delighted to find an American jazz band also appearing, and struck up a friendship with the leader, a big burly negro (as people called them) called Harry Goffey. The circus master, who was fairly unscrupulous, decided to pay the German dancers in German currency. By the evening it was worthless and Jo, in charge of the troupe's finances, was at her wit's end.

"If we can't pay, the landlady will have us all arrested. I shall see if anyone can lend us money to tide us over." She walked miles in Amsterdam's unfamiliar streets. She had two addresses, but one was an empty apartment and the other she could not find at all. In despair she trailed slowly back to the lodging, dead tired. It was midnight when she got back. A single light was burning downstairs. As she entered, she saw a burly figure slumped across the table, head on arms, fast asleep. Harry Goffey! He stirred and sat up.

"I'm sorry to wake you up, Harry. What are you doing here, anyway?"

He stood up and stretched, giving a great yawn.

"Good to see you, Jo! Here, we've brought you a present. Share it out, it's from the band." He pushed a fat envelope into her hands, and shouldered his way out before she knew what he was doing. Jo ran to the door, but he had already vanished. She looked at the gift: a great wad of Dutch money! Enough to pay all their debts and their fares to the next engagement - or even back to Berlin!

At the thought of Berlin Jo had a sudden qualm about her mother. How could she be coping, with money valueless and no Piete to help? She must see her. Jo resolved to use her share of the jazz players' present to return to Berlin. Hans Gérard might find her another engagement in the New Year. She wrote a quick card to her mother before leaving Amsterdam, but realised it would probably not get there before she did. She arrived at the apartment block in Steglitz with flurries of snow channelled along the deep street by a chill wind. Her mind went back to the war-time Christmases, her Oma answering the door to see Uncle Bruno on the step, a sprinkling of snow on the shoulders of his grey uniform and peaked officer's cap.

"Who is it?" The voice sounded thin behind the closed door.

"It's me, Mutti, Piete! Let me in, I'm cold."

The first sight of her mother when the stiff bolts at last gave way and the door opened gave Jo a shock. Was this gaunt, grey-haired woman really her darling Mutti? She threw her arms round her. As she kissed the lined face she tasted salt tears.

"Such a surprise! Why didn't you let me know you were coming, dear child? There is not much Christmas fare here for you."

"We can celebrate together now, Mutti. I have some money - real money." She recounted the story of the jazz band-leader's generosity.

"A black man! My daughter accept money from a negro! What were you thinking of?"

Jo fought back the angry rejoinder that came to her lips. Mutti was imprisoned by her prejudices. She would not change them by losing her temper. She tried to explain how the circus manager, a white man and a German, had cheated them.

"And the band players were fellow artists, Mutti. We all have to hang together." Then, with a pang of conscience, "Are you well, Mutti darling? You look so tired."

"Don't worry about me, child. Yes, I do get tired. But things will be better in the New Year. I have several new pupils starting in January, and now we have the Rentenmark, no more of those stupid, worthless billion-mark notes. Look, I still have some here to change." They laughed together at the flimsy bits of paper.

Jo stayed with her mother over the holiday. Early in the New Year she saw Hans Gérard again, who told her of an engagement with a ballet company in Stockholm and lent her travel money.

"Tu gagneras beaucoup d'argent à Stockholm, mon enfant. Alors, tu me rembourseras."

The new work was exciting but strenuous. The Russian ballet master, a friend of Gérard's, welcomed Jo and appreciated her distinctive style. Her main rôle was as a grotesque Chinese acrobat in a modern ballet sequence, with a black lacquered costume replete with little bells sewn onto it. On the last night of the run, as she was in the dressing-room putting the final touches to her make-up and strapping on her ballet shoes, Signor Godurov, the ballet master, tapped at the door.

"One moment, I'm nearly ready."

"I have some news for you, Jo." He opened the door and his solemn face split in a grin. She did a pirouette, the bells tinkling, and he started laughing. Jo was happy, elated by the success of the run and her own part in it. The laughter was infectious. They were interrupted by the call-girl running up.

"One minute, Miss Mihaly!"

"I must stop laughing. What was your news, Signor?"

"Your mother has just died. A telegram came to the theatre ten minutes ago. Now you're on. Good luck!"

3

By the time Jo arrived back in Berlin her three brothers had taken charge of all arrangements. Her mother had died of cancer. Jo had not seen her brother Gil (Willi Gunther Kuhr) since he left the bank in Berlin for a better paid job in Königsberg. He agreed to take charge of the - pitifully few - possessions of their mother.

"Can you also take my things for now? I have no home once this apartment is handed back."

They had little in common with the two sailor brothers, Ernst and Hans. Both made it clear that they despised Jo - they called her Elfriede - for 'losing the family name' as they put it, as well as for her chosen career.

She was relieved when all was over and she had bade Gil farewell. She stood alone in the empty apartment, stripped now of all identity. 'This is no home for me.' Suddenly it dawned on her that for the first time in her life she had nowhere she could call home. Now she really was a wanderer, a gypsy. She owed nobody anything. The world lay before her. She was 22 years old, fit and independent. She picked up her guitar.

"El Bobo, my faithful friend! You and I shall see the world."

For almost a year Jo was on the road. Her songs to guitar, the well-loved Hermann Löns favourites, "Green is the heath", "Red rose, white rose", "The Mother-to-be" and others, and her own settings of Willi's poems, earned her her bread and board. Germany was full of homeless wanderers, the aftermath of war and inflation. Jo loved the camaraderie, the open friendliness. The Brandenburg countryside burgeoned in the early summer. She loved it all, the liquid bubbling call of the curlew as it swooped along the water-meadows, the high twittering of larks, the muddy lanes, rain-puddles glistening in the sunshine, the smell of turned earth and wild flowers, of the hay-filled barns where she often slept.

One evening late in the year she had earned enough for a meal and bed in a small country inn. A fellow wanderer, a girl of almost her own age, turned up there and they shared their experiences over supper. Lu Eggers also aspired to be a solo dancer.

"Why don't we team up? We'd both be less vulnerable." Some of the experiences they had exchanged were of encounters with drunks and desperate men.

Jo said, "And we could earn more as a duo, if we can work out some routines."

They spent the winter earning what they could as they worked on their dance sequences. Lu knew of an agent in Berlin, and he agreed to take them on for a substantial percentage.

His services found them work, but often in rather un-salubrious surroundings: small, poorly kept inns frequented by tradesmen and workers, often drunk. In Salzwedel came the last straw. A great lout of a builder tried to make advances to Jo and got a vigorous slap on the face for his pains, to the coarse laughter of his companions. In a rage he emptied his pot of ale over Jo's head. The landlord ordered him out, but joined in the laughter at Jo's plight, so they demanded their fee and left as soon as they could.

By the winter they were back in Berlin. The agent proved more rapacious than they had reckoned, leaving them scarcely enough to live on. As the two girls debated what to do - they were making their coffee last as long as they could in the café to absorb the warmth before tramping through the sleet and slush to their chilly lodging - a voice next to them said,

"Join a union. They can stop people exploiting you." They looked round in surprise. A slim dark-haired girl was smiling at them. "Sorry, I couldn't help hearing what you were saying about your agent. There are plenty of these pimps in Berlin. You have to protect yourself."

It turned out that the girl, Lisa Ney's uncle was a Trade Union official and could help. The encounter marked a turn in Jo's fortunes. Lisa was another dancer and had been frequenting the café, a favourite of theatre people and cabaret artists, on the lookout for dancers to form a team. Her uncle had secured for her an engagement with the "Three-Town Theatre

Company" in Upper Silesia. Their headquarters would be in Beuthen, with its famous theatre and opera-house, and there would be appearances in the near-by towns of Königshutte and Kattowitz. The job combined all the things Jo loved doing: dancing, writing - she wrote the scripts for their dance sequences, based on fairy-tales, Old Testament stories or simply from her own fertile imagination - and working with children. These were from the close-knit mining community, lively kids full of energy, mostly gabbling away in Polish.

The work took Jo's mind back to her nursing days in Schneidemühl. A great wave of longing, a kind of homesickness, swept over her. She resolved to visit the little town as soon as she had a chance and wrote to old Schulz, their former coachman. 'He and his wife would love to see me, I know.' No reply, though she sent letter after letter. As the days and weeks went by she began to feel a dread. 'What if they have gone away? No, never! What if Schulz is dead? How could I know?' A temporary closing of the Beuthen theatre for renovations gave her the chance she needed.

What a complex mixture of feelings as the old train pulled in to Schneidemühl station! That station linked with so much of her childhood, the Red Cross centre run by dear Oma, the soldiers and war prisoners, the crushed farmer with his skull split open. And farewells, all the tears, the waving from the platform as her darling Mutti vanished from sight, Werner Waldecker's coffin carried away . . . Jo made her way through the familiar streets to where Schulz and his family lived, no longer over the stables in Zeughausstraße but in a gloomy farmhouse. As she walked through the entrance swifts raced past, as they used to by the coach-house. Their screams accentuated the silence. No-one about. Her timid knock remained unanswered. She pushed and the door opened. She tiptoed into the living-room. No-one! A cat on a bench by the stove looked at her. The pendulum of the clock was still, stopped by a finger. The bedroom door was also ajar. As she drew near she fancied a voice whispered "Come!" Schulz lay in a small bed, his face rigid, waxen hands on the counterpane. Was he dead? A freshly laundered shirt was drawn to his chin, fastened with a brooch. With a start she remembered seeing the brooch on Frau Schulz's Sunday scarf, a pin with three black bees.

"I have come home, Schulz." Her voice sounded hoarse and weak. 'He is deaf, he won't hear me.' The eyelids fluttered and opened as his head moved. Those deep blue eyes, so full of life still! She rested her hand gently on one of his and he drew it to his heart so that she could feel it beating. In all those years of her childhood, when Schulz had been the only father she knew, she had never seen him weep, but now the tears came. She bent to hear his whispered words.

"Here you are! I waited, thought 'one day the child must come, she used to sit on my knee. When Frau Golz had bread she would say spread it thicker for Schulz.' You brought me marzipan at Easter and Christmas. It is as if you are my own child."

She sat silently, her cheeks wet. A dove cooed in the roof. Voices outside. The son-in-law strode by carrying hay on a fork. Frau Schulz saw Jo through the window and spoke to her daughter. 'My old nurse Gurtel! And now she has . . how many children of her own? Eight, ten?' When they all came into the room it seemed at first that the peace was shattered. Frau Schulz greeted her and Gurtel, now buxom, with her hair in a great bun, gave her a timid kiss. Her mother said, quite loudly,

"You have come for Father's last day." Jo was shocked. Would he not hear? The children had followed their mother and clung round her. Jo remembered she had brought some sweets for them. As she handed them round Schulz whispered,

"Mir auch ein Bonbon!" He held it in his fingers without eating it, then took Jo's hand and held it fast. He seemed to sleep a little and Gurtel shushed the children to silence. The sound of a scythe being sharpened came from the farm building. Schulz's eyes opened.

"You - he used 'Du' - belong to us. That's as it should be." He tried to shake Jo's hand, then the fingers relaxed. She bent and kissed the still face and left the room.

Coachman Schulz died as the light faded.

V Wolfgang

1

WOLFGANG WAS with his father when he died. A few moments before the end he had a vivid sense of a door closing, a blind being drawn down. It was a last deliberate act of will and, in the seconds between it and the instant when Carl Graeser's heart faltered and stopped, Wolfgang felt as if a great chasm had opened up. When his mother came into the bedroom she saw the staring empty eyes and instinctively closed the lids with a finger before her own tears came. Wolfgang felt helpless. He put his arm round her and led her to the door, where his brother stood. Hans embraced his mother closely, as her tears came faster. Wolfgang said,

"I shall stay here a while." Hans nodded and took his mother away.

It was very still in the room. Wolfgang sat dry-eyed, his hands folded on his knees. Images passed through his mind like lantern slides: he and his father holding hands on the edge of the Vesuvius crater - he could smell the acrid sulphurous fumes - ; the empty corridors of the Naples hospital, his father saying 'Don't run!'; the first ride with his father in the new Fiat car, down to the "Villa" in Naples; the opening chords of the St Matthew Passion at the Odeon in Munich, his hand once again groping for and finding his father's . . .

'Your soul, my child, your immortal soul!' Hans Zurlinden's words on the Brocken. But there was no immortal soul. He thought of Heinrich von Kleist's memorial stone by the Wannsee, marking his suicide spot, with its futile boast: "Now, immortality, thou art wholly mine!" Professor Dr Carl Graeser. The titles, and the striving that had gone into acquiring them, belonged here, in this mortal evanescent world. Carl Graeser had sloughed them off like a snake's skin, even his name. Who was Carl Graeser? An inscription on a tombstone? As he raised his head Wolfgang found himself looking at himself, his twelve-year-old self-portrait in pastels, which he had drawn for the exhibition. His father had had it framed and hung beside his bed. His eyes seemed held by those in the picture, deep-set, questioning, old in a young face. He remembered how he had drawn and re-drawn them, glancing in the mirror again and again to try and catch himself unaware. He remembered his father's "Why so solemn?" when he first looked at the portrait and his response, "You don't want me grinning like an ape for ever, Papa!" For ever!

'So there I hang, and he sees me no more.' He shook himself as if awakening from a dream and stood up. After a moment he bent over the silent figure and kissed the cold forehead.

"I shall be true, Papa. I promise!"

Before leaving the room Wolfgang re-hung the portrait with its face to the wall.

After the funeral they decided that the big house must be sold. Hans returned to Rome, where he had now settled, so with the help of Johannes Wolf and Paul Müller Wolfgang and his mother took up residence in a small first-floor apartment at the other end of Prince-Friedrich-Leopold Straße, number 6, over a general goods store.

Far from relieving the pressure, his father's death gave Wolfgang a new sense of urgency. The Die Kunst der Fuge article led to several further engagements. At the same time he was following up his interest in Chinese and Asiatic cultures and in mathematics. To offset the cerebral nature of these activities he instituted a strenuous programme of physical exercise, swimming, running, mountain-climbing, pushing his body to its limits, as if to assert his identity, to defy the hollow chasm that had opened as his father lay dying. Hans Zurlinden was a good friend at this time, steady, predictable and undemanding. Wolfgang appreciated his generosity of spirit, while on his side Hans paid homage to his young friend's undeniable genius, indulging him in his sudden whims and accompanying him whenever possible on his physical work-outs.

"How is the athletics book taking shape?" Hans and Wolfgang were lying in the sun on the Wannsee beach after a long swim. In spite of the spell of blazing weather the water had been chill, so it was good to soak up the heat for a while. There was no reply, so Hans went on, "It is certainly timely - and fashionable! Have you seen that book everyone is talking about, Man and Sunshine?"

"Fashionable! I'm not a follower of fashion." Wolfgang sat up, remembering as he did so how his own suggestion to Piete that her 'Dead soldier's dance' would be fashionable had prompted one of her outbursts. With a change of tone he said, " I suppose it is in people's minds just now. Yes, I've seen Hans Surén's book. Don't think much of it. Mine will go a lot deeper . . if I ever get it written." Wolfgang grimaced. "Haven't touched it for weeks. Brigitte thinks it is a big mistake." As he spoke he realised this was the first time he had mentioned the girl to Hans. He was off-hand with his friend's evident curiosity.

"Just one of Steffi Nossen's girls. She lives in Holland."

"I should like to meet her."

"She has left the school now." Relenting, he went on, "If she comes back, maybe. You can see the new building. It is worth seeing."

Wolfgang seemed to himself to be living on two levels. On the one hand there was his physical self and the persona he presented to the world, extrovert, happy, often laughing; on the other his interior life, so much changed by his father's death. Paradoxically, the more public exposure he had following the Bach article, the more solitary he felt. He experienced the loss of his father as 'a great gap in Nature', a gap that carried with it a host of associated feelings and recollections: his self-doubt about his actions after the suicide attempt, that chasm he had sensed just before Carl Graeser breathed his last. Also multiple memories: of roaring into tunnels during his travels between Naples and Zürich, of the constant brooding presence of Vesuvius, the doorway to chaos, throughout his childhood, which had prompted painting after painting - the thirty or so in his exhibition just a small sample - , and water, the luxury of surrender as he dived and felt it close over him.

This last had led, in one of his conversations with Piete, to another bitter argument. She had been telling him of a Wilhelm Hauff fairy-tale read to her as a child which still haunted her. It was about the sunken treasure-ship 'Carmilhan'.

"The greedy fisherman cast a spell to summon the drowned crew back to tell him where the treasure lay and they all gathered round him, all the drowned seamen, or their souls, accusing him of disturbing their rest. I used to hear that eerie cry of "Carmilhan, Carmilhan!" in my dreams. Then when the Russians were pursued by our troops into the Masurian swamps early in the war, and the sinking of the passenger ship 'Lusitania' - oh, all those horrible things we did to our so-called enemies!"

"What do you mean, so-called?" He had turned on her angrily. "They would do the same to us. Drowning might be a good way to go anyway, I love swimming underwater."

"Even sinking into the swamp?" He had thought, as she said that, 'she is not looking at me, she doesn't see me'. She went on, "I used to imagine what it must have been like, the mud reaching to one's mouth, ugh!" shivering as the images came alive in her imagination. How his casual 'they deserved all they got' had sparked off that furious rejoinder, which had taken weeks to heal! And was not healed now, he thought.

Was he destined never to experience the kind of close natural relationship he saw amongst his peers? Was the union he had been conscious of when Piete and he were together in Nikolassee always to be just a fleeting moment, a glimpse of a world never to be inhabited by him? Her world seemed so far removed from his own. She looked ahead with hope to the fulfilment of her dancing ambitions, to directing her energies, her life-force, towards persuading others to renounce war. To him, as to Spengler, this was no more than a chimera. Yet for Piete - or Jo as she now wanted to be called - it provided the incentive for life itself. Wolfgang tried to compare her dynamic with his own, with the 'obstinate force' he had inadvertently named in his letter to Uncle Ludwig. He and Jo were both 'driven', but by what blind power? In his letters to Brigitte Wolfgang tried to articulate something of this, but it was soon clear to him that she could not understand what he was getting at. She had none of Jo Mihaly's impetuousness, nor of his own pressures. She lived in and for the present. Wolfgang envied her her approach to life, but could not emulate it.

In the Spring of '26 a new encounter helped to give the book on gymnastics and dance, which had foundered after several abortive attempts, a fresh lease of life. When he came in from his run one morning a letter from Munich awaited him. It was from his Uncle Anton, a brief note enclosing another in a hand unknown to him. His uncle was merely recommending the other writer to him. He looked with curiosity for the signature: Oswald Spengler. Wolfgang was astonished and thrilled. He devoured the content of the short letter - it was little more than a note. The writer 'would be in Berlin for some days and wished to meet Herrn Wolfgang Graeser, having been apprised of his extraordinary talents in many directions, in particular in the fields of mathematics, philosophy and Eastern culture.' There was no mention of Bach, or indeed of music.

"Mutti, look at this!" He ran downstairs - he had once more found an attic eyrie in the new dwelling - waving the letter. "Uncle Anton sent it. Look who it's from! D'you think I dare meet him?"

Lily read the note. She too was impressed, knowing the writer's fame, though she knew of his magnum opus only through comments and extracts passed on by her husband when the book came out soon after the war.

"You must go and see him, dear. It is quite an honour to be sought out by such an eminent scholar. No more than you deserve, with all your work. Strange that he does not mention the Die Kunst der Fuge article."

"Oh, that is a relief for once. I don't want to be labelled as a mere musicologist any more than Hans did." In fact, he thought to himself, I don't want to be 'labelled' at all.

The meeting took place in the university, where Dr Spengler had been invited to conduct a series of seminars. Wolfgang was at first put off by the 46-year-old scholar's manner. He rose from the desk as his visitor entered: he was shorter than Wolfgang, bespectacled, with thin, rather scurfy hair and a domed forehead. His handshake was limp and damp, and his mode of speech precise and monotonous in tone.

"So young! Of course, of course, your relative informed me. I understand you are interested in my modest attempt to analyse our Western predicament and define the destiny of our civilisation."

The conversation started stiffly, but Wolfgang's obvious awe and respectful responses flattered the older man, so that he soon became more expansive. At one point Wolfgang mentioned the word 'ideals' in relation to philosophy. It prompted a scornful snort from Dr Spengler.

"Ideals are no more than cowardice, my friend. All great thinkers, from Montaigne to Nietzsche, have realised this. In our day, as we sense the closing, the inevitable dissolution of an epoch, scepticism is the only honourable stance. We are beasts of prey, not idealists."

Wolfgang chose to ignore the incompatibility between that belligerent title and the speaker, with his pallid student's complexion and flabby physique. Dr Spengler expressed interest in Wolfgang's idea of a book on physical fitness and sport and asked about its scope and purpose. As the young man warmed to his theme he became oblivious to his companion's dogmatic tones. So much in what the great man had been saying showed the vast range of his intellect. Wolfgang had never known anyone like him. He had greater breadth of scholarship than Professor Müller, and this explained, it seemed to Wolfgang, why he could not take refuge in the idealistic world-view that seemed to inform Müller's attitude to life.

"I believe, Herr Graeser, that your book on sport and gymnastics could be a valuable contribution to the re-establishment of German identity. We need leaders, both physical and intellectual leaders, and such a book as yours could help point the way."

At the close of the meeting - or interview, as it had felt like to Wolfgang - he was surprised and delighted to receive an unexpected offer.

"I should be happy to read over your manuscript and discuss it with you when it is complete."

In return Wolfgang asked if he might dedicate the book, "if it meets with your approval, sir" to 'the revered author of The Decline of the West.' Dr Spengler agreed to this with some complacency.

As he made his way home, elated by the meeting and its conclusion, he suddenly remembered having asked the dancer Mary Wigman something similar in connection with Körpersinn. 'No need now to follow up that idea,' he thought, recognising at the same time how far he had travelled since that theatre outing with Piete Kuhr.

2

He returned to Körpersinn with renewed enthusiasm, and had soon worked out a new more compact structure for the book. If it was to satisfy his new sponsor and fulfil the rôle Dr Spengler had suggested it must be short, but it must also be hard-hitting, in line with the 'New Objectivity' that had replaced post-war Expressionism. Wolfgang rebelled against the decisiveness of tone in the word Sachlichkeit and chose to use instead a more neutral term of his own, Das Neue Etwas. The book would now have nine short chapters, one dealing specifically with dance and music. He looked forward to getting Brigitte's comments on this, but as the plan took shape he realised that the dance chapter would be near the end, 'and it would be no use asking her to read the one on the metaphysics of body culture.' He would aim to give it her as a birthday present in September.

The planned meeting between Hans Zurlinden and Brigitte was not an unqualified success. The day was overcast and chilly and the new building, still raw and staring, with builders' rubble not yet cleared and dirty puddles of rain in the driveway, had none of the expected Bauhaus atmosphere. Wolfgang felt ill at ease and had already decided to make the visit a brief one. He wanted to arrange for more observation in connection with the book now the writing was under way. Steffi Nossen was friendly and agreeable.

"So this is your motor-cycling friend, Wolfgang. Hullo, I'm Steffi Nossen." Hans responded to her evident vitality. Dark complexion, almost Indian. Southern Italy? He could not decide, but was conscious of the pent-up energy which seemed to vibrate from her.

"Has Brigitte come back yet?" Wolfgang had resolved on taking the bull by the horns. "Perhaps she could show Hans round while we are talking."

"Good idea, I'll call her."

Brigitte was pleased to see Wolfgang and courteous to his friend, but obviously not at her best. She had an uncomfortable-looking stye in one eye and lacked her customary ebullience. As they embraced she whispered to Wolfgang: "Not the best time of the month for me. Sorry!"

Before leaving, Wolfgang was able to exchange a few words with her. She would be going home for the holiday, but 'they must keep in touch.' Wolfgang was able to refer to the chapter on Dance and Music.

"I aim to complete it for your birthday."

"And yours, then," she said with a smile. "Perhaps we can really celebrate together this year."

"Will you be back in Berlin?"

"Steffi has asked me to help with the younger ones. I like that. Anna, my sister, keeps saying I ought to find a job, but . . well, this is a job of a kind . ." She tailed off indecisively.

"Will you read the chapter for me?"

"I'll try, Wolfi, I promise. But you know me, I am not clever like you."

They embraced hastily as Hans came up to say, "Bucephalus awaits us."

As they left the dance school Wolfgang was resolutely silent, his face set in the sulky expression Hans now knew well. After trying and failing to discuss the meeting with the Dutch girl he decided to go for a more neutral topic.

"So that was one of Bruno Taut's designs. Not all that impressive to my mind. I preferred the architecture of the next-door house." Bismarckallee 2 was a typical well-to-do brick-built bourgeois residence, bearing the date MCMIX proudly on its stuccoed neo-Palladian front. Wolfgang laughed scornfully.

"An un-reconstructed traditionalist, that's what you are. What about fitness for purpose? What about the way those great sliding windows unite the dance hall with the space beyond? All it needs is time to settle and for the mess to be cleared." He shed his gloom as he spoke. "Hey, Hans! Why don't we pay a visit to Gropius's new Bauhaus building. It has been in all the papers. Dessau is within reach now, not like Weimar. I really want to see what they are doing there. We could easily do it on your trusty machine."

Soon they were covering the 140 kilometres to Dessau. At Hans Zurlinden's request they stopped for refreshment in Wittenberg, in the shadow of the Stadtkirche with its twin towers. Before going on Hans insisted, to Wolfgang's sardonic amusement, in stopping to look at the door of the Schloßkirche where Luther had pinned up his 95 theses.

"Bronze lasts longer than paper and wood." (Luther's wooden doors had been burnt down during the Seven Years War). "Will Martin Luther and his works outlast these doors, do you think?" Before Hans could reply he went on, "We need a new set of theses from Walter Gropius, or Mies Van der Rohe. Mount your Bucephalus, friend. Let's shake the Protestant dust from our feet."

Hans was impressed in spite of himself as they approached the stark new Bauhaus building beyond the railway lines in Dessau - two straight-edged blocks with flat roofs, clean white surfaces, lots of glass. As they entered they picked up a copy of the new art school's magazine with its striking cubist three-dimensional design: a cone, a sphere, a cube casting clean-cut shadows on a printed page headed bauhaus in functional modern lettering.

"Fitness for purpose, that is the focus here." Wolfgang was excited by the whole experience of Bauhaus culture, the sense that everything from ash-trays, chair-legs, tea-pots to the building itself was conceived as a unity. No stuck-on ornamentation, no waste yet plenty of space. As he scribbled in the old dog-eared notebook he always carried he found in it a jotting from an article read in preparation for the visit: 'Every epoch demands its own form. Our task is to lend new form to our world by modern means.' Would his book achieve this? It was a worthwhile aim.

After this visit the book rapidly took shape. With his new patron in mind Wolfgang widened his field of reference, ranging - not without a certain intellectual arrogance - from ancient Chinese culture to Mussolini and fascism, from Greek Euclidian geometry to modern gymnastic and dance patterns, from Renaissance to contemporary art-forms. In the longest chapter, on 'the metaphysics of body-culture', he attempted to elucidate, partly for himself, the dichotomy he always sensed, defining it here as chaos v. cosmos, darkness v. light, the Yin and Yang of being. His text was liberally sprinkled with scholarly references, including several to Oswald Spengler, betraying both his youth and his naiveté. By the time the book was to be in print a year later Wolfgang would already have grown beyond this sort of display. For the present he looked forward to the autumn, and to his birthday present for Brigitte.

In spite of his speed and clarity, it took the whole summer to get the book into shape. Oswald Spengler wrote from Munich expressing his interest and asking for drafts. Wolfgang at first demurred - he never liked showing anyone unfinished work, it had been one of the few disagreements he had had with his father and Uncle Johann when they insisted on his adding that set of rough sketches of hands to the art exhibition - , but when Spengler told him that he had made representations on his behalf to the well-known Munich publisher C H Beck, who might even make an advance on royalties, he felt obliged to comply and copied out the first three chapters. 'He should approve of the one on metaphysics at least.' Wolfgang was, however, determined that Brigitte should be the first to see chapter 7: Dance and Music. As he read through the draft before packing it off to Holland he was wryly aware that it owed more to Piete Kuhr than to her. He was also conscious of the contrast between the two recipients of his work: the dry, precise scholar in Munich, whose immense studies with their global sweep had generated in their author only a world-weary determinism, and the vital, happy-go-lucky girl of his own age, with her laughing eyes and lissom body. Where did he belong in relation to these two? His eyes rested on a passage in the chapter:

'True dance is created only when the outer form of the body becomes a transparent vessel (durchsichtige Gefäß) for living essence and its impulse.'

This was what Jo Mihaly was aspiring to with her individual, expressionist approach to her craft. She had a purpose in her life driving her on. But what was the point of his own physical training, the early morning runs, the exercises - he even had a pair of dumb-bells in his room now, which he used daily before the evening meal - ? Spengler talked of man as 'a beast of prey'. Was he, Wolfgang, merely preying on Brigitte, on all his friends? As so often, he felt torn apart.

Shaking off his speculations, he read rapidly through the rest of the chapter. He felt more sanguine about Brigitte's reception of it. She would recognise his observation of the Grunewald Palucca School dance class in his comments on Von Laban. He was pleased with his provocative description of Laban's choreography as 'a text-book of three-dimensional Euclidian geometry.' He had also managed to include something about the evening with Piete and Mary Wigman's dance group: the almost religious, abstract quality of Wigman's dance patterns. 'Perhaps one day I shall give Piete a copy of the book, if our paths ever cross again.'

Lily Graeser had met Brigitte van Schaer once, when one of their bike rides had ended in Nikolassee, and she liked the girl's high spirits and open friendliness.

"So much less complicated a person than your other friend, Wullie, though Piete is nice too. I liked the way she talked with your father, so respectful."

"I have lost touch with Piete. She calls herself Jo now, Jo Mihaly. I think she's touring with a ballet troupe. Did I tell you that Brigitte's birthday is only two days away from mine. We'll be twenty together." Lily had done no entertaining since her husband's death, but this gave her an idea.

"Why don't you have a joint birthday celebration here? I should like to see Brigitte again."

The 'celebration' was a muted one. After thanking Wolfgang for the chapter and agreeing to talk about it later, Brigitte told them that she was giving up her work at the dance school.

"I told you about the other Wolfgang, didn't I, Wim's college friend from Göttingen? He has asked me to marry him."

Wolfgang was shocked. "You once said that no-one in their senses gets married before they're twenty-five." She laughed rather self-consciously.

"Yes, well, one says these things. Wolfgang is good fun. He's not like you, Wolfi, not really an intellectual - though he is quite bright. I think you would like him. He is a scientist, electrical engineering. He's been offered a job with Siemens, so we'll have lots of money."

The news put a damper on the birthday celebration for Wolfgang. He could not work out his feelings. Of course he had no claim on Brigitte, they had never been close in that way - or had they? In any case he felt let down. After their simple meal, the birthday cake baked specially by Lily giving it a little more gaiety, Wolfgang asked if Brigitte felt like talking about the dance chapter.

"Don't expect much from me, Wolfi. I have read it as carefully as I can, but your writing is well over my head." She turned to Lily. "Has he shown you any of his new book?"

"I read the beginning. Wullie is an intellectual, as you say, so his ideas often go far beyond my poor capacity. He misses his father when it comes to discussing his work. Has he told you that Dr Spengler, the great historian philosopher, is backing the book?"

Wolfgang cut into the conversation impatiently.

"Shall we go up to my room? I have all my papers there, so it might be easier - if you don't mind sitting on the floor."

The room was indeed bare, with little more than a writing table with a plain Van Gogh-like chair, shelves of books and papers, a chest for clothes, a plain, off-white carpet. The bed against one wall with its Indian cotton quilt cover in dusty reds provided the only spot of colour. Dr Wolf had made Wolfgang a present of the elegant little clavichord, which stood in a corner. Brigitte surveyed the room with interest.

"It's a cell, a monk's cell! No wonder your writing is so . . so elevated." She was amused to see the dumb-bells stowed under the bed. "So that's how you keep so fit."

"I spend so much time at my desk these days. There is also this." Wolfgang hooked down two hand-grips on ropes suspended from two big hooks in a rafter. He quickly swung himself up and over, landing lightly on his feet. "It's useful when the weather is too bad for running. If I am writing about gymnastics I need to feel what it's like." He hooked the two ropes out of the way.

Brigitte watched him with admiration, then looked about her. "I'll sit on the floor as you suggested, your chair looks very uncomfy."

The discussion began awkwardly. Wolfgang wanted to know whether what he had written made sense to Brigitte as a dancer.

"There were some things I really liked. All that about rhythm, for instance, its origin in breathing and the pulse-beat." She thumbed through the sheaf of paper. "Here it is, near the end: 'Rhythm is in reality another word for living, for being alive. Where rhythm fails, there comes death and rigidity.' I like the whole passage. And I recognise that bit about Laban's choreography. That is pure Steffi." She smiled up at him. "The style is good too, you have a vivid way of putting things. There is much that I didn't know, about the origin and history of dance. Your three links between dance and music - I couldn't quite understand the second one, something about abstract, sacral quality?" She referred to a number of other passages she had found obscure. "You keep talking about chaos, it seems often to be in your mind."

Wolfgang blushed at this; she had touched a sensitive spot. He tried to explain by referring to the Orchestra poem that had so fascinated Piete, with its idea of the universal dance, the music of the spheres arising out of primeval chaos. Brigitte was equally charmed by it.

He asked her, "What did you think about what I said of the need for a spectator? That is near the end of the chapter. I was thinking of my visits to the Palucca School, where I, the non-participant, sat watching you the dancers."

"Your problem is that you want to be both, a dancer as well as an observer. You just can't be in it and outside it at the same time. I am not sure I agree with you in your comparison of the dance observer with the deaf person playing the piano and only aware of the movement - I suppose that is a kind of dance - of his fingers. It is a vivid image, but I don't see that the purity of dance, as you call it, is destroyed or compromised by the need for spectators. After all, music is nothing without listeners. Our dances weren't any different when you were watching us."

This led to animated discussion, with Wolfgang striding about, Brigitte sitting cross-legged in the middle of the floor. They both sensed that their respective views were incompatible. The conversation came to rest on a passage in the centre of the chapter, in which Wolfgang traced the development of rhythm out of primeval chaos, through mediaeval and Renaissance music to the 'absolute purity' of a late Beethoven string quartet or Bach's Die Kunst der Fuge.

"Ah, that is your great work, Wolfi, I know."

"Not mine, Bach's. I have simply tried to re-discover his original conception."

"I wouldn't say 'simply'. Please play me something from it and I'll listen like your musician listening to Beethoven, with my eyes shut." Wolfgang bent down and kissed her forehead, then took his chair over to the little keyboard of the clavichord.

"Bach loved his clavichord next to the organ. I like it too, it is so responsive and intimate and it doesn't disturb the household, being so quiet. I'll play you the opening 'Contrapunctus' - that's what he called the fugues - and one of the canons. Do you know the subject, the theme tune?"

"Wolfi, I don't know anything about it. I need to be educated."

He explained the structure of the work briefly, playing the twelve-note subject in its original form. "And sometimes he turns it upside-down." He played the reversed theme and a part of the fourth fugue. The girl was naively astonished at the way the subject could be used like this and still make music.

"Here is one of the two-part canons." He picked out Contrapunctus XV. "Bach called it 'a canon with augmentation in contrary motion' - but you needn't worry about that." He laughed at her puzzled expression. "It opens with a subtle variation of the subject -" he played the first four bars - "then the top part starts doing all sorts of things, with the bottom part just meditating on the theme." She settled herself to listen, closing her eyes as she sat cross-legged in the centre of the carpet. After the canon he played the opening four-part fugue in a steady tempo. The gentle, muted sounds of the clavichord scarcely disturbed the stillness in the bare attic room, a shaft of sunlight from the small window resting with fortuitous grace on the girl's fair hair. After the final unison he rested his hands in his lap. The silence took over. Brigitte remained with her eyes closed for some moments, then got up, stretching like a cat.

"I think I begin to understand why the work fascinates you. It is a dance of notes. That canon is a pas de deux. Bach is the choreographer. And so beautiful!" Her eyes were shining with tears.

"But he had to leave it incomplete, all that beauty. He died and the whole great structure died with him, unfinished." Wolfgang left the instrument and turned to her unsmiling. "Perhaps the only way to experience the finish, the completion of anything is to die."

Suddenly it seemed to the girl that this cell-like room was a prison. She shook off the feeling, opening the door and saying,

"All this brainwork and sitting has made me restless. Let's get some fresh air."

They walked slowly together to the S-Bahn station. Wolfgang was conscious of that other parting there, with Piete. How much older he felt after all that had passed! They embraced closely, and Brigitte whispered,

"You will always be special to me, Wolfi. We'll keep in touch, won't we?" He did not reply, except for holding her more tightly before letting her board the train. Their linked hands were pulled apart as it started moving. He watched until the curve blotted his view, then stood motionless until all was quiet again.

VI   Berlin 1927

1

IT SEEMED that Germany was at last emerging from the sombre post-war era, from the pariah status of defeated nation, the wild revolutionary excesses, the financial chaos and its consequences. In 1926 she was accepted as a member of the League of Nations beside her victors. The statesman Gustav Stresemann's acceptance of reality, his political Sachlichkeit, had led him from leadership of the National Liberals and monarchism, even to the extent of supporting the Kapp putsch in 1920, through 'rational republicanism' to whole-hearted acceptance of the new republic. Thanks to Schacht and Dawes, foreign capital, no longer suspicious of the 'socialist' republic, poured into Berlin. Big business had discovered how to resist those socialists in the administration who sought control through nationalisation: they formed cartels. The chemical industries showed the way in 1925, when six concerns united to form the giant I G Farben. A year later the four largest steelworks amalgamated and the motor-car firms of Daimler and Benz linked to produce Mercedes cars.

Berlin was the sounding-board for the new Germany, with its unique mixture of old-style Prussian imperialism - the ponderous architecture, the 'Siegesallee' of mediocre statues to military heroes, irreverently dubbed by Berliners the 'Puppenallee', even the triumphalist Brandenburg Gate - and bustling modernity. By 1927 it was the most cosmopolitan, exciting city in Europe. Hundreds of newspapers poured from its presses, commercial aircraft constantly soared overhead or landed and took off in the new Tempelhof airport, trains, elevated railcars, motor-cars, buses and taxicabs filled the ravines of the streets with with noise and fumes day and night. The great apartment blocks and their courtyards, the markets, spilling into the streets themselves, the cafés and restaurants teemed with life. Berlin was a magnet for art and science, for theatre and cabaret, as for industry.

To some Berliners all the apparent prosperity, the advertisements, department stores, factories, the visible affluence, showed that Weimar socialism was working, that republican-style democracy had come to stay. If the conservative author of Buddenbrooks and The Magic Mountain espoused it together with his socialist brother Heinrich, if even the hero of Tannenberg could preside over it, who could deny it? Yet the very openness of Berlin, its cultural ferment, the breadth of its society, gave nourishment to quite different forces. The judiciary, entrenched in the past, gave derisory sentences to right-wing murderers and stiff ones to socialist and working-class petty criminals. The murdered Luxemburg, Liebknecht, Rathenau were still fresh in people's minds, while the pathologically energetic demagogue of the Munich beer-cellar 'Putsch' and his Brownshirt supporters preached and acted out a different kind of 'national socialism'. Untainted by Versailles and 'stab-in-the-back', they could safely denigrate the Reichstag parliamentarians as an ineffectual bunch of Jews and fellow-travellers. They alone, they claimed, could provide the leadership that the new Germany needed. It was a message with a strong appeal to the middle classes as well as the disbanded and disaffected Junkers, especially those impoverished by the financial incompetence in 1923. It also had a certain intellectual respectability. Had not Nietzsche, partly influenced by Schopenhauer, shown the need for strong leadership, for the 'superman'? One thousand metres up in his Black Forest fastness the philosopher Martin Heidegger seemed to be supporting the same line of thought with his new book Being and Time, while closer to hand Oswald Spengler, philosopher-historian author of The Decline of the West, derided the ruling powers. His 1920s pamphlet "Prussianism and Socialism", often reprinted, passed from hand to hand finding ready readers for its differentiation of 'English socialism' (a way of denigrating Marxism consistent with nationalist chauvism) from true (German) socialism. Wolfgang made sure of his father's copy before he and his mother moved down the road in Nikolassee, and it now carried the author's autograph on its title-page. Spengler's publishers, the Munich house of C.H.Beck, who were to accept Wolfgang Graeser's Körpersinn two years later, had issued in February 1924 another stirring pamphlet by the historian, a speech given to college students in Würzburg - at the very time when 17-year-old Wolfgang was taking his Abitur in the Mommsengymnasium - on "The political duty of German youth."

Gentlemen! At present Germany finds itself in a situation of deceptive peace . . . We are play-acting. We have learnt and forgotten what we were as a people in the world community. We are not merely miserable, we are also dishonourable . . . While all round the world armies and navies are preparing for new decisive action, we pay with German gold for a French army on German soil. That is what our anti-militarism amounts to! . . . It is my hope that through you, the new generation, we Germans, the youngest and least exhausted amongst the European peoples, will be able once again to play an historic rôle consonant with our inner strength, our undamaged virility - in spite of all that has happened - and our creative capacity. It is your sacred duty, my friends, not merely to be enthused, but to train . . .

For Wolfgang, caught up now in his abstruse university studies in mathematics and Asiatic culture, such stirring words from his new friend and advocate seemed like a breath of fresh air. He remembered his father's approval and felt proud to know the famous man, whose call to German youth, based on penetrating analysis of the whole sweep of western history and culture, could not be dismissed as mere fashion. After all, he, Wolfgang, was a German too, wasn't he? The Obenauses were a good Bavarian family and his father always called himself German, in spite of the accident of being born in Switzerland. He felt pleased that he too had addressed something, his new book, to 'the new generation' - his own contemporaries.

The message was especially welcome to Wolfgang at this time. His new realisation, or as he preferred to call it, restoration of Die Kunst der Fuge had appeared, handsomely printed by Breitkopf and Härtel of Leipzig as a Supplement to the Bach Gesellschaft Edition, in their dignified 40cm.by 30cm.-volume format: 35 scholarly pages covering the history of the work from its inception in 1750, with facsimiles from the first editions, followed by 130 more pages of music, including the chorale dictated by the dying master. It had been enthusiastically received by critics and by some Bach scholars, and Wolfgang assumed that the immediate talk of a performance would soon bear fruit. Here, however, the difficulties began, possibly owing to the youth and obscurity of this upstart, claiming to teach older and more experienced Bach specialists their job. A performance planned by Dr Straube, the Thomaskantor in Leipzig, for the 13th Bach Fest in Essen was cancelled. Professor Georg Schumann put an end to another scheduled for the 14th Bach Fest in Berlin. It was left, appropriately enough, to Karl Straube himself, the holder of Bach's own post, to rescue the work and prepare for its first performance in Leipzig, but this was still not to take place until the year after it was published.

Wolfgang was both a part of Berlin cosmopolitanism and apart from it. At times, when he was making his way through the crowds of shoppers, window-gazers, beggars and cripples to the university, or threading a path through the teeming back streets, he felt like a disembodied ghost, hearing and comprehending the babel tongues while identifying with none. In the main streets he sometimes realised, with a curious shock, that while these different races so cheek by jowl - French, American, Chinese, Italian, Russian - remained mutually unaware and as it were deaf to each other, like planets each in its separate orbit, he was linguistically and to some extent culturally linked to all of them. Yet who, what was he - an intellectual? a man of the world (he laughed to himself at the cliché)? a philosopher? a scholar? a musician? an artist? an athlete? German? Swiss?

Italian? Just now, immersed as he was in his university studies yet increasingly forced into the public eye through his growing fame as musicologist and Bach scholar, Wolfgang felt at times as if he was spinning out of control, like that wooden top being whipped back into equilibrium there on the street corner.

He had stopped to watch a familiar enough street scene, two little boys in a patch of sunlight absorbed in keeping their spinning bobbins upright, while the slant sun cast shadows of their moving bodies and of a long-shafted handcart beside them. Wolfgang had taken a short cut after playing second violin in string quartets with some former friends at the Music School - an unusual indulgence for him these days, only entered into on the insistence of his mother. A strident woman's voice from the entrance to a courtyard called the children in. One wooden top lodged by Wolfgang's foot. He picked it up to hand to the boy, but the mother had already grabbed him by one ear and was hauling him away in spite of his howls. Rather at a loss, Wolfgang followed them through the cavern-like gateway into the courtyard of the apartment block, a working-class Mietskaserne, the like of which he had never before seen or been aware of. The noise and accumulated stench hit him like a wall as he emerged into the courtyard. Cries and calls of children, hammerings, shouts from the windows to those below, fumes from the multiple kitchens and basements, damp from the clothes hung out on the drying-frame in one corner, tobacco smoke. The square of sky diminished by the tall walls with their grime and cracked plaster. A negro street musician had wheeled his barrel-organ in and was adding to the din; he had attracted out a few drab housewives, who had linked arms to dance on the dirty paving. The musician, a bass drum on his back beaten through a foot pedal, cranked the handle of his tired machine. He had a battered imperial Stahlhelm on his head, enlivened with a home-made contraption of tiny bells fixed to its spike which tinkled in time to the tune. His monkey, sitting on the organ top, spotted Wolfgang as he drew near and jumped across onto his shoulder, chattering and scratching at his hair. The women laughed; one saw his violin-case.

"Give us a tune then, young 'un!"

Wolfgang blushed, trying to dislodge the animal and shaking his head. The musician chuckled.

"He won't harm you, young sir. it's just his way of being friendly. Here, Jacko!"

Finding a few groschen in his pocket, Wolfgang was able to distract the creature, hand over the top and make good his escape. He was thankful to breathe even the street air with its petrol fumes after the fetid stale atmosphere of the courtyard. Yet for thousands, perhaps millions of his fellow Berliners that was the first air they breathed as they awoke each day and the last before they crawled into their beds at night.

One crack of the whip for Wolfgang came early in the New Year, when he was invited to talk to musicians and critics in Munich. It was a strange feeling returning to the familiar surroundings of the Bavarian capital. Compared with Berlin everything here, buildings, streets, business-men, even the shop-assistants with their 'Grüss' Gott!', seemed staid and old-fashioned. Uncle Anton, his soldierly body now filled out and corpulent, met him at the station with a shiny long-bonneted Horch motor-car and chauffeur.

"Wolfgang my boy! So pleased to see you." He pumped his nephew's arm mercilessly. "So you are a famous man, eh!" with an avuncular slap on the back. "We'll just take a snack at home before the talk. Ettie will be happy to see you."

Aunt Ettie was a quiet rather mousy woman with straight grey hair pulled back from her thin features into an untidy bun and scared-looking hare's eyes that were constantly glancing at her husband as though expecting an outburst. She had set out an ample cold buffet, with a whole roast chicken and a large stone jug of foaming beer, of which Anton partook in generous measure. Wolfgang, nervous of the coming ordeal, drank water and ate sparingly in spite of his uncle's full-mouthed urgings to the contrary.

When he entered the great salon of Baron von Schrenk-Notzing's palace, with its crystal chandelier, panelled walls and succession of tall windows, Wolfgang felt a sinking of the heart. This was worse than the Swiss Embassy in Berlin, worse than the Theresiengymnasium . . . There was some polite clapping and a subdued buzz of talk as he made his way past a table on which his Bach-Gesellschaft Supplement was prominently displayed, took his place at the rostrum and spread out his papers. The lights glinted on numerous pairs of spectacles, professors from the Academy of Music who were hosting the meeting. A daunting assembly, almost entirely male, dark-suited, unsmiling. Amongst them he spotted several with note-books and pencils, no doubt reporters for the music journals. He took a deep breath.

"All that I have to say today derives from the twelve notes you see behind me."

He had asked his uncle to arrange for a large poster to be set up with the Die Kunst der Fuge subject writ large. Once into his theme Wolfgang's nervousness vanished. He read his lecture with animation and even managed to raise a few chuckles at some of the less perceptive dismissals of Die Kunst der Fuge, in particular at his quotation from C Debrois van Bruyck in 1867: 'This is no longer music, but has degenerated entirely into a barbaric, abstruse kind of catterwauling.' He found the questions after his talk positively stimulating. The formal part of the evening ended with genuinely rousing applause and several 'Bravos!'

When Wolfgang arrived back in Berlin his mother surprised him.

"Your friend Piete telephoned while you were away."

The news came as a shock. All that he associated with Jo Mihaly seemed so remote from his current obsessions. He recalled his idea of giving her a copy of Körpersinn. Amongst the accumulated mail at Nikolassee was one from his Munich publisher to say that ten copies would be despatched to reach him on 1st March.

"Where was she when she rang? She calls herself Jo now, Mutti, Jo Mihaly. Her professional name as a dancer."

"In Berlin somewhere, she didn't leave an address or telephone number. She said she might ring again. But wait! She did say she was appearing at the People's Theatre."

Wolfgang toyed with the idea of going to see her there. How would she react? Why had she tried to make contact? He could not sort out his own feelings about another possible meeting with this fiercely independent, unpredictable person. He allowed other matters to overlay the enigma.

Partly as a result of his Munich talk and its favourable reception in the musical press, there were renewed representations in Berlin for him to be awarded a research stipend, in the absence of one from his home country of Switzerland. Thanks to Minister Schmidt-Ott, the current president of the German Science Association, they succeeded. In the light of the Graesers' reduced circumstances this was welcome news. The monthly 150 marks felt like affluence to the 20-year-old scholar. An immediate consequence was his purchase of one of the new wirelesses, a handsome radiogram in a veneered walnut cabinet, with two little doors that opened to reveal the loudspeaker and amplify its sound. In the last few months of his life Dr Carl Graeser could often be found with headphones on, listening to broadcasts from Radio Berlin, but when Wolfgang and Lily moved after his father's death there was not room for the unwieldy wireless set with its accumulator and aerial. Now, besides the broadcast programmes and music, there was the excitement of buying the new shiny black gramophone records. An early purchase was a fine recording of Beethoven's Op.130 string quartet and Grosse Fuge made by the young Budapest Quartet for the English company His Master's Voice, with its touching picture on the black label of a little dog listening at a phonograph trumpet.

2

The cavernous Mietskaserne that had so shaken Wolfgang with its noise, smells and airlessness was just two blocks away from another in the same street where Jo Mihaly's dancing partner Lu Eggers had managed to rent a room. It was to this that Jo returned after her visit to Schneidemühl, the town she still thought of as home. She was strongly aware of the contrast between the quiet farmhouse with its country scents and sounds and this cramped, noisy, stinking environment; but at least it was a shelter and friendly, with the solidarity of the poor. Lisa Ney's father had procured the engagement at the Volksbühne for the dance trio. One advantage of moving back to Berlin for Jo was the opportunities it gave her to develop her solo work, performing dance sequences of her own devising in cabarets and clubs, often coloured by her anti-militarist convictions or her experiences as a vagabond. She even tried out the dance that had originated all those years ago when Uncle Bruno gave her the bloodstained helmet and army boots.

The telephone call to Wolfgang had been a sudden impulse as she caught sight of the poem he had introduced her to - she always kept it pinned up by her bed alongside one or two other precious mementos: one of Gil's songs, a shrivelled flower, Mutti's delicate lace handkerchief, its perfume long since dispersed. She was disappointed that Wolfgang was away, but her life was so full that the impulse was soon swallowed up.

"Miss Mihaly! A package for you!" The cheeky back-stage page-boy at the People's Theatre met her as she ran in - always at the last minute after her long walk to avoid the street-car fare - to dress for the performance. She took the parcel hastily and threw it on the dressing-table amongst the grease-paint and bits of soiled cloth. Probably another fan. Jo was accustomed to these offerings, flowers, cards, boxes of chocolate, always from male admirers. Jo was the most striking of the dance trio and was nearly always the first to get such attention.

"Aren't you going to see what it is? I just fancy a bon-bon." Lu spoke with a touch of envy. By now they were back in the tiny apartment after the show, the block mercifully quiet at this late hour.

"Oh!" As she unwrapped the present she sat down suddenly on the edge of the bed. "It is a book." Wolfgang had written inside the cover of Körpersinn:

'For my friend the dancer Jo Mihaly from the author - remembering Mary Wigman (page 113)'

Lu Eggers looked at it curiously: a substantial little 150-page book neatly bound in brown cloth, with a plain printed dust-jacket like a school text-book. Jo had spoken once or twice about her clever friend.

"'Gymnastic, Dance, Sport'. He seems to have got everything here, Jo. Is he a dancer?" She saw the dedication 'to Oswald Spengler in veneration and thankfulness'. "Spengler! That horrible man!"

Jo was also taken aback by the dedication. They both knew of Spengler's inflammatory speeches and how they appealed to the chauvinist lunatic fringe of the youth movement. And hadn't Wolfgang said he might dedicate it to Mary Wigman? Lu went on,

"The Brownshirts have taken up Spengler now, all that talk of the need for a strong leader is just what they like to hear. That ranting Austrian demagogue with the small moustache, Hitler. That's their größe Führer."

"I don't think Wolfgang is that sort of a person, Lu, I really don't. He is a bit naive because he spends all his time with his head buried in books. His father is very conservative, ex-army. Wolfgang just follows on."

Lu still had the book in her hands. "It looks pretty heavy going, Jo. What about this: 'the metaphysics of body culture'; 'the hierarchy of the world of the senses'." She laughed as she showed Jo the table of contents. Jo did not share the joke. She felt protective towards Wolfgang; the book made him seem somehow vulnerable. She turned to the page he had indicated, in the chapter headed 'Dance and Music'. As she read she warmed to him again.

"This is good. Listen, Lu. He is comparing dance and music. 'The great moments in dance for a Mary Wigman are genuinely abstract. Higher dance forms, like music, belong in the realm of religion and worship.' That's great! That is what I think too." She told her friend about the evening with Wolfgang at the Theatre in Nollendorf Square.

"But you don't want to be abstract, Jo. Your dancing is very down-to-earth."

Their talk went on far into the night. The next morning Jo scribbled a note of thanks, saying she hoped to see Wolfgang soon and talk about the book. The following evening there was a letter for her at the theatre. Wolfgang asked if she would like to come with him to a concert of Beethoven string quartets: ' . . . The famous Havemann Quartet are doing a series, playing all Beethoven's quartets this month. I should be glad of your company. Please come if you can.'

Jo telephoned to make the arrangement. His voice sounded strangely remote over the phone, but he seemed pleased that she could join him for one of the concerts, which were being held in the concert hall of the

Hochschule für Musik. They met on the steps, at the very place where they had parted four years before. Both were shy and embarrassed at first, taking in the changes those years had wrought in each. Jo, animated as ever, but slimmer, more wiry, her hair now short like a man's, the bones of her face more strongly marked. She noticed the dark shadows under Wolfgang's eyes, which in an odd way emphasised the youthfulness of his face with its smooth cheeks, now with a soft down blurring the lines, and still the unruly lock of hair on his forehead. His first words had been to ask after Jo's mother. He was shocked and saddened to hear she had died.

"Cancer again! So we have both lost a parent." Jo was also genuinely sad to hear of Carl Graeser's death. The news seemed to her a fitting prelude to the sombre, tranquil cavatina of Beethoven's B flat quartet Op. 130, which moved her to tears.

"I have a proposal for you, Wolfi." They were sitting over a coffee after the concert. Conversation was now easier, as each had brought the other up-to-date with their lives. Jo had expressed a wish to see his mother again and offer condolences. She asked,

"Do you have a wireless?"

He told her about the new acquisition with some of his former boyish enthusiasm. "Why do you ask?"

"I've been told there is going to be a broadcast next week of one of Bert Brecht's plays. Have you heard of him?"

"I know the name. Some sort of Marxist, isn't he, from Bavaria?"

"Lots of my friends think he is one of the best German playwrights since the war. Yes, he is a socialist, but so are the Bauhaus artists. So am I, for that matter."

"What is the proposal, then?"

"Can I combine a visit to your mother with listening to the play on your wireless?"

Lily Graeser was pleased to hear that Jo Mihaly was coming. She worried about her son's increasingly withdrawn, self-obsessed life, with its strict routine of exercise and study and its lack of personal contacts apart from public engagements. He even saw Hans Zurlinden only rarely these days, and all the Music School acquaintances had dropped off. (It was she who had arranged for him to be asked to play quartets.) 'So like his father!' she thought with a sigh, recalling the strenuous war-time days in Naples, with their unremitting work burden for poor Carl at the hospital, which had possibly nourished the seeds of his final illness. More and more she traced Carl's features under the youthful lines of Wolfgang's face and in his gestures and mannerisms. Her mind would go back, in spite of herself, to the grey face, shallow breathing and empty syringe of that frightful moment.

The evening before *Man equals Man* was broadcast, Brecht himself gave an introductory talk on Radio Berlin. Up to then the playwright had been no more than a name to Wolfgang, so he made himself listen to the talk. Bertold Brecht was introduced in very fulsome terms as 'the most significant original talent on the German stage.' Wolfgang thought how his father would have disliked such extravagant claims for a 'red'. The dramatist's dictatorial manner did nothing to change Wolfgang's antagonism and he began to regret having agreed to listen to the play. Once the talk got under way, however, he found it both arresting and disturbing. Brecht's analysis of 'the decline of a broad stratum of humanity' was uncomfortably similar to Spengler's, but his 'new human type' was very different from Wolfgang's patron's ideas about leaders and followers. This new human type, Brecht claimed, became strong by losing his individuality, by identifying himself with the mass. Wolfgang found himself saying "no, no!" as he listened. Had not J S Bach defied 'the mass' when he wrote his masterpiece Die Kunst der Fuge? Even his sons thought he was wrong, but compare his work with the fashionable music of his brother Hans's chosen composer Telemann! Nevertheless, when Brecht pronounced, in his harsh voice with its Bavarian vowel sounds, that 'any work that has nothing to do with [the new human type] is not alive and has nothing to do with anything', Wolfgang had a sense of collapsing walls, of disintegration.

The group round the elegant polished walnut cabinet of the new radiogram listening to *Man equals Man* the next evening made an unusual trio: Lily, quiet and grey-haired in her upright armchair, her hands busy with darning, her eyes downcast but glancing ever and again to her son; Wolfgang sprawled on the rug, his chin cupped in his hands, a sulky expression on his face, looking younger than his twenty years; Jo sitting next to him, her mobile features alive to the changing moods, laughing from time to time, her hands unconsciously gripping the sides of the chair. The frank sensuality of Widow Begbick in the play made her feel embarrassed for Wolfgang's mother, whose colour rose in her cheeks at the most outspoken parts, but Wolfgang was silent and almost motionless throughout. At the horrifying close, with the transformed Galy Gay storming the Tibetan fortress and the cries of '7,000 refugees, peasants, artisans, shopkeepers, friendly hard-working people', Wolfgang jumped up and switched off the set almost violently.

"I need some fresh air," and to Jo, "Coming for a walk?" Jo looked to his mother. She nodded.

"The night air is lovely here in Nikolassee, with all the trees and water we have nearby. I shall brew some chinese tea ready for your return. You like that, Wullie." She had been aware of his growing hostility to the play.

Once out of doors Wolfgang almost ran towards the open common land beyond the cemetery, the scene of that first walk with Piete such an age ago. Jo kept pace, but did not speak, waiting for him to break the silence.

"It is not a play at all. How can you believe in those four men and their ridiculous antics?" The forcefulness of his accusation provoked Jo into a heated defence of the play.

"The actual events may be far-fetched, but that is how people behave. I saw lots of soldiers in the war. Those four were typical soldiers - fighting, beer and women! But that's not the point."

"What is the point then?"

"Identity. Galy Gay lost his identity and found his strength."

"That doesn't make sense to me. How can you call anyone strong if they let themselves be manipulated like that? Who was he at the end of the play?"

Wolfgang was so intense that Jo couldn't help smiling. "I . . I don't know who he was. But it doesn't matter. What mattered was that he could lead the attack. He found his strength. When the play began he was a nonentity, just a porter, running errands for his wife."

Wolfgang looked at her, then turned and set off again. Jo put an arm over his shoulders.

"Come, Wolfi, let's not quarrel. You must agree there were some funny bits." She was surprised to find that he seemed to have memorised the whole play. They were still discussing it when they returned to the apartment. The evening ended abruptly when they realised that Jo needed to catch the last train back into town. She scribbled her address before leaving the flat, with a warm invitation from Lily Graeser for her to come again.

Once more Wolfgang found himself watching the lights of a departing train. As he walked slowly back from the station he compared his feelings now about Jo with that first visit of hers to the big house when his father was alive. To think he had fancied himself in love with her! Yet she was beautiful in her special way. He would like to see her dance, even the dead soldier dance she had described to him. The Brecht play, that was her world, not his. He had been aware as they were listening of her total absorption. Yet the play was deliberately, aggressively non-illusionist. Brecht seemed to demand that his audience stayed detached, observers not participants. Why then had he found it so disturbing? Dr Spengler said in that pamphlet of his father's that power belongs to the whole, that individuals must serve the whole. But how different that was from Brecht's talk of 'the mass'! Brecht meant the Marxist proletarian masses, dictatorship of the proletariat, that 'English socialism' exposed so mercilessly by Spengler. As Wolfgang pondered this he recalled his Mietskaserne experience, the stinking, crowded, noise-filled, filthy courtyard. That was 'the mass'. Hand over power to that? He recoiled from the very idea. In one of their many arguments when he first got to know Piete Kuhr she had called him élitist. Very well, he accepted the soubriquet. So was J S Bach, so was Nietzsche, so was Spengler. He mentally squared his shoulders as he dismissed the argument and returned to his studies.

3

The Spring of 1927 was mild and balmy. One of Wolfgang's chief relaxations from work pressures and his increasingly voluminous correspondence was cycling in the gentle, watery Brandenburg countryside, with its lush meadows, streams and lakes. He often thought of Brigitte when on these excursions, their carefree times together, pretending they were really twins, laughing at nothing, holding hands like children. He still wrote to her regularly. The marriage had been postponed as her father said she was too young; they must wait until she was 21. Meanwhile Brigitte was living at home in Holland and helping in the local school. Wolfgang had still not been there, but Brigitte had sent him a sketch she had made of the house by the canal, tucked away below the water-line, a windmill in the distance. He always looked first when he emptied the mail-box for her big childish hand-writing, and felt a lifting of the heart when he saw it.

This was one such day. It lent wings to his feet as he set off. He had reached a natural pause in his studies, so had resolved on a day in the country. He kept to the small lanes, sometimes forced to dismount and push through brambles and undergrowth. Water, glimpsed through the saplings on his right! By now he was warm and sweating. Why not? He dropped the bike and tore off his clothes. He would swim out to that islet and claim it as his own. He stepped gingerly over the stones to the water's edge. The lake lay calm and shining, there was little sound - ripples at the water's edge, the bleat of a sheep. He hung his sweat-soaked undervest on the shrubs as a mark. The stones, the size of cricket-balls, fists, flat-irons, hurt his feet as he stumbled to the water and into its cool anonymity. A metre out and the stones gave way to soft sand. He gave himself to the dark lake, pushing through weeds to the deeps beyond. From this angle the island seemed further away. Nevertheless he would claim it, possess it. Seven minutes' strong swimming, to more harsh rocks, for 'his' island was little more than a heap of them with a few stunted trees clinging to it. An overhanging branch supported him as he clambered on to his kingdom. "I claim this land for . ." His voice sounded strange and thin in the great sleep of the lake, stretching away to the distant rugged shoreline. Breathing less heavily now, he picked his way across the islet to where a smooth boulder - 'my private jetty' - invited him back to the water. He would circumnavigate his new realm. But hidden rocks bruised his legs, forcing him further out into the lake. A blessed stretch of deeper water, black below his pale limbs. His mark on the shore? He could just make it out as he rounded the island. So far away! 'If you should get cramp . . .' Some words of Hans's came into his mind. He would sink without trace, the nearest help kilometres away, even his discarded clothes and cycle hidden. His breath came faster, his arms ached, the water neutral to taste, the cold embracing him. Was this how it could be, should be? Why go on striving? He turned on his back, blotting out the near shore, gazing across the great expanse of shining water, its calm penetrating his soul . . .

Teeth, what was it between his teeth? That tough woody sprig broken off from a shrub on the islet, tight mauve flowerets on a single stem - a souvenir for Brigitte, to put in his reply to today's letter. As her laughing face came into his mind he struck out strongly for the shore, his eyes fixed on the distant white navigation mark. It was a tough swim, even though Wolfgang was exceptionally fit. He had not realised how far out he was. The stones bruised his knees and feet as he scrambled out, panting heavily. ('An obstinate force drags me along over rocks and stones.') He dressed, wet as he was, then wrapped the sprig of blossom carefully in some leaves before setting off for home. Yin and yang, chaos and cosmos, life or death. Increasingly Wolfgang was aware of the see-saw in his consciousness. That sense of profound calm as he abandoned himself to the lake haunted him.

He enclosed the little sprig in his reply to Brigitte, saying where he had found it but not how it had changed him. A few days later, as he was in his room, wrestling with a particularly opaque Chinese philosophy text, came the familiar toot of a horn, followed by Hans Zurlinden's cheerful voice below. Wolfgang looked up from his book. Sun streamed through the small attic window, the dust-motes dancing in its beam. He threw down his pen and charged down the stairs.

"To horse, to horse! Just let me get my gear." Lily laughed at this burst of energy.

"Don't forget Dr Schweitzer's talk. You must be back for that, both of you."

Albert Schweitzer was on a rare visit to Berlin - his last as it turned out - in the course of a lecture tour to raise funds for the Lambaréné hospital in French Equatorial Africa. While working on Die Kunst der Fuge Wolfgang had exchanged letters with him, and looked forward to meeting the great man.

The motor-cycle ride was exhilarating, westwards into the sun to Werder, on the lakes. The cherry blossom was in full flower. They stopped to buy brötchen and cakes in Potsdam. Soon they were lounging by the water, munching and at ease. Hans filled his pipe, a treasured relic from student days with curved stem and ornate carved bowl, and leant against a tree trunk as he puffed away.

"So Körpersinn is out now. I hope you have kept a copy for me, I'm looking forward to reading it."

"You have read most of it already - but of course there's a copy for you if you want it. Anyhow, that book is history now. I'm embarrassed to read some of the things in it."

Hans looked at him curiously. His friend was so mercurial, so unpredictable. "What about Brigitte? Does she like it?" Wolfgang laughed.

"She can't make head or tale of most of it, she says. But she approved of the bit about Von Laban. That came out of the visits to the Palucca School." He went silent for a moment, then said suddenly, "She is getting married later this year, did I tell you? Another Wolfgang."

Hans was surprised. He knew of the continuing correspondence and had speculated on the possibility of something more to the friendship, had even mentioned it in talk with Wolfgang's mother. He studied his friend, but Wolfgang's tone and manner were neutral, detached, and he did not pursue the topic, asking instead about Hans' plans.

"You still aim at the diplomatic service? Not returning to God, in spite of Luther! Remember our trip to see the 95 theses?"

Hans chose not to respond to the hint of mockery. "One can serve God in many ways. Yes, thanks to Hermann - you remember Ambassador Rüfenacht? - the path is now fairly clear. It looks as if I may get a posting to Bucharest when I leave Berlin. I shall be 36 next month, you know, so it is time I was actually in service."

Wolfgang sat up. "36! What an age! You don't look it, Hans, I must say. What does it feel like to be so old?"

"You'll find out soon enough, young Graeser. What are you now, 20, 21?"

Wolfgang lay back in the grass, stretching his arms over his head. "I want to be always twenty. That is enough for me. Once you are 21 and over, all sorts of trouble. Brigitte's father told her she couldn't marry until she was 21." He jumped up, with one of his abrupt changes of mood. "Come on, let's go. I want to hear Schweitzer."

When they arrived for Dr Schweitzer's lecture the hall was already full, though there were many minutes still to go. Wolfgang was intrigued by the difference between this audience and his own in Munich earlier in the year. Admission was free. Schweitzer insisted that no-one should be prevented from hearing about his work in Africa. He always made his purpose clear: to raise funds in order to continue the work, his life's work. The collection bowls, hand-made wooden bowls which the doctor had brought back specially from Lambaréné, were always filled to overflowing at the end of his talk.

"Where else could one see such an audience?" Hans Zurlinden was also aware of the unusual mix in the hall: an age-range from small children with their parents to the very old - several in wheel-chairs - and from all social strata. Workmen and women in their working clothes, housewives, even street-walkers, rubbing shoulders with businessmen in dark suits, college professors, actors and musicians. As Wolfgang and Hans took their seats they spotted Jo Mihaly at the other side of the hall with a group of theatre people.

Schweitzer, a legend in his own lifetime, was impressive, with his tall now slightly bowed figure, leonine head, rugged workman's face and heavy moustache, his coarse hair brushed back from a high thinker's forehead. "Reverence for life!" Those were the opening words of his talk, spoken first quietly then in ringing tones. The achievements of this extraordinary man, wearing so lightly his four doctorates, of theology, philosophy, music and medicine, made Wolfgang, like many others in the hall, feel puny, insignificant. Starting with early childhood experiences in Günsbach in the Alsace, the doctor went on to describe the profound effect on him of Bartholdi's sensitive sculpture of an African native, one of four figures round the central statue in Colmar, near Schweitzer's grandparents' home. It was like a talisman for him, a sign on the road leading eventually to the Ogowe river mission field in the Gabon, where he built, sometimes literally with his own capable hands, his first hospital just before the war. As he held up his hands in illustration, Wolfgang's mind went back to the childhood obsession that had produced all those drawings, studies of his own and his father's hands. He looked with awe at these hands, reflecting on all they had achieved, both with a pen and with cruder tools, the organs they had played, built and repaired, the timbers shaped in Africa, the surgical operations done and medicines administered. Schweitzer brought the story right up-to-date with the triumphant completion of his new hospital only a few months earlier, at the beginning of the year. He ended by explaining his need for continued financial support. He sat down in a hushed, respectful silence, followed by prolonged applause, most of his audience standing, some cheering.

For Wolfgang, Schweitzer's account of his work seemed exotic, so far removed from his own esoteric preoccupations, yet compelling. He found himself stirred and disturbed in ways he could not define. Here was someone who, like himself, had achieved intellectual and artistic eminence in one field only to move on to something quite different. Like himself, Schweitzer was an internationalist, thinking, writing and speaking with equal fluency in French and German, having spent his childhood in the uneasy, beautiful Alsace, now French, now German. Like himself, this man seemed 'driven', but his dynamo was a faith in God and humanity that Wolfgang found incomprehensible, even repellant. Was not his philosophical manifesto The Decay and the Restoration of Civilisation a deliberate refutation of his sponsor Oswald Spengler's work? After the lecture was over Wolfgang waited for an opportunity to approach the famous man. Hans knew one of the organisers, who introduced them.

"Ah yes," Dr Schweitzer smiled as he shook hands with Wolfgang. "The discoverer of Die Kunst der Fuge. Thank you for your letters. They have given me much food for thought. I have seen your work in the Bach Gesellschaft Supplement - a remarkable piece of scholarship. It has made me think again about that extraordinary work."

Wolfgang flushed with pleasure at this, from so eminent a Bach scholar. The hall had now cleared and helpers were counting up the contributions. Dr Schweitzer suggested that the three of them adjourn to a café nearby on Potsdamer Platz.

"When they have counted up my African funds I have to be on my travels again, but we can talk over a coffee."

At first Wolfgang was silent, rather overawed by being in the presence of a person so often referred to as a living saint. Schweitzer was interested in Hans Zurlinden's decision to leave the church for the diplomatic service, questioning him about his motives.

"And this young man, your friend?" He turned to Wolfgang. "You are still at the threshold of your life. What will you make of it?"

Wolfgang was taken aback by the stark question. "I . . . I don't know how to answer that, sir. At present I am studying Eastern philosophy and culture. And mathematics, of course."

"Yes, yes, study is necessary. You are right to look to the East. I plan to write something on Chinese philosophy before I die. We in the West can learn much from them." He smiled. "But you have more time ahead of you than I. You are twenty-one?"

"I shall be later this year."

"That is a good moment to plan one's life. I made a simple vow on my twenty-first birthday. I would continue to follow the arts and the world of knowledge - science in the old Greek sense - until I was thirty. But afterwards I would spend the rest of my life giving rather than receiving. No, it was not benevolence, atonement rather, for all we 'civilised' people have done, especially to the coloured races in Africa. That is why I turned from theology, philosophy and music to medicine. Your father was a doctor, I think. You will know all about how a doctor can serve humanity."

Wolfgang made no direct response. He recognised that here was a kind of challenge, but it was one he felt unable to take up. He muttered something about his father's hard life as a doctor, before relapsing into silence again. The older man looked keenly at him, then, sensitive to his discomfiture, turned to Hans again, asking about his work with Swiss expatriates in Berlin. As Wolfgang listened he came to recognise the strength of Schweitzer's concern for humanity in the mass - he thought wryly 'this is Brecht's "mass"' - and his real humility. Yet this missionary doctor was also a great Bach scholar, a philosopher. Wolfgang felt the need not to let the opportunity slip. At a lull in the conversation he interposed, almost abruptly,

"Your words about Bach's subject in Die Kunst der Fuge are often in my mind, sir: 'a still and serious world'."

"Bach knew he was about to approach his Maker. He was a profoundly religious man." Schweitzer went on to talk of the St Matthew Passion and the central place of the chorale in all Bach's work. "I was glad you included in your edition that great chorale, dictated shortly before his death by the blind composer to his son-in-law Altnikol, Vor Deinen Thron tret' ich hiermit - a glimpse of heaven for us poor mortals!"

The conversation flowed more easily after this, Wolfgang encouraged by the great man to talk not only about Die Kunst der Fuge but his other studies, in particular his exploration of Chinese and other Eastern philosophy and culture. The discussion came to an end when Wolfgang referred to Schopenhauer. Dr Schweitzer dismissed him as "one of these latter-day pessimists, or nihilists, like your friend Spengler," and rose. "I must leave you, gentlemen. I have a busy schedule."

As they stood outside the café, he put both hands on Wolfgang's shoulders, looking him in the eyes.

"You have been given great gifts, young man. Don't waste them. They are for the world." He embraced him briefly, shook hands with Zurlinden, then turned and walked away, his upright figure noticeable as he made his way along the crowded pavement back to the hall.

4

Jo Mihaly had noticed Wolfgang in the hall. She tried but failed to attract his attention, then lost him in the press of people after the lecture. She too had been stirred by the great man's account of his work and the difficulties he had had to surmount to establish his hospital in Lambaréné, but in a very different way from Wolfgang. For Jo this was inspiring, strengthening her in her resolve to devote her life to combating war, violence and hatred.

"What a man! He could have done anything, been rich and famous. Instead he looks after lepers in Africa." Lisa Ney, her dancing companion, had been with Jo in the hall. She was impressed more by what Schweitzer had given up than by the work itself. Jo answered indignantly,

"He is famous, and saintly too, to my way of thinking. If there were more people like him the world would be a better place."

"I wonder what your friend made of the lecture, that intellectual young man."

"Wolfi? Wolfgang Graeser is his name. He is a Bach scholar too. That's probably why he came. But Schweitzer hardly mentioned music at all. I must telephone him and talk about it."

The call was not a success. Jo wanted to share her elation at the lecture, but Wolfgang was monosyllabic, almost, it seemed, resentful. He did reveal that he and Hans Zurlinden had met Schweitzer after the talk, but when Jo wanted to know more he brought the conversation to an abrupt end.

"Sorry, Jo, I can't talk just now. Let's meet somewhere when things are easier. Oh!" he paused, then, "My mother says she would like a word. I'll hand you over."

Jo was surprised to hear Lily's gentle voice. She invited Jo to visit them again soon, then, dropping her voice, said, "I am worried about Wullie - Wolfgang. There is something wrong. He hardly eats and I think does not sleep. Please come soon if you can. Tomorrow?" The anxiety in her voice was palpable. Once again Jo felt how vulnerable, how exposed Wolfgang was, in spite of his cleverness and fame. She arranged to visit the small Nikolassee flat the next day.

After Schweitzer left them Wolfgang and Zurlinden parted; Hans had to visit a Swiss family in Zehlendorf while Wolfgang made his way on foot to the State Library. In Mauerstraße he found himself surrounded by Brownshirts, mostly young men, coarse-voiced and bullying. They were gathering at the "Clou" variety hall, evidently for one of their inflammatory rallies. Out of curiosity Wolfgang let himself be drawn in with the crowd. As he entered there was a hush, then, as if at a signal, everyone stood up, right arms raised stiffly in salute, and "Heil Hitler!" shook the rafters as the platform party took their places. Next to the ample, be-medalled ex-Air Force Marshal Göring Hitler looked small with his slim build. Next to him the angular form and skull-like monkey face of the NSDAP press spokesman Dr Joseph Goebbels, and behind the trio a phalanx of brown uniforms. After some brief introductory remarks, Göring introduced the main speaker, "our present and future Führer, Adolf Hitler." Wolfgang felt intimidated by the almost animal roar that went up as the speaker rose. He turned to leave, but found himself pushed back into his seat. While shrinking from the human contact in the crowded, overheated hall, he was impressed in spite of himself by the speaker's fluency and power. So much of what Hitler said echoed uncomfortably what Wolfgang's father used to say: the betrayal of Germany by "the enemy within", the Jewish war profiteers, the need for resolute leadership "as defined by Nietzsche", the great Aryan traditions of "our Fatherland".

"Oswald Spengler has revealed the significance of this moment in the history of the West. We can seize and transform it. Germany will be mighty again!"

The speech went on and on, its hypnotic power evident from the rapt audience. At last Wolfgang was able to squeeze his way out, pleading sickness and the need for air. He felt drugged, battered by the torrent of words. As he walked up Glinkastraße towards the State Library his mind was in turmoil, trying to absorb and reconcile the two talks. No, they were irreconcileable: Hitler's vision of the greater Germany, 'Deutschland über Alles!', was at opposite poles from Schweitzer's 'reverence for life'. When Wolfgang reached his table in the hushed, echoing State Library he held his head in his hands, unable to turn his attention to his books. He could feel those other hands on his shoulders, strong, work-worn hands, and heard again the tones of the great man's voice: "You have been given great gifts." Given? By whom, or by what power? And for what? He remembered the words he had penned, involuntarily, in the letter to Uncle Ludwig: 'I am not under control. An obstinate force drags me along over rocks and stones, I do not know whither, but I must follow.' The spinning top coming to rest against his foot on that street corner. Miss Jones used to say "Look, it 'sleeps' now," when he had whipped his top into spinning equilibrium.

"That means it has found its centre from the centre of the earth." The centre of the earth! And the gaping mouth of Vesuvius was the doorway to it . . . The young man shook himself and looked around guiltily, as if caught unawares on some nefarious exploit. He pushed the books aside, shouldered his satchel and left the library.

For several days Wolfgang was unable to work. He spent hours in his bare attic room, picking up book after book only to abandon them after a page or two. Lily would bring up a glass of milk and his favourite semmeln, but he often left them untouched or only took a mouthful while she was there, forgetting it as soon as she had gone. At night he threw himself onto the bed but came to dread letting go of consciousness, for the shapes and visions that crowded in, a tortuous mixture of images, the lava-filled crater of Vesuv an ominous leitmotif. That ranting, compelling voice with its "Deutschland! Vaterland!", the open mouth like a tunnel into which he was drawn, as in a vortex, spinning to the earth's centre . . . He would wake cold and sweating, staring at the square of sky framed by his small window.

"Wullie, I asked your friend Piete round this-evening. Can you be sure to be back in time?"

"Jo, Mutti, not Piete." They had come out into the yard from their apartment. After a perfunctory breakfast Wolfgang was fetching out his bicycle from the basement. "Yes, I'll try to get back. She wanted to talk about Schweitzer. But isn't Uncle Johann coming this-evening?"

"I'm sure he won't mind if your friend is here."

Wolfgang leant on the machine, half muttering, "I must get away, right away from here." He nodded to Lily, jumped on the saddle and pedalled furiously round the house into the street.

Lily asked Johannes Wolf to come sooner. She needed to share her anxiety over her son.

"His instinct is right, Lily. We must get him right away for a spell, before he has to go to Leipzig for the first performance; he has to be fit for that." Karl Straube, Thomaskantor in Leipzig, had at last finalised the performance of Die Kunst der Fuge. It would take place in Bach's own church on 26th June. "He overtaxes his brain and takes on too much - Chinese philosophy, higher mathematics, the new book on Bach's later work, and now that other idea for a sequel to Körpersinn called Hörsinn. Then there are the speaking engagements and all that correspondence." He pointed to a heap of unopened letters. "Too much for anyone. Could he not stay with those old friends of yours in Capri?"

Jo Mihaly failed to turn up, rather to Wolfgang's relief. What could he possibly say to someone like her about Dr Schweitzer? He still felt the pressure of those hands. When he heard of Dr Wolf's idea he agreed at once. "I have some money from Breitkopf - a good use for it. Napoli again, how I long to be there!" The following day, in the great vault of the Anhalter railway station he boarded the dark-blue Nord-Express to Munich, en route to Naples.

When Jo telephoned Lily to apologise for not coming she was distressed to discover that she had missed the chance of seeing Wolfgang. Her absence had been unavoidable. On the day of the visit she herself had an unexpected visitor. She was in the cramped two-roomed apartment when she heard a gabble of children's voices outside. She opened the door to see a darkly handsome man with deep-set, penetrating eyes, a strong Jewish nose and a fuzz of curly hair. He had obviously attracted a crowd of children playing in the courtyard below. They had followed him up and were round him like seagulls at a ship's wake. He was laughing, swinging one of the small ones, an urchin with a very dirty face and bare feet, up in the air, to his screams of delight. When the door opened he set the child gently down and took out a handful of small coins from his pocket.

"Share these out and be off with you!" He beckoned the biggest child and poured the coins into her cupped hands. As she watched with a smile, Jo realised that she knew this man. The features were unmistakeable, even in the absence of greasepaint.

"Corbaccio, the profiteer! I saw you in Stefan Zweig's play at the Volksbühne. Come in, please!"

"Steckel, madame, Leo Steckel at your service. And you are Jo Mihaly the dancer. You see, I know you too." He had come with an unexpected offer of new work. He had seen one of her dances at a cabaret and his enthusiasm had succeeded in persuading his director Viktor Schwanneke to audition her for a part in A Midsummer Night's Dream. The audition was to be that same evening, with the run starting the following week.

"Shakespeare! How can I possibly learn a new part in that time?"

"Don't worry, my dear." Steckel put an arm on her shoulders. "It is a non-speaking part, perhaps three words, no more. It is your miming skill and stage presence we need. Your task as one of Titania's fairies will be to light all the lamps."

"And you, Leo? May I call you that? What part do you play?" Jo was heating some coffee in a pan on the stove. She brought two cups to the scrubbed wooden table. He laughed, lounging back on the little chair so that its joints creaked.

"A good rest for me after Ben Jonson's Corbaccio. It was an English play before Zweig took it over, you know, a contemporary of Shakespeare's. This time I am Francis Flute the bellows-mender, who takes the part of Thisbe. Can you see me in a dress!" He sprang up, crouched behind the chair and adopted a cracked falsetto voice:

"'O wall, full often hast thou heard my moans,
For parting my fair Pyramus and me!
My cherry lips have often kiss'd thy stones,
Thy stones with lime and hair knit up in thee.'"

The transition was so sudden, so complete, that Jo was convulsed with giggles. Steckel broke from the part, straightened up and smoothed back his hair. "Laugh now, but not when we're on stage. So you'll take it, Jo?"

"Of course I will. What a chance! I'll be there at seven."

The production was successful, in spite or because of its modernity. Since Leopold Jessner had shattered the illusionist, comfortable theatre with his scandalous production of William Tell just after the war, the serious Berlin stage had become increasingly stark and uncompromising. In this very year of 1927 Jessner wrote: 'Since war and revolution set their seal on the times, appearance has been annihilated by reality. Spilt blood, the cry from the streets, these replace the glittering colours and tuneful melodies of the past.' Shakespeare remained perennially popular, but even his plays were made to reflect the times. Two years before Der Sommernachtstraum Erich Engel had called on the radical Bert Brecht to join him in directing Coriolanus at the Lessingtheater, complete with 'Jessnertreppe' and overt political resonances. In Der Sommernachtstraum the deluded lovers might have been seen at any time in the Tiergarten, Puck was a muscular, wicked negro boy, the 'rude mechanicals' were uncomfortably reminiscent of the transvestites who minced along the Kurfürstendamm and the fairies were gymnastic, other-worldly, rather than the prettified creations of former times. Jo, with her strong athlete's body and unfettered freedom of movement, fitted in well. She loved the symbolism of lighting the lamps for the fairy scene and, as with her dance trio, was soon picked out for her virtuosity.

At the dress rehearsal, as she crouched still and silent at the side of the stage, she was aware of a whispered voice behind her:

"Jo, I'm after you!" followed by two hands clasping her round the waist. Had she not trained herself she might have screamed involuntarily, it was so unexpected. She turned and looked straight into the dark eyes of Steckel.

"Leo! You startled me, creeping up like that."

"I'm after you, Jo. You know that, don't you."

She had been aware, ever since his visit to her flat, that Steckel liked her, and she found it exciting to have so well-known and handsome an actor taking such an interest in her. She had lived amongst show people long enough to know that this was more than a casual attraction. Soon after this declaration they were engaged. The marriage took place towards the end of May, an informal affair, the brief civil ceremony followed by a lively backstage party. As Steckel already had an apartment in the artists' quarter near Breitenbach Square it was logical for Jo to join him there. It pleased her to be moving so much closer to the old Steglitz home she had shared with her mother.

As soon as she knew the date of the wedding she phoned the Graesers. It was a disappointment that once more she had missed Wolfgang. The day after she rang, a card came for her from Capri. She studied the picture - 'Isola di Capri. Panorama della Via Circumtelegrafo' - with its rocky coastline and lovely blue seascape, the gentle slope of the headland west of Naples in the misty distance. Jo felt a sudden pang of longing to be there with Wolfi, not in this crowded city with its stale air and constant noise. She turned the card over. Wolfgang's rapid fluent hand-writing - 'Capri Villa Emilia Augusto'. She imagined him on the terrace, looking over that view, thinking of her. How would he respond to the news of her marriage? She thought, 'How different these two men of mine, Wolfi and Leo!' then reprimanded herself for the thought. Wolfgang had no claims on her, nor she on him. Reading the card, she discovered that he was planning to return for the Die Kunst der Fuge performance in Leipzig at the end of June, after which he hoped to see her again in Berlin.

5

The weeks spent with Violetta, once his and Hans' Italian nanny, and her family at Villa Emilia Augusto in Capri gave Wolfgang time and space to calm his spinning mind and face the world again. The familiar sights and smells, the soothing rumble of the surge at the foot of the rocks mingling with his dreams, even smoking Vesuv over there to the north-east, all revived childhood memories. By screwing up his eyes against the glare he could just make out, across the bay, the white walls of Papa's hospital up above the "Villa", as they called the great park where he used to play and ride his bike, or cross on the way to the beach at Posilipo. Violetta, now ample in girth, her quiet husband and four dark-eyed smiling children, were a rest-cure in themselves, she with her 'Signor Wolfi' and comfortable ways. He would stay as long as he could before the big day, the long-awaited first performance of Die Kunst der Fuge. Capri also revived memories of his godfather Uncle Ludwig, whose rare visits to Naples were such joyous times. He remembered how he used to write out for his uncle the programmes of their home concerts at Christmastime. 'I wonder if he kept any of them. Aunt Elli is a great hoarder.' He could see himself sitting there, one elbow on the table, shaping his letters in the newly learned 'joined up writing', then looking up to see Hansi fixing candles on the Christmas tree. After Hans went away to school Uncle Ludwig, Wolfgang and his father used to have their 'three man expeditions', one of them that fateful day here in Capri when Papa was crushed against the wall by the carriage. Wolfgang shook himself to expunge that memory with its fateful consequences. He sent off cards to Hans Zurlinden and Jo Mihaly in Berlin and Brigitte in Holland, then to Uncle Ludwig von Hofmann in Dresden.

On his return he took in Dresden on his way to Leipzig. He wanted to be sure that his uncle and Aunt Elli could come to the performance. They greeted him warmly, though Aunt Elli, plump as ever, shook her head as she looked at him.

"You have been starving yourself in Italy, Wolfi dear. Look at you! So thin!"

"I am very well, Aunt Elli, never fear. 'Letta fed me like a pig in Capri, olive oil with every meal. I take lots of exercise, you know." At this she looked down at her own ample figure and was silent. "I have a question to ask, Auntie. Do you remember when I used to send you programmes of our Christmas concerts in Neapel? I was thinking about them when I was there."

"Such sweet letters you wrote to Ludwig! Of course I remember. I can even show you one, I was looking at them the other day." She rummaged in her little ecritoire and brought out the letter. They studied it curiously:

'. . . Heute Abend kämt ein Gast und wir machen ein Konzert und spielen
1. Napolitanisches Lied
2. Schlaf herzens Sönchen, mein libling bist du
3. Sah ein Knab ein Röslein stehn lif er schnelles nah zu sehn
4. Guten Abend gute Nacht von Rosen bedacht
5. 1 Largo von Händel

6. 1 Andante von Gluck

7. 1 Rondo von Beethoven

Mama dekt schon den Tisch.

Also viele Grüsse von erem lieben   Wolfi '

"Such beautiful handwriting, Wolfi, for a five-year-old!"

Wolfgang laughed. "Miss Jones made me write like that. She had copy-books, a space under each line. I remember how I hated them. I can still sing you that Neapolitan song, though!" He did so, to his aunt's delight. His uncle, a keen and accomplished amateur cellist, wanted to know all about the coming performance.

"It will be an unique occasion: the first performance of a major work by J S Bach more than 175 years after his death. You will be famous, Wolfgang, and not just in Germany."

In Leipzig he collected mail left at the offices of Breitkopf. Amongst it was a letter from Jo Mihaly with an invitation - now out-of-date - to her wedding. And later this year, after their linked 21st birthdays, Brigitte as well! Wolfgang held the letter in his hand. Could he face Jo now, married to a Jewish actor? He thought of their argument over the Brecht play, of the Schweitzer talk. Their worlds had drifted far apart since that first visit to Nikolassee. She saw her path ahead clearly - acting, dancing, perhaps children. That was her 'obstinate force'. And his . . ? 'I want to be always twenty!' He heard himself saying it to Hans Zurlinden, as he stood with Jo's letter in his hand. He shook himself, as if waking from a dream, crumpled up the letter and left the office. Tomorrow was to be Bach's day. Let him think solely of that.

Dr Straube had asked that he should come to the final rehearsal. As he entered the cathedral-like Thomaskirke, so hallowed by association with the great master, Wolfgang felt churned up inside. He wanted to walk on tiptoe, to pray. How did one pray? The idea had never entered his mind before. Knowing little about the practicalities of orchestration, he had prepared the Breitkopf edition simply in open score, with no indication of appropriate instrumentation. This had been one of the handicaps when it came to discussing a performance. Two musicians, Karl Straube and Generalmusikdirektor Weisbach in Düsseldorf, had backed Wolfgang in his insistence that, as it was a work on the scale of the B Minor Mass or the St Matthew Passion it was probable that Bach had contemplated similar orchestration to one of these, probably the latter. Both were respected Bach scholars, and Wolfgang was happy to leave this technical side of the performance in their hands.

"Ah, Wolfgang! Good, good! We were just about to begin." Karl Straube's voice sounded loud and secular as he shook Wolfgang's hand. "Gentlemen! This is our reason for being here today and tomorrow. Allow me to introduce Herr Graeser." The players smiled their greeting, slapping their instruments in appreciation. Wolfgang blushed and nodded, before retiring to the front of the congregational seats.

"Not there, sir, if you please!" Straube explained that they were principally there to finalise the positioning of the players and check the balance. "If you could sit near the centre or towards the rear, your help would be valuable. We are not playing the whole work today, mostly just beginnings and endings."

Although he knew, thanks to letters and telephone conversations exchanged with Straube, what instrumentation had been employed, to actually hear the Gewandhaus players bringing his work to life was a shock. Wolfgang was glad to have this foretaste; he was nervous of the performance itself, the culmination of those long solitary hours, days, weeks, poring over the Berliner Autograph, checking and re-checking the complex fugal patterns, hearing in his mind the colossal structure by the dying master, its longest span, the unfinished 19th fugue, autographed in music with the notes B A C H before expiring like its creator, its work unfinished. His own closing words of introduction to the new edition came to mind. Was not that a kind of prayer? 'May this publication be an effective means of deeper penetration into this wondrous great imaginative work of the German nation, the like of which cannot be found in the whole history of art of all times and peoples.'

The great day had arrived at last, a bright sunny June day. Wolfgang's friends and family foregathered for Mittagessen in "Auerbach's Keller", scene of the famous comic episode in Goethe's Faust. His brother Hans had arranged his leave from the bank in Rome in order to be there. Hans Zurlinden had come by road, Johannes Wolf and his mother by train from Berlin. Wolfgang was surprised and delighted that Paul Müller his old tutor, now bent with rheumatism and walking with a stick , had made the effort to join them. "Couldn't miss an occasion like this, my boy, even if I do have cloth ears." Wolfgang had invited Dr Straube to join them for the meal, but he had declined.

"We must expect a full church and I have much to do before 3 o'clock. I shall try to call in briefly to greet your mother and Dr Wolf."

The Thomaskantor, with the help of Breitkopf and Härtel, had publicised the occasion well. As the family party made their way on foot along Grimmaischestraße to the cathedral they found themselves part of a great throng all heading the same way. When they emerged into the open space outside the Thomaskirche, with its statue of the great former Kantor, Mendelssohn's tribute to the master he too, in his way, had re-discovered, people were converging from all directions. It was fortunate that space had been reserved for the family as the church was already almost full and people were streaming up into the galleries.

Promptly at 3 o'clock, as the hours sounded from the clock tower on the Alte Rathaus, the church doors were closed and the great crowd was hushed. The Director of the Music Conservatory spoke briefly about the significance of the occasion:

"Ever since Johann Sebastian Bach died in 1750 this church has maintained continuity with his music. Scarcely a week has gone by without Bach's creative genius living again here and rejoicing our hearts. Today, however, thanks to the vision and the genius of one person, we shall be listening for the first time to a major work which even the master himself was never able to hear. This is a solemn, an historic day in the musical life of our church, our city, our nation."

He resumed his seat, his steps echoing in the hushed building. The orchestra tuned briefly then the Thomaskantor strode to his rostrum. He stood until the silence was complete, profound. The first eight notes of the theme, played on a solo violin, floated out pure and still, to be followed, like the awakening of a sleeping giant, by the solemn opening fugue. This first performance was planned in two parts, as Dr Straube judged that the complexity of the work made exceptional demands on an audience. The chromatic eleventh Contrapunctus, one of the longest and most intricate, announced its variant of the theme in four three-note sections, each separated by a crotchet rest. After the triumphant alto F sharp resolution of the cadential chord into D major the musicians fell silent. Straube stood for a few moments before leaving his place, then the great church gradually emptied, the vast crowd blinking as they came out into the bright sunlight, like a visual echo of that final chord.

During the break Herr von Hofmann, Wolfgang's Uncle Ludwig, had arranged for the Graesers' party to join them at the house of a friend, one of the orchestral players. Everybody wanted to congratulate the young genius and to talk about the music, but he discouraged all approaches and Lily, sensitive as always to his feelings, deflected them. Wolfgang felt suspended between the two parts of Bach's mighty structure. He had lived with it and in it so intensively that this enforced hiatus was almost painful. His mind went back to his two exercise ropes in the attic room in

Nikolassee. It was as if his soul was swinging on two ropes of sound. As soon as he could, he took Hans Zurlinden aside.

"You have your motor-cycle here? Good! Can we get away for an hour or so? Make our apologies, I can't face company just now."

Hans nodded and explained to their host. Soon they were speeding out of town towards Torgau, into the flat Saxon countryside. As they crossed the bridge over the Mulde in Eilenburg Wolfgang shouted,

"Let's turn off here and find somewhere quiet."

Hans swerved right, down a narrow lane signed to Kollau, and after a bumpy ten minutes they found themselves at the little settlement, no more than sprawling farm buildings and a few cottages. They propped the machine against a fence and sought refreshment from the farmer's wife: two steaming beakers of milk warm from the evening's milking and thick slices of coarse home-baked bread smeared with butter from the dairy. Leaving the farm, they scrambled over fields to the river, reedy and slow-moving here. Hans respected the other's silence as they threw themselves down in the lush grass. The calm deepened around them. Watery whispers from the river, a bubbling curlew swooping across the meadow, a light breeze stirring the tops of the rushes.

"What to do about the nineteenth contrapunctus?" Wolfgang muttered, almost to himself. Hans looked questioningly, "The unfinished fugue?"

"Mm. I tried to continue it - impossible! I soon knew how futile. But in spite of its length - you know it is the longest fugue he wrote - it's only a torso, like one of those Greek fragments of sculpture, head and limbs missing, but still shapely, perfect in its way. So it dies with its creator." He sighed. His fingers closed on a pebble, so he lobbed it idly into the sluggish stream, watching the widening ripples until they touched the bank. Then, with one of his sudden changes, he laughed.

"The old wizard signed it anyway, before he left us. Remember that tenor entry five bars before the end?" He sang the four notes B A C H as he scrambled up. "Come on, let's face the rest of it now."

It was almost eight o'clock by the time they had washed and changed. The sonorous clock tower began its strokes as they slipped into the great church and took their places. Once more Karl Straube waited until the last noises died away and the cathedral, gloomy with the gathering dusk, enclosed silence. First came the four two-part canons, each with a different pair of instruments, chosen to emphasise its individual character. Then the three pairs of 'mirror' fugues, the first pair three-part, the others four-part. Before beginning the final nineteenth 'torso' a solo cello played the musical autograph B A C H , the notes Wolfgang had sung as they left the water-meadow. The echoes died away, then came the sombre opening bars of the Fuga a 4 soggetti, played on cellos and basses. This colossal 'fragment' of a fugue was in three parts, like the movements of a symphony. As the busy second part closed with a cadence at bar 193 Wolfgang took a deep breath. It was as though he needed to hold it until the whole great structure collapsed after the author's name. He remembered those words in the Berliner Autograph, in the hand-writing of the composer's son Carl Philipp Emanuel: 'During this fugue, marked fittingly with the name BACH, the author died.'

After bar 239, ending in mid-phrase, the musicians laid down their instruments. Again the echoes died. Silence, like a dark flood, surged up and filled the great space of the Thomaskirche, a mighty tomb. The solemn notes of the chorale Vor deinen Thron tret' ich hiermit, played on the organ, set a seal on the evening. The audience left quietly, silent or talking in whispers. Many had handkerchiefs to their faces.

6

It was as if the Leipzig performance had at last opened the floodgates. Within days Wolfgang Graeser's name was known in musical circles throughout Germany, Austria, even Switzerland. There the influential Neue Zürcher Zeitung carried a favourable review, describing the work of 'the extraordinarily gifted 16-year-old Swiss Wolfgang Graeser'. Over the next few months performances of his new version of Die Kunst der Fuge took place or were planned in Hamburg, Flensburg, Breslau, Cologne and as far away as Oslo. Dr Weisbach ensured a fine performance in Düsseldorf, the first of several there, and Lily Graeser's family helped to set up another in Munich. Later on came performances under Hermann Scherchen in Graeser's home country, first in Winterthur then in the cupola of the Tonhalle in Zürich and in Geneva.

Wolfgang smiled his way through the inevitable congratulations and lionising after the Leipzig concert. He returned to Berlin to face a mountain of accumulated correspondence. As the pressures mounted he felt drawn back to the mountains of his childhood pictures and dreams. His nights were disturbed by dreams again, especially that one. He stirred uneasily under the thin coverings on his narrow bed. Bemused between dream and waking, its dimensions were still vivid - the smooth freshly laundered white linen sheet inexplicably crumpled and awry. More vivid was his feeling of numb despair at the spoliation, the meaningless, apparently wanton stupidity. As he woke the dream resonated in the familiar way, growing less sharp-edged but linking itself uncomfortably with the twelve-note subject and its disintegration, bringing down the whole airy structure of the great nineteenth fugue. The kind, stupid, wrinkled face of Hanno, their handyman in Naples, floated into his memory. How bewildered the old man had looked when little Wolfgang tried to explain his nightmare . . "Incubo! Incubo!" He sighed and leapt out of bed. That dream must be exorcised, the sheet must remain pristine, snowy. He must finally escape from the 'obstinate force' revealed in that unguarded moment in the letter to his uncle after his father's death. He had written 'I must follow', but now the question repeatedly in his mind was Why? Why should he continue the struggle? Why not just sign his name, like Bach, and let go? He had heard people talk of 'completing their life's work': what did it really mean? Was Bach's work incomplete? Of course not! Wolfgang had been accustomed to thinking of that unfinished nineteenth fugue, collapsing into silence in mid-phrase, as a tragic loss. Could it not also be seen as a triumphant gesture, a snapping of the fingers at fate? What was it Schopenhauer said: 'Death is the consequence, the summing up of life. It reveals in an instant what life teaches us in fragments . . .' That is how to complete one's life's work. He saw his own intellectual projects - the studies in Chinese philosophy, in psychology, mathematics, Greek and Egyptian culture, the major work on 'the later Bach', the follow-up to Körpersinn, tentatively titled Hörsinn in an article dashed off for the Beethoven Centenary publication - as another great unfinished fugue, as so many ice-covered peaks rearing up ahead of him, like those in his pastels for the Munich exhibition. Peaks! Yes, that was what he must do.

"I shall leave for Zürich, Mutti. I want to do some climbing."

"So soon! You have been here hardly a week, Wullie. And your friends, they all want to congratulate you. Jo Mihaly rang this-morning while you were in your room. I think she came to the Leipzig concert, but we didn't see her."

"I must go, Mutti. I need the air and the exercise." He smiled ('What a sad smile!' she thought, seeing the pain around his eyes). "Those Engadiner peaks are calling. Do you remember my pictures of them?" His face clouded. "I'll try to see Jo before I leave. You know she has married that Jewish actor? I suppose I'll have to see him as well."

After her marriage to Leo Steckel Jo was still with him in the Midsummer Night's Dream production. It was now in repertory at the Peoples' Theatre, which gave her time to continue and develop her solo dancing. She resolved to try and attend a big dance congress planned in Magdeburg during June as part of a major summer exhibition (May to September) devoted to the theatre. The dance congress was the brain-child of Rudolf von Laban, working with Oskar Schlemmer, the professor of theatre studies at the Bauhaus in Dessau, and was to include scenes from Laban's own group dance creations like "Titan" and the famous "Knight's Ballet", as well as Schlemmer's semi-abstract "Triadic Ballet". When she saw the programme Jo was disappointed to discover that, owing to some misunderstanding or disagreement, Mary Wigman would not be there, nor would any of her followers. It all looked rather intellectual, especially the first day, with its four high-powered speakers: Professor Oskar Bie on the history of group dance, Andrej Levinson on classical dance, Fritz Böhme on 'dance in our time' and Adolf Loos on the physiology of modern dance.

"Much more Wolfi's cup of tea."

"Who is Wolfi?" Leo and Jo were for once dawdling over breakfast of rolls and coffee by the window of their Breitenbach apartment, looking out at the June sunshine along Kreuznacherstraße.

"You know, Wolfgang Graeser, my friend from Nikolassee. Don't you remember that book he gave me, all about gymnastics and dance? I can just see him lapping up all that about the history and physiology of dance."

"Don't you want to attend the congress then? I thought you were . . ."

"Wolfi!" She interrupted him suddenly as a thought struck her. "It is his first performance on Sunday in Leipzig. I must try and go. Will you come, Leo?"

"What, to a gymnastic performance in Leipzig? Sounds odd."

Jo laughed. "Not gymnastics, Dummkopf, music. He re-discovered a great work by J S Bach called Die Kunst der Fuge."

"Bach!" Steckel sounded alarmed. "No, Schatz, not for me. You know I don't have your musical training."

Jo finally managed to attend part of the last day of the dance congress, when the speakers concentrated on the place of dance in theatre. She was pleased to have the chance of hearing Oskar Schlemmer talking about 'the abstract in dance and costume' and took notes so that she could discuss his ideas with Wolfgang. A dance drama on the floating stage, Schlemmer's "Nacht", made a memorable closing image, its lights reflected in the darkening waters of the Adolf-Mittag lake. There were many of Jo's friends and acquaintances in Magdeburg, dancers and theatre people. Amongst them she was delighted to come across Lu Eggers again, who was working in the theatre, and stayed with her before taking the train on Sunday for the two-hour journey to Leipzig.

Once there she was just in time to squeeze into one of the few empty gallery seats for the first part of the concert. She picked out Wolfgang from the mass of heads below her, but by the time she was able to leave the church he had vanished. After the emotional close of the work later in the evening Jo was too overcome even to look for him. She made her solitary way to the station for the night train to Berlin, her footsteps echoing in the empty streets, her head full of the magical theme, the pregnant silence after the last fugue had disintegrated and the solemn organ tones of the chorale.

"So you came to Leipzig. I should thank you for that." It sounded grudging. Wolfgang had overcome his reluctance and agreed to meet Jo Mihaly at a café near the theatre in Bülowplatz where she was working. Jo was aware of his unease. He looked so boyish, with his smooth cheeks, tousled hair and the familiar sulky expression. Jo was reminded again of the old days with her brother Gil, another uneasy soul. Today Wolfgang seemed on edge, unable to relax or be his usual open self.

"It was wonderful! You are the one to thank, Wolfi. I was overwhelmed." Her admiration was so genuine that it momentarily overcame his reserve. He smiled and blushed. She was bubbling over now. "Hearing it like that, in its entirety, made me realise how it all stems from that opening theme and how the theme gives the whole work unity. Was it your idea to have it played first on a solo violin?"

"Yes, I think it worked. The listener has to have the subject clear in his head at the beginning. Otherwise one can't appreciate all the variant forms."

"I don't know that I recognised them all. Sometimes it sounded as if it was upside-down!"

"It is equally effective either way up, that's the cunning of it. Sometimes at half the speed. Bach was a great mathematician."

"Mathematician?" Jo was taken aback. "Surely it is not just numbers, like a machine? You told me once that it is as great a work as the B minor Mass. Bach must have been inspired. This was for him another way of worshipping God." At this Wolfgang laughed, a short, bitter laugh.

"God! What does that mean? Die Kunst der Fuge is Bach's not God's. He spun it out of his own entrails like a spider." Jo wanted to challenge this, but Wolfgang was launched. "Whenever people are confronted by a work of genius they try to explain it away, because genius diminishes them, makes them feel small."

"What about Schweitzer, then? He said he is doing God's work in Africa."

Wolfgang paused. Then, speaking more calmly, he said,

"Albert Schweitzer is a great man, a great human being. If religion helps him to fulfil himself . . ." He shrugged. "But it is his own individual choice. He told us after the talk, Hans Zurlinden and me, that when he was 21 he made a deliberate decision to change his life when he was 30 and work for others. Even if one doesn't see things his way one can admire such single-mindedness and sense of purpose." Wolfgang sat back in his chair, looking across the table at Jo. "That gives the lie to your friend Brecht, with his idea that you need to lose your identity to find your strength. Communistic claptrap!"

Jo was roused by this. "Brecht is a man of vision. Leo - my husband - has worked with him. The communists have made mistakes, I know. And paid for them - remember Luxemburg and Liebknecht! But they hold out more hope for humanity than the nationalists, with their Brownshirt roughnecks roaming the streets terrorising people."

"Humanity! What is humanity? Do you mean the masses, the proletariat?"

"I mean people, you and me. I would trust myself more to Brecht, and Zuckmayer, Toller, people like that, than to Adolf Hitler."

Wolfgang fell silent at this, his mind returning to the hysterical atmosphere of the rally in the "Clou" variety hall. His face darkened. Sensing his discomfiture, Jo said,

"I haven't told you about Magdeburg, Wolfi. A professor from the Bauhaus in Dessau was talking about the abstract in dance and costume. It made me think of your book. I even made some notes, if you are interested."

"That book is history now."

"I don't understand. History?"

Wolfgang shrugged his shoulders. "I wrote it in a fit of enthusiasm after the Bach work. It's full of mistakes. I shall try to re-write it one day with a different title. Something like Vita Nova." He glanced at her and added uneasily, "Did you manage to read it right through? Another friend of mine - I think I told you about Brigitte - she said it was too abstract. I was trying to say too much in too short a space."

"I can see what she means, but that wasn't my problem with the book. I think you are trying to do the impossible."

Wolfgang said shortly, "You know what they say: difficult things I can do straight away, impossible ones take a little longer. What do you think was impossible?"

"You tried to approach emotional, physical matters intellectually, to intellectualise them. That bit about swimming and skiing, remember? I could see what you were getting at. I hate all this competitive, stop-watch sport too. I like to swim like a fish . ."

"All right, so we agree. What's your problem?" He sounded defensive, prickly, but this time Jo was intent on following up her train of thought.

" . . but you can't start analysing the feeling of swimming or skiing, that joy in freedom, sense of liberation, love of the open air. Poetry can sometimes call it up, Goethe's "Harzreise im Winter" for instance. I remember loving that as a child. It is not accessible simply through the intellect - even for someone as clever as you, Wolfi. Because, because . ." she paused, gazing into the air, "because one loses oneself in the movement, like in a dance. You become the dance."

As he saw her rapt expression Wolfgang was conscious once again of collapsing walls, disintegration. He tried to take refuge in irony.

"So I suppose you become a dead soldier in that dance of yours, like Brecht's Galy Gay."

"Exactly!" She was roused by his tone. "You are laughing at me, I know, but that's exactly right. I do become the dead soldier. That is why my dancing is effective. It changes the way people feel about war." She looked at him. For an instant he looked like a scared child, so she went on more quietly. "I did read the whole book, Wolfi, because it was by you. 'By Love's persuasion, Nature's mighty king' - you remember the poem?"

"Oh love, love! Why do people always try to bring love into it?" He spoke harshly. "Here we are, at the back end of a civilisation, and all they can talk about is love. What Germany needs is toughness, courage, the fighting spirit again like it had in 1870. Since the Versailles fiasco we have gone soft."

Jo was shocked by the violence of this response to her innocent remark, so out of proportion and, it seemed to her, out of character.

"Is that why you dedicated the book to Spengler? Those are his ideas, aren't they?"

He turned on her. "You call Brecht a man of vision. That is much more what Spengler is. He is the only thinker capable today of surveying the whole sweep of civilisation and defining our rôle in it. Our Western, Graeco-Roman culture is at the end of its cycle. We in Germany need to face up to it." His features had set in a scowl and his body was tense, rigid. Jo saw the two vertical lines in his forehead and quailed. He seemed like a stranger. She felt powerless, but filled with pity. At last she was able to respond. She did so as gently as she could.

"We didn't come here to talk politics, Wolfi. When do you leave for Switzerland? Will you do some climbing?"

She had chosen well. Wolfgang relaxed immediately, speaking of his early obsession with the mountains and of his paintings. Noticing her surprise - she knew nothing of his childhood artistic activities - he spread out a paper table-napkin with a resumption of boyishness, took out a pen and quickly sketched a mountainous skyline.

"Look, Jo. Here are the three Engadiner peaks called Piz Palü. They are a well-known test climb. I plan to take up the challenge and climb all three in a single day." He stared at the drawing then looked up, his eyes far away. "That is where one is free, on the mountains. Goethe was right about that."

Their shared enthusiasm for Harzreise im Winter brought the rendezvous to a more tranquil close, but they were both aware of a new coolness in the relationship. As they rose from the table Steckel appeared at the café entrance. He spotted them and strode over. Jo's happiness was evident. She put an arm round his waist.

"Wolfi, meet my husband Leo." She looked up at him affectionately. "This is the unlucky fellow who has undertaken to be my partner."

Seeing this swarthy Jewish-looking stranger and their mutual absorption, Wolfgang shrank back into his shell. They shook hands formally. Steckel broke the awkward silence.

"Jo has told me about your great Bach work. I offer you my congratulations."

"Thank you. I understand you were unable to come to Leipzig."

"Ah. Your classical music is above my head, Herr Graeser. I am just a poor man of the theatre."

"Shame on you, Leo!" Jo turned to Wolfgang. "He is a brilliant actor, Wolfi, and famous too." The conversation faltered in spite of her, so Steckel soon made a reason for leaving. They parted outside the café, Jo and her husband to the theatre, Wolfgang to the Staatsbibliothek on Unter den Linden.

VII   Wolfgang

1

AMONGST the accumulated mail when he returned from Leipzig was one in Brigitte's big rounded script. Wolfgang set it aside while he dealt with the rest of the correspondence. After the meeting with Jo and the encounter with her husband he felt the need to remind himself of this easier relationship in a more suitable setting. He stuffed the letter unopened into a pocket and set off to cycle along the familiar roads by the water to the Palucca Dance School in the Grunewald. As he leaned his bike against the wall he heard children's voices from the garden beyond. Instead of going in - what was there to go for? - he sat within hearing in Bismarck Square by the flower-beds to read his letter.

My dear Wolfi,

How are you? This is not just a form of words, I have had a feeling lately that you are not happy. I am sorry that we ('the other Wolfgang' as you call him and I) could not come to your first performance. We planned to meet in Leipzig for it, but he had an examination and my headmaster would not release me from work. It must have been a great occasion! There were even reviews in our Dutch papers!! So you must feel rewarded for all your hard work. You <u>should</u> feel happy! I really wanted to come, Wolfi, not only to hear the Bach but to see you again after all this time. I often think of our cycle rides and walks and what fun we had. Do you remember when you lost your boot in that bog and how cross you were when I couldn't stop laughing? It was comic, you with your arms and legs all covered with mud, scrabbling about trying to find your boot, and that great <u>SQUELCH</u> when you pulled it out and fell backwards!!! 'The other Wolfgang' and I plan to get married as soon as we can after <u>our</u> (yours and mine, Wolfi dear) birthday. You will get an invitation, of course. I should like you to meet W and he wants to meet you. He says he is nervous of meeting someone so famous! Please write and tell me how you are and what you are doing. Do you have any new writing projects? Do you still visit Steffi's school, or was that only for Körpersinn? I want to go there again, but . . . Well, I won't go on about changes - marriage and so on.

Lots of love - and a kiss!
Brigitte

Wolfgang sat for a long time with the letter in his lap, staring sightlessly at the trim municipal flower-beds of Bismarck Square. With a part of his consciousness he was aware of the children's voices, laughter and faint music from the dance school in amongst the trees behind the wall. The same wall where he and Brigitte exchanged that first kiss. "and a kiss!" - he saw the words at the end of the letter. In three months or less 'the other Wolfgang' would be the beneficiary. Wolfgang silently reproved himself for such sentimental reflections, put the letter away and retrieved his bike. As he prepared to mount he glanced down Bismarckallee. The first big house next to the new dance school, Bismarckallee 2, the one Hans had admired, seemed with its ponderous Prussian solidity, resplendent with wrought-iron balconies and neo-Palladian stucco pillars topped with the proud date MCMIX, to be asserting its permanence beside its upstart neighbour. The Palucca School's clean functional lines and lack of ornament struck a new note in this respectable bourgeois neighbourhood. 'But which will last longer?' he thought. The dance school, with its horizontal planes and modular construction, for all its 'fitness for purpose' looked flimsy by contrast. 'It is a machine, not a monument. Thine evermore, most dear lady, whilst this machine is to him.' As he rode back through the leafy Grunewald with all its Brigitte associations, Wolfgang had a presentiment that any response to her letter was to be more harshly qualified by 'whilst this machine is to him.' At the end of Shakespeare's play both the writer of those words and their recipient were dead.

Brigitte's letter with its news of the imminent marriage hastened Wolfgang's plans to give himself to his beloved Swiss mountains. He had been in Capri for Jo Mihaly's wedding; he would be on the Alps for Brigitte's. Both, in their different ways, rejected his Körpersinn, though it was aimed at their - and his own - generation. He thought of Jo's words - 'one loses onself in the movement . . one becomes the dance.' Very well, he would put it to the test with the three peaks of Piz Palü. Perhaps the Engadine would give him inspiration, as it had done for Nietzsche with 'Zarathustra'. For reading-matter he took with him only one book, Martin Heidegger's Being and Time, the sequel, as it were, to Nietzsche.

In spite of their strenuous excitement, the weeks spent in the mountains could not be more than an interlude. Wolfgang loved the undemanding comradeship of fellow-climbers, many of them army people on leave, with a sprinkling of young recruits. Their animal high spirits and absence of academicism were refreshing. He recognised the appeal of army life, its good fellowship and discipline, its uncomplicated existence. On impulse he made some steps towards volunteering, as a Swiss national, for the Swiss Army.

"The thin clear air of the mountains helps to free one's mind." (He was writing to Hans Zurlinden while resting between climbs in a small chalet.) "Nietzche discovered this too here on the Engadine. Yet to what end is all this empty philosophy since Nietzsche, Heidegger's existential inquiries into the problem of Being? Here one is in touch with Being itself. When I come down to the flatland again I plan to join the army. . ."

Zurlinden was disturbed by this letter, its uncharacteristic tone as much as its content. He discussed it with Lily Graeser on one of his frequent visits to the little apartment in Prince Friedrich-Leopold Straße. Together they prepared and despatched a reply, setting out all the arguments against so rash a step: his university studies and forthcoming doctorate, further performances of Die Kunst der Fuge, the plans for a book on the later Bach, his Oriental studies . . . Hans added the point of Lily's isolation if both sons were permanently out of Berlin. When it arrived in Zürich, where Wolfgang was staying with relatives, this letter certainly gave him pause, but what finally deflected him from going ahead with enlistment was a chance meeting. He had been to collect the necessary forms for recruitment and was standing on the Quai-Brücke gazing out over the lake when a hand rested on his shoulder. He turned to see a smiling 42-year-old man.

"Herr Graeser, I believe. Andreas Speiser. Do you remember me?"

"Of course! How good to see you. I had you in mind this very day, as it happens. I was reflecting on Heidegger's contention that since Descartes mathematics has had a narrowing, restrictive influence on the true sources of our Western philosophy, on our appreciation of what Parmenides, Plato, Socrates did for us." As he spoke Wolfgang became more animated, his intellect racing once more with its customary ferment after its enforced rest. His remark led to a prolonged philosophical discussion, first standing on the bridge, then continued in a café nearby, to the mutual delight of the two scholars. Before leaving the bridge Wolfgang ceremoniously tore up the army papers and scattered the fragments on the green waters of the Lippat below.

Professor Speiser reminded him about the proposed study trip to Egypt.

"Are you still game for that, my friend? I should greatly value your assistance. And what better place to investigate Parmenides' philosophy than the coast of Greece! When we discussed the matter before, you undertook to be my photographer. I have cleared my teaching schedule for March and April next year."

"How could anyone resist such an opportunity to visit the wellspring of Western culture, Rome, Greece, Egypt! Thank you for asking me. I'm your man!"

The conversation jerked Wolfgang's mind back into more familiar channels. In the mountains he had lived entirely in the present, moment by moment, relishing, almost glorying in his physical prowess, sensible only of the blood coursing in his veins, the ache in his muscles, the sensation of the wind on his face and his lungs ingesting great draughts of the clear, thin mountain air. He had 'celebrated ' his birthday alone amongst the snow-clad peaks. At night he threw himself down on the narrow chalet bunks and slept dreamlessly. Now Andreas Speiser, so like Wolfgang's father in those distant carefree Napoli days - he even looked like him, Wolfgang thought - , had opened up the future again with his study trip to the ancient world. The future? He paused at this. Was it not more the past? Was he, in fact, running away from the future. 'I want to be always twenty.' Yet now he was 21, like Brigitte. Her life lay tranquilly ahead of her: a husband, a comfortable home, children . . . With a pang of dread he felt again Dr Schweitzer's strong workman's hands on his shoulders - "You have been given great gifts . . ." Schweitzer had used his 21st birthday as a moment of decision. Should not he also?

During the long, tedious rail journey back to Berlin Wolfgang had plenty of time for such reflections. This 22nd year of his life would now be marked by two things, his Berlin doctorate of philosophy and the Egyptian adventure. Papa always said that good things came in threes. He would approve of the first, at any rate. When brother Hans had achieved his doctorate in Munich, Wolfgang remembered how his father, in a rare burst of feeling, laid his arm round his shoulders, saying, "You next, my boy. I want to be there when you receive your award." A vain hope! He remembered the touch of his lips on that chill forehead and his histrionic - as it now seemed - vow: "I shall be true." What would be the third thing?

He was agreeably surprised, when the big locomotive at last pulled in to the cavernous Berlin Anhalter Station in a cloud of steam, to see his mother and Hans Zurlinden together on the platform. Lily, looking small and trim beside his friend, embraced Wolfgang quickly,

"Hans wanted you to arrive home in style. He has the Embassy car waiting for us. You look very fit, Wullie dear. The mountains have done you good." At the same time she was aware of a strange, remote, haunted look in his eyes, awaking the old feeling of dread for her brilliant, tempestuous child. Nevertheless, Wolfgang was laughing with something of his old gaiety.

"Hans, you devil! How have you managed this?" The porter had brought out Wolfgang's luggage and was duly impressed by the black limousine with its crest and uniformed chauffeur.

"I persuaded Hermann that the discoverer of Die Kunst der Fuge deserved nothing less. Come on, there's room for all of us."

The unexpected luxury made the journey out to Nikolassee pass quickly. Wolfgang's replies to questions about his time in the mountains were vague and neutral, but his encounter with Professor Speiser and the invitation to accompany him to Egypt prompted something approaching his old boyish enthusiasm.

"He is an interesting man, Mutti, a fine mathematician and a philosopher as well as a classical scholar. I wish Papa was here to talk with him."

"I am so pleased for you, Wullie. It is a fine opportunity. But your doctorate . . ?"

"That will be all over before we set out, don't worry. One shouldn't take things like that too seriously. Remember the Abitur?"

Over the remaining part of the year Lily allowed herself to think that her son, by resuming his normal academic routine, had recovered from his crisis earlier in the year. He attended the university regularly, concentrating on mathematics in preparation for the planned geometrical study of Theban tombs in Egypt, but spending most time on Oriental culture. He had rapidly acquired reasonable fluency in Mandarin Chinese and spent long hours contemplating the Eastern art treasures in the Asiatic Museum. One day he arrived home with a fine Japanese tea-set in delicate porcelain, the bowls shell-thin, almost transparent.

"I found it in a little shop behind Alexanderplatz. Probably looted in the war, Mutti, but who cares now! I've seen bowls like this in the Asiatic Museum. Aren't they beautiful! It replaces that Meissen service you had to barter during the 'Millionenkrankheit'. We can use it for the tea ceremony." Lily accepted the gift with a feeling of relief. This was a flash of Wullie's old self, the open, generous-hearted boy. Perhaps he was emerging from the cloud after all.

2

Thanks in part to Hans Zurlinden's insistence, Wolfgang had taken to attending concerts more frequently, usually with Zurlinden or by himself, sometimes with his mother, occasionally the three of them in a party. The Berlin season was particularly brilliant this year. Artur Schnabel was playing all 32 Beethoven piano sonatas in a series of matinée recitals at the People's Theatre, to great applause. Wilhelm Furtwängler, now commuting between Berlin and Weimar, invited the great Arturo Toscanini from Milan to conduct his Berlin Philharmonic in a group of concerts. In September Paul

Hindemith, famous - or notorious, depending on your point of view - for his advocacy of Gebrauchsmusik (utility music), was soloist in his own new viola concerto under the baton of Otto Klemperer, the newly appointed music director of the Kroll Opera on the Platz der Republik. Wolfgang, scornful of what seemed to him merely a pandering to fashion, had spurned Hans' invitation to hear it, but when Hermann Scherchen, who had conducted his Die Kunst der Fuge more than once in Switzerland, invited him to another concert of new music he felt he could not refuse.

Three years before, when Schönberg took up his appointment in the Academy of Arts and when the first staging of Alban Berg's opera Wozzek had taken Berlin's music scene by storm, Wolfgang had been immersed in his Bach research. He knew of Schönberg's music, in particular the Gurrelieder, which he remembered describing as 'Wagnerish and tonal' in a letter to Uncle Ludwig years ago, but considered that atonalism was a futile experiment, a negation of music as he understood it. This was his first exposure to the serial music of the Viennese school. The main work, Berg's chamber concerto for piano, violin and 13 wind instruments, composed as a 50th birthday present to his teacher Arnold Schönberg, shook Wolfgang. He had approached the concert sceptically: the idea that tonality was exhausted seemed so alien to his own musical experience, and his mother simply dismissed it out of hand as 'rubbish'. But the clean lucidity of texture and the sheer excitement and virtuosity of Berg's music forced him into a re-evaluation, whilst also undermining his self-confidence. From the opening piano statement, the delicately placed eight letters of Schönberg's name A D S C H B E G, followed by Anton WEBErn on the violin and AlBAn BErG on French horn, he had been arrested, compelled to listen. Like Coleridge's hapless wedding guest, he could not choose but hear. Using so many of the musical techniques Wolfgang knew so well, canonic writing, rhythmic variation, baroque embellishments, Berg still avoided any suggestion of conventional harmonic structure. Yet, far from seeming anarchic, the piece was taut, disciplined, controlled. It was witty, virtuosic, eclectic music, sufficiently self-assured to employ elements of jazz or waltz rhythms, to explore new sonorities, new potentialities of the 15 instruments, like the arresting little duet between violin and muted trumpet in the second movement. Wolfgang's overriding impression was that Berg had broken free, escaped from the tyranny of diatonic harmony, that he had succeeded where Wagner or Richard Strauss, even perhaps Mahler, had failed. Was not this also, like Die Kunst der Fuge, woven from a theme stated at the beginning? Instead of Bach's melodic subject, the 'still and serious world', as Schweitzer called it, there was this sequence of notes discarding all the harmonic contrapuntal complexity that had drawn him to Bach, yet - as he had to admit when listening - creating what he must still call music, with the magical number 3, hinted at in Berg's motto for the piece 'Aller guten Dinge . . .' ('All good things [come in threes]', his father's motto), binding it all together, like a mocking echo of Bach's own puzzles in The Musical Offering. It was as though Berg, like himself, had chosen to climb from the flatland of diatonic harmony to the wild Engadine and had found freedom there. But had not Wolfgang decided, especially after talking to Andreas Speiser and resuming his university studies, that that freedom had been an illusion, a chimaera? The great final piano flourish sounded through the concert hall, its duration precisely punctuated by five arpeggios on the other instruments, so timed that, at the very end, the last of the violin's four pizzicato notes coincided with the moment when the piano chord died into silence. It held for some tense seconds, then the applause burst like a breached dam. Wolfgang's mind was in turmoil. If this was today's music, of what value was his attempt to present Bach's Die Kunst der Fuge to the world? Was it all an exercise in futility?

After the concert Scherchen introduced him to the musicians. To his surprise they loved the music, both the challenge it mounted to their skill and the music itself.

"Such a relief after the tedious 48! I suppose I shouldn't say this to you." This was the pianist, who had recently played all Bach's 48 preludes and fugues in a series of concerts. It seemed like sacrilege to Wolfgang, dismissing Bach, the god of his idolatry, in so cavalier a fashion. While he was with the players he slipped naturally into his public rôle as the celebrated young musicologist, but once back in his study 'cell' in Nikolassee he felt the darkness lapping around him. He thought of Piete Kuhr's vivid sense of horror as she recounted the plight of the Russian soldiers engulfed in the Masurian bogs, of his Vesuvius imaginings, of the black holes of tunnels . . . He looked about him, as if waking from a nightmare. It was very quiet in the house at this late hour. A sliver of moon glimpsed through his small window, his papers spread out on the desk, the exercise ropes swinging from their hooks. He jumped up, grasped the hand-holds and swung himself about until his muscles, hardened though they were from the alpine climbs, screamed for mercy. He hitched the ropes back up then went through the rest of his morning sequence of exercises before throwing himself on the bed, physically exhausted.

For days afterwards he could not settle to anything. He attended no lectures, sitting listlessly in the university library, unable to concentrate. At home he would climb to his attic room, look at the mess of papers and come down again, or moodily trace the familiar paths across the common beyond the Protestant cemetery. "After life's fitful fever they sleep well!" Macbeth's despairing words seemed to fit his mood too, with his restless, image-filled nights. His mother knew him too well to question him, but his haunted looks and the dark shadows under his eyes made her heart sink. Always sensitive to his changing moods, she racked her brains for something to jolt him out of this resumption of his former depression. A lucky chance prompted her to make him a proposal one morning.

"Dr Wolf, your Uncle Johann, has offered us seats at the opera, Wullie, Der Rosenkavalier. You know it is one of my favourites. Please come! He has given us three tickets, so Hans can come as well if he's free. It is at the Municipal Opera under Bruno Walter. Apparently Walter has found two new singers for Sophie and the Marschallin and people are raving about them."

The fin-de-siècle lushness of Richard Strauss was not at all to his taste, but his mother was so insistent that he agreed to join the party. Lily revelled in the music, its idiom so reassuringly within the romantic traditions of her own musical training. In spite of the antiquated stage machinery of the opera-house the production was brilliant and the new stars, Elisabeth Schumann a naive, innocent, beautiful Sophie and Lotte Lehmann a full-voiced, world-weary Marschallin - though not much older than the other in real life - , made a remarkable duo, a foil to the coarse Baron Ochs, superbly portrayed by Richard Mayr. As the evening wore on Wolfgang felt more and more alone. It was evident that his mother, that Hans, even Uncle Johann were captivated like the rest of the audience by Strauss's rich romanticism, but for him, mentally comparing it with the astringent economy of Alban Berg, it came across as blowsy and overblown. He almost disgraced himself by laughing immoderately at one technical hitch in the production, when a man-servant put a taper to the lights on one side of the stage and those on the other side were illuminated. The party had seats in the front stalls and Walter looked round angrily, while Lily tried to hush him.

"I know I shouldn't have laughed, but it was funny, you must admit." They were on their way home in Uncle Johann's big motor-car. Lily was pleased, at least, that Wolfgang's mood seemed to have lifted. It was late when they arrived at the small apartment so they could not prolong the party. Instead she invited Dr Wolf and Hans Zurlinden for the next afternoon. When both accepted, Wolfgang had an idea.

"As it is Sunday, why don't you join us for the Japanese tea ceremony? That should blow away some of these Straussian cobwebs."

Dr Wolf had arranged to pick up Hans Zurlinden so that they could arrive together. Wolfgang had been very insistent on this as a necessary preliminary to the tea ceremony.

"It is one of Sen Rikyu's rules - he was the greatest Japanese tea-master - that the host should welcome the guests and lead them in."

Hans and Johannes Wolf wanted to enter into the spirit of the occasion, but on the way to Nikolassee they discussed it as a kind of game of Wolfgang's. They would humour him by conforming to his rules. When they arrived, walking from the car round the house to the courtyard that the Graesers' apartment door gave onto, Wolfgang stood waiting for them. His expression was serious and calm. He wore a plain snowy-white collarless shirt and baggy trousers. His feet were bare. He greeted the two men formally and led the way into the flat, where Lily also greeted them quietly.

"I must explain a little about the ceremony as we have adapted it." While Lily was in the kitchen completing preparations for a light meal as a prelude to the ceremony proper, Wolfgang sat with his guests. "We use my room as the actual tea-house. This room, where we have our meal, is the yoritsuki or waiting-room and the stairs to my room constitute the roji or path which breaks the connection with the outside world. The essence of the tea ceremony is sabi, tranquillity. All who participate must do so, as far as they are able, with a clean face, clean hands and a clean heart. After our meal you can prepare yourselves. Once in the tea-house there must be no discussion of worldly affairs, no flattery or pretence. Sen Rikyu emphasises how the setting and the carrying out of the ceremony are designed to cleanse all the senses. Please remember this as you mount the roji and enter the tea-house."

Hans and Johannes looked at each other. This was a more serious undertaking than they had anticipated. Lily now invited them to the table, where she had laid out a simple meal:white fish with rice, fresh peaches, cool water to drink. There was desultory talk during the meal. Dr Wolf wanted to engage Wolfgang in discussion about the opera, but Wolfgang simply smiled gently and turned the conversation. It was clear that he wished to avoid anything that could be construed as part of his professional 'persona'. Lily was a little more forthcoming.

"What a pure soprano that girl had, the one who was Sophie! Ideal in the part, and such a pretty thing too. I don't think I have ever heard so true a voice."

Johannes Wolf agreed. "She will go far, that one. She bears a famous name, anyway. I wonder if she sings her namesake's Dichterliebe?"

Wolfgang was the first to rise after the meal. "I must prepare for the ceremony. Mutti will explain; you give me a signal when you are ready." He bowed, hands clasped, and padded silently out of the room. Johannes looked at Lily.

"This is a serious matter, evidently."

"It means a lot to Wullie. I'm so glad you have been able to join us, both of you." She seemed strained and anxious. She explained that Wolfgang was giving the guests and herself time to wash and prepare their minds. "Then we sound this little gong before going upstairs. He puts the water on when he hears the gong. Two sounds, to cleanse the sense of hearing, you see, the gong and the water. I must lead, as the oldest, then you Johann, then Hans. When we arrive outside his room you will see a scroll on his door - the cleansing of the sense of sight. Once in the room you will appreciate how the other senses are also purified."

Dusk was just beginning to fall as Lily beat the gong with a leather-covered stick, a clear gentle tone. It reverberated up the stair-well, quickly dying away. They had all removed footwear and washed feet, hands and face. The parchment-like scroll hanging on Wolfgang's door had been painted by him. In subdued blues, browns and greens it depicted a countryside with trees and hills. There was Japanese lettering down one side, the signs formed in precise brush-strokes. As they contemplated it, Wolfgang opened the door and beckoned them in. The room was clean and bare. The exercise ropes had been taken down, the bed and desk pushed to the walls and covered with cotton drapes. The light was so hooded that it illuminated a thin clear glass vase containing a single perfect arum lily bedewed with water-drops. Its perfume mingled with a faint smell of incense whose source was invisible. They took their places in a circle, sitting on the floor. Wolfgang sat Buddha-like, legs crossed. Beside him the iron kettle sang gently on a small spirit stove. The tea-set he had brought back for his mother was laid out ready. Johannes reached over to examine one of the bowls.

"May I?"

"Of course!" Wolfgang smiled. "They are beautiful, are they not? It is good to feel them in one's hands."

As the sound rose in the kettle then changed to the boiling he quoted from the Ch'a Ching, Lu Yu's classic eighth century book on tea. "'At the first boiling there is a faint sound and the eyes of a fish appear on the surface. Then we hear the gurgling of a brook, with pearls at its edge. For the third boiling turbulent waves appear.'" He poured water onto the green tea-leaves. After leaving it for some minutes Lily filled a bowl for each of them and the aroma from the steaming bowls was added to the lily's perfume.

"Now we can taste, the last of the senses. You first, Mutti!"

As they sipped, all sensed a harmony of spirit. They conversed in hushed voices, as though in a church, about the scroll, the shape of the lily, the design of the tea-set, the delicate flavour of the tea. The daylight died away as they sat. Lily had explained that it was not necessary to bid farewell before leaving the tea-house. Each could leave at the moment when he or she felt it was time. Johannes Wolf was the first to go. He looked round the circle as he rose. Wolfgang had been sitting perfectly still, his eyes downcast. He smiled faintly as Johannes nodded and left the room, followed by Lily. Soon Hans went after them, leaving Wolfgang alone.

"Beautiful! I have not felt so at peace for many a year." Dr Wolf was making ready to leave. "Your son is something of a mystic, Lily my dear."

After they had gone Lily sat alone, the tears now coming fast. She felt her love for Wolfgang as an oppression of spirit. 'He is drifting away from me and there is nothing I can do.'

3

For Wolfgang too the tea ceremony had felt like a valediction. He had shared in the cumulative tranquillity as they sipped their tea, but for him the ceremony was also a means of clarification, a gleam of light through cloud, penetrating and beginning to disperse the turmoil of the two years since his father's death. After converting his room to its normal function, replacing the two stout exercise ropes on their hooks, removing the drapes and pulling the desk out to its proper place, he joined his mother downstairs. Noticing her tear-stained face, he felt guilty and contrite.

"I fear it has all been too much for you, Mutti dear." She shook her head dumbly. How could she explain?

"No . . Yes, perhaps you are right, my darling child." She smiled. "But you are no longer a child, Wullie. You are a famous man." She rose, busying herself with putting the room to rights. "It was a beautiful ceremony. Johannes was deeply moved, and Hans too. He is a faithful friend. It is sad that he will be leaving us next year."

"He will still be in Berlin for my doctorate in February. Then I must leave you too, Mutti, for a while. You remember, the study trip with Andreas Speiser?"

He looked ahead to this expedition with keen anticipation. What a coming together it might provide of so many of his interests - or obsessions!

The classical source of all Western culture, the ontological significance of geometry in the Theban tomb inscriptions, even - he could at least speculate - the shadow cast over the great Mediterranean civilisations by the Orient. Moreover, as both mathematician and philosopher, Andreas Speiser was the ideal companion for such an adventure. Wolfgang found himself pursuing his university studies with renewed vigour.

One chance episode this autumn came when he was with Hans Zurlinden in the bustling centre of Berlin one evening. They had paid their 60 pfennigs to see a new film by Walther Ruttmann which claimed to portray the essence of the capital: Berlin: Symphonie einer Großstadt. It traced a day, from dawn to midnight, in the life of the city, using the medium skilfully to suggest a bustling modern metropolis, busy and orderly.

"Interesting to see how an instantaneous image can direct your thoughts," Hans Zurlinden said as they came out. "Those quick shots of cattle interposed between those of the factory workers!"

Wolfgang was less impressed. "That was Vicki Baum's Berlin - skimming the surface. Yes, cinema can suggest ideas. Another one was that argument on the telephone, then two dogs fighting, and in the next act a street fight between two men. It was cleverly done, but what was it trying to say, that men are animals?"

Zurlinden laughed. "Animals make good movie actors! I liked the elephant lying down after the lunchtime café scenes."

"Clever, I grant you, but where was it leading? I was aware of only one bit of serious comment on Berlin, when it flashed up the headlines 'Money!' 'Money!' 'Money!' while filming the newspapers pouring from the presses. The way Berliners are shown enjoying themselves - sport, cabaret, dancing, those yankee Tiller Girls showing their legs, cocktails and roulette - that was pure Vicki Baum." Wolfgang laughed ironically. "The Berlin I know offers a good deal more than that for entertainment." His mind went back to the stinking crowded Mietskaserne. "And it is a lot dirtier. Not many beggars or cripples in Ruttmann's Berlin."

"Come, Wolfgang, you can't expect a movie to depict your rarefied life-style. I agree that it skated round the seedier aspect of the city. The skating was good to watch, anyway!"

As they strolled along Münzstraße in search of a place for coffee, Wolfgang's eye was caught by the name on a garish poster outside one of the many cabarets:

JO MIHALY, solo dancer

Zurlinden saw it at the same time. "Shall we go in?" He was aware that since her marriage his friend had dropped all references to Jo Mihaly. Wolfgang hesitated, then shrugged his shoulders.

"Why not? Jo can't be worse than the movie and it will pass the time."

The place was crowded and stuffy, the air thick with tobacco smoke. Many young people, one group with swastika arm-bands of the NSDAP presided over by a sweaty, bald-headed man in a brown shirt, all in the group loud-mouthed and the worse for drink. There was also a sprinkling of older people, some obviously actors and artists. The two friends waited a long time for service, while the small stage was occupied by a very indifferent singer of indeterminate sex. His or her act elicited jeers and obscene gestures from the noisy youths, encouraged by their leader. The stage remained empty for some time, then the patron came on to announce,

"Ladies and gentlemen, here is what you have been waiting for, JO MIHALY." A cheer went up. "Many of you have seen her at the People's Theatre. We are lucky indeed to have her with us tonight. She will perform two of her inimitable dances, introducing the second one herself. First, your hands, please, for "Flower in the Back-yard". Jo Mihaly!"

Jo ran onto the stage, blinking a little in the strong lighting. She acknowledged the applause briefly, then, as the lights dimmed, was absorbed in her rôle, a girl finding a single flower that had struggled into life in the dim yard. With no props beyond the tattered costume of a pauper child, dirty and bare-footed, and with only a piano as background, she conjured the scene to vivid life by mime and gesture. The audience was silent, as absorbed as the girl herself. Some titters and shuffling from the group of youths was indignantly 'shushed' to silence by those around them. The fluidity of the dancer's movements, her expressive, eloquent hands as she caressed the little flower, transported the watchers to the scene. Jo then took the part of the flower itself, its upturned face pleading for sunlight, a single shaft of light shining down. As the sunbeam faded and vanished the flower closed, wilted and laid down its tiny life. The dancer was now the girl again, discovering her lost friend. As she crouched in silence on the stage the lights came up, to a storm of applause. She rose, as if from a dream, smiling shyly and acknowledging it before running off.

"What an artist your friend has become!" Hans, who like many others had stood up to applaud, smiled at Wolfgang. "She almost hypnotised us then. I felt I was in that back-yard, didn't you?"

Wolfgang was prevented from replying by Jo Mihaly's reappearance, this time wearing a shabby army tunic, badges roughly torn off. With a shock of recollection Wolfgang recognised it as the one she had described to him, her brother's discarded uniform. She wore clumsy army boots and carried - yes, the very helmet! The buzz of talk died down as she made her introduction.

"Most of you," she surveyed the crowded room, her glance pausing a moment on the two friends before moving on, "like me, were conscious of living through the war years. You will know what it means when I tell you that this," she held up the battered Belgian helmet, "came from Verdun. I call this dance 'A Vision of War'."

As the lights dimmed, leaving the stage glaringly lit, the piano struck up a crude military march. She was now a soldier. At this point the group of Nazi youths, stirred by the music, started jeering and hissing, egged on by their leader. Jo signalled to the pianist to stop playing and stood stock-still in the centre of the stage, until the proprietor, with two muscular assistants, ordered the party out. They left with an ill grace. Before beginning her act again Jo said,

"Those too young to have known what war is are easily led - or misled. I wish they had stayed to see."

There were sounds of approval and some clapping, then all was silent as the dance sequence got under way. It delivered a powerful message. The soldier fought, was killed. There was a fragment of a Dead March, a brief silence, then the insistent bugle call, hammered out high on the piano. The 'dead' soldier stirred, rose, resumed his fighting posture, face smeared with blood . . . Once again the dancer's absorption in her part was absolute, the controlled fluidity of her movement gripping. After the last shattering, dissonant crash on the piano, symbolising a death-blow, the soldier, mortally stricken, crawled off the stage into darkness. The silence in the stuffy, crowded space was profound. The lights came up on an empty stage and the clapping began spasmodically before building up. The proprietor came on.

"Jo Mihaly has asked me to thank you for your attention. She is too tired to thank you herself."

Hans Zurlinden looked inqiringly at Wolfgang. "Do you want to find if she . . .?"

"Let's go!" Wolfgang spoke abruptly. His face was clouded and Hans knew him too well to press the suggestion. They parted in the street outside.

The emotional power of Jo's artistry had shaken Wolfgang's new-found poise. He realised that when he wrote about dancing in Körpersinn he had been unaware of the direct, sensuous power of dance. After the movie, which he had dismissed as essentially frivolous, this live 'entertainment' had come as a shock. He was uncomfortably aware of the overt political import of the dances, demonstrated by the reaction of those swastikaed youths and their unsavoury leader. He had been aware that Jo's eyes rested on him, but he shrank from any closer contact. However, the experience prompted him to turn down an invitation which he received the next day from Oswald Spengler. The historian was to be principal speaker at a conference in Weimar entitled "Nietzsche and the 20th Century", a topic that a few months before would have attracted Wolfgang's enthusiastic interest and support. Spengler wrote in his letter of invitation:

"I feel certain that my analysis of Nietzsche's philosophy in relation to our times will engage your interest, especially as we share our admiration for the Italian Übermench Benito Mussolini. . ."

As he scribbled a brief note of apology he paused, pen in hand. Was this not a breach of faith with Papa? He would have urged him to go at all costs. 'Rest, rest, perturbed spirit!' He must exorcise this ghost. He would do so next February - Dr Carl, Dr Hans, then Dr Wolfgang.

Jo's dance and the behaviour of the NSDAP youths and their companion or Fuhrer had brought about a deeper revulsion of feeling over Spengler's interpretation of Nietzsche, indeed, his whole outlook. For all his learning, his analysis of the rise and fall of civilisations, was he not shutting his eyes to the possible consequences? Mussolini might be no more than another Lenin, whom Wolfgang had always seen as a single-minded power-hungry fanatic. Hans Zurlinden had described to him a visit to the Russian theatre troupe appearing at Piscator's theatre on Nollendorf Square, with its powerful socialist message. They called themselves the "Blue Blouses" and seemed to be subscribing to Brecht's ideas about finding strength through loss of individuality. When Wolfgang thought back to the play Jo Mihaly had made him listen to and their subsequent arguments, it was as though he felt the ground shaking under his feet.

He tried to dismiss such thoughts by burying himself in his studies. He was hardly aware of the end of the year. He and his mother both hated the tawdry commercialism of Christmas in the city centre, so spent the time quietly in their tree-lined suburb, now bare of leaves. Zurlinden went to Switzerland for the holiday but was back in Berlin in January. From time to time Wolfgang strolled along Prince Friedrich-Leopold Straße to visit his old tutor Paul Müller, now very arthritic and more or less house-bound, though his mind was alert as ever. He too questioned Spengler's philosophy.

"Nietzsche was a poet, a visionary. Your patron, Wolfgang, for all his learning, has no poetry in him so misses the point over and over again." He was aware of his former pupil's discomfiture at the topic so changed the subject. "Come, let us leave the politicians to their dirty game. How are your Eastern studies progressing? Have you heard from your new friend the mathematician?"

"Professor Speiser? Yes, the plans are going ahead for our visit to Egypt."

"I envy you, young fellow. Ah, I wish I had my youth again." He sighed, shifting in his chair, a hand pressing the small of his back. "I tell you, young Wolfgang, one of the worst things about growing old - apart from my aching spine! -" he smiled ruefully, "is seeing one's friends die around one. Your father now, a fine man cut off in his prime. Yesterday I heard of another old friend - well, he was younger than me by a year or two . . ."

"I shall never be old!" Wolfgang said it with such violence that the old man looked up in surprise. Wolfgang's tone moderated. "I am not looking any further than Egypt for now. There is so much to learn before we go."

"What about the doctorate?"

"Oh that!" Wolfgang grimaced. "Remember the Abitur? This is just such another. I can't take it very seriously. I suppose it will be nice to call myself 'doctor'. Papa would like it At the moment I am absorbed by Max Reger's music, fascinating stuff. But . ." he laughed, "it is no use telling you that, with your 'cloth ears', as you call them."

On the day of the 'viva' examination he met Zurlinden for coffee at the Café des Westens on the corner of Joachimsthaler Straße. He had cycled into town and locked his bike to the railings. Hans Zurlinden looked at it in some consternation.

"You take your life in your hands coming into town on that." He was only partly joking; the pressures of motor transport in the congested city streets, mingled as it had to be with pedestrians, horse-drawn vehicles and advertising stunts, was already taking an almost daily toll in accidents. Wolfgang shrugged.

"My life is always in my hands. Come on, let's have coffee."

The café was fairly crowded. At the table next to them sat a family, two children, their parents and an old lady, obviously the children's Oma. They kept Hans and Wolfgang amused with their delight at the unfamiliar treat and setting.

"Look, the old lady has gone to sleep. She's had too much of her grandchildren's antics."

Was she asleep? It seemed a bit of a joke at first, the old lady nodding off after an unaccustomed feast. Then someone noticed the dead pallor in her face, the shallow breathing. Suddenly all was movement in the cramped, crowded corner of the restaurant. Wolfgang tried to move their table back to give her more space. A plate shattered, a water jug overturned. The old lady's head lolled on her chest. The older child, a boy of eight or nine, was looking with dispassionate interest at his grandmother as two uniformed medical assistants came in with a stretcher and lifted her on.

"Is she dead, Mutti? Will they bury her in a grave?"

"Hush dear. Your Oma is just . . unwell." The boy looked at her sceptically and said no more. Once the café had settled down again, Hans said,

"When is your viva, Wolfgang?" Wolfgang hauled out his pocket-watch, his father's rather ponderous repeater on a chain.

"I had better get moving. It's supposed to begin in ten minutes. Can you settle for the coffee?"

He cycled off up Budapester Straße, weaving through the traffic. 'My life in my hands,' he thought. 'And that old lady? was her life in her hands?' He remembered his words to Paul Müller as he saw again her slumped body, the white-grey pallor of her face reminding him vividly of his father.

4

So now he had completed the trio of doctorates. The conferring of the degree would take place in May, and Papa's soul would perhaps then be at rest. As Wolfgang looked back over the last four and a half years since that momentous discovery in Otto Haas's cluttered bookshop in Bernburgerstraße, he wondered what it had all been for. What next? How was it that Hans Zurlinden could see so clearly his diplomatic career stretching out ahead of him, that Albert Schweitzer could, at his own age of 21, plan the fine, selfless life for others which now inspired and dominated him? He felt again those hands on his shoulders, but still repudiated Schweitzer's view of his 'gifts'. Jo too, dancing out her convictions, focusing so clearly on the futility of war, the social evils of poverty. He could not help recognising that their way of making the business of living - 'whilst this machine . .' - meaningful was more admirable than Spengler's fatalism. 'Or nihilism,' he thought. How different Spengler's, or for that matter Schopenhauer's pessimistic appraisal from Johann Sebastian Bach, spurning the baroque extravagance and prettiness of his contemporaries, even his own children, to create that mathematically elegant, complex yet visionary musical monument! Yet that too ended in a question mark. In his mind he heard again the echoes of that broken 239th bar dying away in the vault of the Thomaskirche . . .

As Wolfgang made his preparations for the Egyptian expedition he tried to suppress such cogitations. At least, with Andreas Speiser as a companion, he might hope to find some answers during their travels to the cradle of Western civilisation. In a mental gesture of defiance he included in his sparse luggage a shabby copy loaned to him by Paul Müller of Plato's later dialogues. 'Let Socrates speak to us in sight of his homeland.' After meeting Speiser in Zürich the journey on, with its childhood recollections, did much to lift his thoughts out of the slough of despond. The mathematician and philosopher, now at the peak of his academic career, had something of the same questing, mercurial temperament as his young friend. They completed the journey to Egypt by sea, boarding the package steamer "Bienna" at Venice and sailing down the Adriatic and across the Mediterranean to Alexandria. Thanks to his seaboard childhood in Naples Wolfgang proved to be a better sailor than Speiser. To take his friend's mind off the state of his heaving stomach Wolfgang brought out the Plato volume.

"Let's see what we can make of the Parmenides, Andreas. That should settle you."

Fortunately the weather smoothed out as they steamed past the mountains of Corfu, giving them a spell of almost flat calm down the Greek coast. They took mutual delight in each other's mental agility, their conversation sometimes deliberately emulating the Socratic elenchus as they worked their way through the eight deductions of the Parmenides dialogue to its negative conclusion.

"Wolfgang, I think you are a disciple of Aesculapius. You have cured my sea-sickness!"

The crossing to Alexandria was uneventful, and their six weeks in Egypt was packed with activity and travels. Wolfgang had been as good as his word when Speiser had first proposed the trip in Zürich, equipping himself - at his colleague's expense - with the latest Leica photographic apparatus. He enjoyed the technical challenge of its mechanism, especially when taking pictures of the Great Mosque of Ibn Tulûn in Cairo with its many windows. Islamic art was a revelation to Wolfgang. The two scholars travelled up the Nile to Aswan and on to Luxor to the mighty ruins of Thebes, where he took hundreds of photographs as a more permanent record to supplement his drawings of the graves with their geometrical patterning. The mathematical sophistication apparent in the inscriptions and architecture fascinated him. They returned to Cairo via Asyut and El Minya. The Cairo Museum's store of treasures from the ancient tombs was another magnet. More than once Andreas found Wolfgang standing silent before the great statue of the proud 5th Dynasty courtier Ti, gazing at the elaborate bas-reliefs depicting the scenes the dead man wished to participate in 'on the other side', banquets, hunting, fishing, even farming, vivid, sometimes witty action scenes. He chose a picture postcard of one lively hunting scene to send to his uncle. Once he turned to Speiser:

"They understood what constituted ideal beauty even in these ancient kingdoms. We seem to spend our time trying to rediscover what they already knew. So much for the advance of civilisation!"

On their return from Egypt in May Wolfgang felt satisfied, or satiated, yet ill-at-ease. The lengthy investigation into the Plato dialogue left him feeling like the young Socrates, with an intellectual mountain still to climb before he could hope to reach the truth about existence. He first busied himself with putting into coherent form the notes, sketches and photographs to send off to Andreas Speiser in Zürich. On the surface he was his usual self, with a multiplicity of new projects - a full-length study of the Later Bach, work on the music of Max Reger, the sequel to Körpersinn, developing ideas touched on in chapter 7 of the earlier book, further explorations into East Asian language and culture. Only Lily was aware instinctively that this was all a sort of smoke-screen. Yet she could do nothing about it, only observe, with a sinking of the heart, the steady withdrawal of her son.

Although they occupied the same small apartment, mother and son spent much time alone. Wolfgang's routine of early-morning exercises and solitary study, either in his room or at the university, assumed a monotonous regularity. Occasionally Lily would persuade him to join her in violin and piano music or at a concert. He still visited Paul Müller now and again, their conversation ranging as widely as ever, but without the sparkle of those early days in Berlin. Hans Zurlinden was now in Switzerland, Brigitte happily married and living kilometres away in the Ruhr, Jo pursuing her own career, with which he felt neither connection nor sympathy. The spate of performances of Die Kunst der Fuge immediately after the Leipzig première had continued into the new year and more were being planned for the autumn and winter, including, at last, the Berlin première in October. This was to be a big event, directed by Erich Kleiber at the State Opera on Unter den Linden.

"It will be a great occasion for you, Wullie dear, after all the disappointments. It is right and proper that your work . ."

"Bach's work, Mutti."

"Very well, that Bach's work rediscovered by you should be heard here, so that all your friends and colleagues can hear it and congratulate you."

"We shall see." Wolfgang seemed curiously uncommunicative about the performance. Lily thought, 'his head is too full of Chinese these days. The Berlin première will do him good.'

Soon after hearing about it came the degree ceremony at the university. It seemed to have a calming effect on Wolfgang. His brother Hans travelled up from Leipzig, where he now had a responsible, highly paid job in the public relations department of the Koehler-Volckmar concern. After the ceremony itself Dr Wolf joined them in Nikolassee for a small celebration. Lily was happy that Wolfgang seemed his old self, reminiscing with Hans about Italy and with Uncle Johann about the war years in Munich. It prompted Dr Wolf to ask,

"And your friend Dr Spengler? Are you in touch with him still? A very clever man."

Wolfgang made a grimace. "Clever, yes. The Egyptian experience with Andreas did make me wonder if he was as infallible as I used to think in his analysis of our Western culture." It was evident that he had no wish to pursue the topic, harking back instead to Naples. "I have been making some notes about those days, Hansi, and of my time in Zürich, when you were in Glarisegg. It is interesting going back over those years."

"You should include Munich, those grim last years of the war, with the revolution." Hans mused, "I was more of a Red than you. Most of the university students were in those days."

Johannes Wolf broke in: "Your biographer will be glad to know of such things, Wolfgang. You must remember that you are a famous man now." Wolfgang dismissed the idea with a smile, questioning Lily, nevertheless, about how and when she met his father.

"You must talk to Uncle Ludwig too. I'm sure he and your Aunt Elli must have lots to tell you. Elli never throws anything away." Wolfgang amused them by telling how she had shown him his own letter with the family concert programme.

"She even had a card I sent when I was six or seven with a picture for Uncle Ludwig, five little devils. I remember being fascinated by the idea of devils dancing about in the Vesuvius crater."

The Vesuvius crater. How that seething cauldron from the underworld had been a part of his life! It had linked itself with the alpine tunnels, their entrances so many gaping mouths, and with that persistent dream - or nightmare - of the crumpled sheets that had been with him since early childhood.

Soon afterwards, on 23rd May, the day after Hans Zurlinden's birthday, Wolfgang wrote him a long letter including the biographical notes.

" . . . You asked me once to let you have some information about my family background. Here it is, a late birthday present for you. . . .

. . . Three years ago I lost my father. I can never forget that dark hour; the memory of it came back to me today. In such moments one needs the blessed warmth of courage to face life. It is that which spurs us on to new creative endeavour, which protects us from the harsh encroachment of fate. That is always lying in wait, an enemy to life threatening us. With heartfelt sympathy I insist on an affirmation of life, on that vital circle that must close around all who need to find strength for new life, spurning the hostile forces that surround us. As a true friend I give you my hand,

Wolfgang Graeser."

When he read over the letter, which had been written with his usual speed, his pen racing to keep up with his thoughts, he looked for a long time at the closing words. They took his mind back to that almost involuntary comment to Uncle Ludwig four years before, at the time of his father's attempt to end his life: 'I am not under control. An obstinate force drags me along over rocks and stones, I do not know whither, but I must follow.' Hans Zurlinden must accept the letter as 'an affirmation of life', but he now knew that this was not for him, unless he could put any faith in Pythagorean metempsychosis. He and Andreas Speiser had talked much about that; somehow it had made sense when they were within sight of the very place where the concept originated. Now he would defeat that obstinate or hostile force, smooth out the crumpled sheet.

Early in June Lily Graeser's sister in Karlsruhe invited her for a visit. She had been disturbed by the tone of Lily's letters and wanted her to have a break from 'the hectic Berlin scene', as she called it. Lily was at first reluctant to leave Wolfgang, but his quiet cheerfulness after the degree ceremony had persisted, so she allowed herself to be persuaded by him, backed by Johannes Wolf, to join her sister in the faraway Baden capital. Wolfgang accompanied her to the station, the same vaulted Anhalter Bahnhof where she had stood with Hans Zurlinden to greet him on his return from the mountains. She was touched by the unaccustomed warmth of his farewell embrace. After releasing her, Wolfgang stroked her cheek gently, looking into her eyes.

"Look after yourself, Mutti dear, for all our sakes. I sometimes think I have been a poor sort of a son . . ."

"Wolfi darling, don't say such things."

He went on as if she had not spoken. ". . . but you have Hans. He is head of the family now." Lily was close to tears, so he smiled, saying, "Don't fret for me, Mutti. Everything will be all right."

"I shall be back within the fortnight."

Wolfgang just repeated, "Everything will be all right," as he left the compartment. She went to the window as the train started moving. He stood, very upright, one hand raised, his face serious, the wind from the train's movement just stirring his fair hair. That image would remain etched in her memory.

On his return to the empty Nikolassee apartment he fetched writing paper and implements down to the small dining-table. There were letters to write, to Uncle Ludwig, to brother Hans, to 'Uncle' Johann, to Paul Müller. Before sealing the last he included a note for his mother. 'You will know when to give this to Lily. I bid you farewell.   Wolfgang Graeser.'

As he signed his name for the last time the notes BACH came into his head and he smiled. It was evening before he had ended all these tasks. Now he must traverse the roji and enter the tea-house. That night, the night of 12th June 1928, after he had completed his preparations, Wolfgang slept dreamlessly and quiet. His eyes opened to the grey early morning sky. Behind the moving film of cloud a large lop-sided moon, half concealed. Then it vanished as the grey seemed to solidify. He stirred and considered rising, but that hypnotic, damaged white disc held his eyes to the patch of sky framed by his narrow window. And now a bright rim emerged, as over the side of a cistern. He watched as it slowly eased itself clear of the stifling greyness and floated up, a pock-marked round of a visage with one side distorted as if by some paralysis. He rose and made himself ready. 'I shall never see that round made perfect, the full moon.'

Epilogue

"Isn't this your friend, that young musician?" Leo and Jo Steckel were enjoying a leisurely breakfast, putting off as far as possible the need to face the day, which was cool, with drizzling rain from grey, overcast skies. Leo was, as usual, sitting back with his coffee, the newspaper, Vossische Zeitung, spread out in front of him. He folded it to point out an announcement under the heading "Family News":

This-morning died suddenly our dear son and brother
Dr Phil. Wolfgang Graeser
at the promising age of 21
In deepest sorrow
Frau Professor Dr Graeser
Dr Hans Graeser
Berlin Nikolassee 13 June 1928
Funeral 15 June at 3 o'clock Nikolassee Cemetery

As Jo took in the bald announcement with its black border the blood drained from her face.

"So it has come."

"What do you mean, my love?"

"I knew, when I saw him in that cabaret with his friend and they never came to see me. I knew, I knew!" Her shoulders shook with uncontrollable sobs. Leo went to her, putting an arm round her shoulders, but she shook her head as the tears flowed. For once in his life Leo Steckel was lost for words. After the first paroxysm, Jo's crying subsided. She groped for a handkerchief, sniffing as she tried to stifle her grief. Seeing there was nothing he could do, Leo stood by the window. Jo put her arms on the table, her head resting on them. The rain beat on the panes. For a while, that and the faint street sounds were all that could be heard. At last she mopped her eyes to look again at the announcement.

"It's today, the funeral. I must go, Leo. Will you come?"

"Do you want me to?"

She rallied at this, going to him and kissing him closely.

"I'm sorry, darling. Please come! Of course I want you to." She paused, then, "Poor Lily!" At this new thought her tears began again, but she dashed them away.

After washing her face and changing she felt more herself. By good fortune they were free until the evening performance, so could take the S-Bahn out to Nikolassee in the afternoon. They made their way to the Protestant cemetery on foot, walking along Prince-Friedrich-Leopold Street, past number 6, where there seemed to be nothing amiss, then past the big doctor's house, number 17, on the other side. As they reached it Dr Müller, using two sticks, hobbled out from the house opposite. Recognising Jo he nodded a greeting, saying nothing. She looked at him inquiringly and would have spoken, but he forestalled her with the one word, "Selbstmord!" It dropped like a stone in her heart, as she realised that that too she had already known.

Leo and Jo adjusted their pace to accompany the old man. A fine drizzle turning to rain, clouds driving across, rain-puddles on the asphalt, reflecting the bushes as they drew near the cemetery entrance. A small gathering by the Chapel of Rest: Lily in black clothes, her face veiled, Hans beside her, very upright, Hans Zurlinden, who had flown from Zürich on hearing the news, Dr Johannes Wolf with a group of university people. Wolfgang was buried beside his father. Soon the headstone would record the final resting-place of the two Drs Graeser, father and son.

Jo and her husband both found it hard to face the thought of the evening performance of *Der Sommernachtstraum*, but when it came it helped to restore some kind of normality to Jo's life. After a short visit to the apartment at number 6, at Lily's pressing request, she and Leo had accompanied Paul Müller back to his house. He was living alone now, so welcomed their company. From him they discovered that Wolfgang had hanged himself on one of the exercise ropes in his room, leaving everything very orderly and so arranging it that his mother would not be the first to find him. Müller went on:

"He was very deep into Eastern culture. Dr Wolf and Zurlinden told me about taking part with him in the Japanese tea ceremony not very long ago. Apparently Wolfgang described the stairs up to his room as the roji, which is supposed to be the path breaking the link with the outside world. He found peace in his tea-house."

Jo warmed to the old man and promised to visit him again. Her mind went back to all those other untimely deaths, César van Glabeke, Werner Waldecker - no older than Wolfgang -, the farmer crushed by the horse, Uncle Georg Otter with his pipe, accidentally burned to death, Toni Renkowitz on her bier, so quiet and still, all the little children in the hospital . . . so many cut off from life, that was still beautiful, still worth fighting for.

Wolfgang's death had the effect of reinforcing her determination to follow her own mission, to defy the forces of darkness. Her solo dancing took on a greater intensity, attracting increasing critical attention, so that she was now having to turn down engagements and could choose the most favourable venues, her choice guided by her need to proselytise as much as or more than to entertain.

Steckel's family were poor - they were very proud of their famous actor Leonhard - and like so many Berlin Jews, in the clothing trade. His grandfather, a fine, devout old man, was a skilled tailor. They lived in the inappropriately named Hirtenstraße (Shepherds' Street), one in the maze of crowded little roads to the north of Alexanderplatz. One never saw a motor-car there and the streetcars didn't run down it. Trucks and hand- or horse-drawn carts made up the traffic. Empty shop windows, occasionally one with baked Jewish dishes, black bread, poppy-seed bagels. On one family visit old Grandfather Steckel, who had taken a liking to Jo, beckoned her over.

"I have something to show you, my dear, something fine, but not here. It is in the tavern close by." Leo was talking to his mother, so Jo allowed the old man to lead her next door, down the worn steps into the little bar and through to the back room. The proprietor greeted him as an old friend. Jo recognised the smell instantly: fish stuffed with onion, a favourite Jewish dish. It took her back to her Schneidemühl childhood, to her Jewish schoolfriend Sybilla ('Bylla) Löwenthal's family, their little hot kitchen and warm friendliness.

"There! Look at that! This is Mr Frohmann, who has come here from the Ukraine. Jews are not popular there."

"Where are Jews popular, my friend, tell me that?" Mr Frohmann spoke sadly. He too was old, though younger than Grandfather Steckel. He had a wispy grey beard and wore a small black skull-cap. He turned to Jo:

"You wish to see my seven years' work? There it stands."

On the table stood a miniature copy of Solomon's great Temple in Jerusalem, true in every detail, Solomon's cedar and gold represented by spruce wood, papier-maché and gold paint. Every curtain was there, the courtyards, the towers with their pinnacles, the sacred implements on the altar. Jo, who used the Old Testament as a quarry for her dance themes, recognised it for what it was, which pleased the old man. As she studied the intricate model more closely she gasped with delight, peering through the doorways, touching the curtains with a finger.

"Seven years! I can believe it. A labour of love!"

"Yes, seven years of my life. Not love, madam, this was not a hobby. An act of devotion. I cannot worship at the one wall left standing. This is my prayer at that wall, my supplication that the temple may one day be re-built."

"It must be much admired by your compatriots, Herr Frohmann. Such precision, attention to detail, so much exquisite workmanship."

He shook his head. "The old ones already know the temple and the young, those of the same generation as your husband Leonhard - yes, I know your fine man! - they want to build streets and houses in Palestine, not temples."

The planned October performance of Die Kunst der Fuge at the State Opera was dedicated to Wolfgang Graeser's memory. Many of his friends and professional colleagues were there. Dr Johannes Wolf sat beside Lily, dressed simply in black. As at the world première in Leipzig, there was no applause at the end, and many had handkerchiefs to their eyes as they left the opera house.

The great post-war Weimar experiment was drawing to a close as the decade ended. With hindsight one could see it had been doomed from the start, the socialist government always vulnerable, first to those who saw Versailles as a betrayal, then to the growing power of the army, particularly since the Locarno Treaty, and even to the impractical idealists in their own ranks. Everyone was aware of the increasing polarisation between left and right, the left drawn towards the Spartacists and communism, the right to a brutalising, anti-semitic nationalism, with the NSDAP and its Führer Adolf Hitler showing the way, cunningly wooing the two sources of real power, the army and big business, with the declared aim of ousting the feeble and divided socialists.

In such an environment the Berlin theatre inevitably, like the English Elizabethan theatre in not dissimilar circumstances, was highly politicised. Leo Steckel, like that other Leo, the controversial director Leopold Jessner, a Jew and proud of his race, was amongst the leading actors. In September 1927 Erwin Piscator had opened his innovative and short-lived Piscatorbühne on Nollendorf Square. Steckel's face grinned out from the pages of Programme No.1, in company with Piscator himself, Ernst Toller - whose play "Hoppla wir leben!" with its boxing matches was the first production - , Leo Lania and other leading theatre personalities, most regarded as left-wing. Steckel had put as caption to his picture, 'I was fat and full and saw myself in the year ahead growing fatter and fuller. Because I was worried, so as to be in the opposition, so as to rouse myself up and to get thinner; that's how I came to Piscator.' In the introduction Piscator had written, 'This theatre has been founded, not to pursue political ends, but to free art from politics.' Nevertheless he concluded the 'manifesto' thus:

'In these days pure art is not possible. Art which has a consciously political purpose, insofar as it remains uncompromised, is in the final analysis alone possible, and can set out to establish a pure art for our times.'

By her emotionally charged dancing and her championship of the downtrodden, Jo was, in her way, also a political radical. Her vagabond years led her to supporting the 'king of the vagabonds', Gregor Gog, for whose journal "The Tramp" she wrote frequent contributions. It was not to be wondered at that, when the aftermath of the Wall Street crash finally gave Hitler and the NSDAP the opportunity they needed to seize power, both Leo and Jo were marked people. Her daughter Anja was born in February 1933, the year of the Reichstag Fire and Hitler's rise to power. In July Steckel, already engaged by a theatre in Switzerland, had to risk the return journey to Berlin to fetch out his wife and baby daughter.

Jo, exhausted from the journey but smiling, her little Anja asleep in her arms, looked round her new home, the small apartment in Zürich's Spiegelgasse on the east bank of the Lippat.

"This is sanctuary! As we crossed the border I could not help thinking of poor Wolfi, who was born here. He was another seeking sanctuary, a safe haven."

"There are many ways of finding freedom," Steckel said. "He chose one way, we have chosen another. For us the struggle continues."

Jo embraced him, their warm bundle of new life between them, still peacefully sleeping.

"I would not have it otherwise."

—————————— finis ——————————